HYPNOSIS AND ITS THERAPEUTIC APPLICATIONS

edited by Roy M. Dorcus, Ph.D.

Professor of Psychology, Professor of Psychology (Medicine), and Dean, Division of Life Sciences, University of California at Los Angeles; Consultant, Veterans' Administration Hospitals, Long Beach and Sawtelle, California

THE BLAKISTON DIVISION

McGraw-Hill Book Company, Inc.

1956 NEW YORK TORONTO LONDON

HYPNOSIS AND
ITS THERAPEUTIC
APPLICATIONS.

V

Library of Congress Catalog Card Number:
55-9542

CONTRIBUTORS

Frank J. Kirkner, Ph.D. Chief, Clinical Psychology Section, Veterans' Administration Hospital, Long Beach, California; Associate Clinical Professor of Psychology, University of California at Los Angeles.

Milton V. Kline, Ph.D. Lecturer, Department of Psychology, Long Island University; Chief Psychologist, Westchester County Department of Health; Research Consultant in Hypnosis, Research Division, Prosthetic Devices Study, New York University.

George F. Kuehner, D.D.S. Private Practice, New Ulm, Minnesota.

Harold Lindner, Ph.D. Chief Clinical Psychologist, Criminal Courts Psychiatric Clinic, Washington, District of Columbia.

Frank A. Pattie, Ph.D. Professor of Psychology, University of Kentucky.

Theodore R. Sarbin, Ph.D. Associate Professor of Psychology, University of California, Berkeley.

G. Wilson Shaffer, Ph.D. Professor of Psychology, Director of the Psychological Clinic, Dean of the University, The Johns Hopkins University.

PREFACE

In 1952, when the Division of Postgraduate Medical Education, Extension Division of the University of California at Los Angeles, decided to offer courses in the field of hypnosis, a problem arose concerning appropriate texts and reference books that were available and suitable for use in the course. Most of the texts were either fairly obsolete or were so specialized that it became necessary to prepare an extensive bibliography. This was unsatisfactory since many of the practitioners who were students in the course did not have ready access to libraries with journals containing the references. The participants, therefore, had to prepare their lectures in mimeographed form for distribution. This material supplied the basis for *Hypnosis and Its Therapeutic Applications* which is, we believe, a valuable contribution to a very complex field.

Our courses seem to have given impetus to a number of books in the field. Some of these recent books are of excellent merit and tend to cover the various aspects of the field in a very satisfactory manner. No one of them, however, incorporates the theoretical, experimental, and therapeutic aspects of hypnosis in a single volume. Either they are strictly experimental and theoretical in approach, or they are almost entirely clinical in approach. It was felt, therefore, that a volume in which all the various aspects of the topic were brought together would be most satisfactory to students and instructors in such courses. This volume is aimed at accomplishing this objective. The authors are specialists in various portions of the field and have incorporated their experiences in their chapters. The approach is essentially eclectic, since no one single theory seems to account for all the facts. If any single theory has received greater emphasis, it is the theory of *role-playing*. With regard to the problems of induction, emphasis has been placed on the technique of adapting the approach to the subject. The therapeutic applications have been treated in a systematic fashion, but caution is recommended in the application of hypnotic techniques, since the authors do not perceive hypnosis as a panacea but simply as a tool in diagnostic and therapeutic procedures.

ROY M. DORCUS

CONTENTS

Frank A. Pattie, Ph.D.

1

THEORIES OF HYPNOSIS

THERE IS NO SCARCITY of theories of hypnosis. Of the making of books, it has been said, there is no end; there is likewise no end of theorizing. Moreover, the variety of theories offered is perhaps greater in this field than in any other field of psychology, since members of all schools of thought have contributed. The psychoanalysts have produced theories, and so have the "brass-instrument psychologists" of the laboratory as well as all kinds of psychologists and medical men between these two extremes. There are theories "from above" in which the emphasis is on the person and his motivations, conscious or unconscious. There are theories "from below" which begin with the simplest building stones of behavior, in particular the conditioned responses. There are "molar" and "molecular" explanations which correspond roughly to the theories "from above" and "from below" respectively. Fortunately, the theories are sometimes supplementary and can be combined in a larger synthesis. While as yet there is no adequate theory of hypnosis, all of them contain some measure of truth.

The account to be given in this chapter is selective rather than exhaustive. It is intended to show the principal trends in theorizing at the present time, rather than to explain any theory in detail or to mention all theorists.

The theories which enjoy some vigor at present may be grouped thus: (*a*) the theory that hypnosis is a form of sleep or a partial sleep, (*b*) the dissociation theory, (*c*) ideomotor and conditioned-response theories, (*d*) the theory of goal-directed striving, (*e*) theories originating in psychoanalysis. The first two of these are the ones least favored at the present time by psychologists in English-speaking countries.

The theory that hypnosis is a form of sleep

This, the oldest theory of all those worthy of consideration at present, has two origins. The first suggestion that mesmeric phenomena might be connected with sleep came from the discovery of artificial somnambulism, or the sleeping trance, by the Marquis de Puységur in 1784. The Marquis was not theoretically inclined, and his attention was focused on the supernormal abilities of his subjects. Nevertheless, the term *somnambulistic sleep,* which he used, linked the phenomena with sleep. The Abbé Faria (who disagreed violently with Mesmer's theory of a physical force, animal magnetism, passing from the operator to the subject) changed the name of the mesmeric phenomena to *lucid sleep* after discovering that he could put persons into trances by giving them the mere command to sleep. James Braid called the phenomena *neurohypnotism* (nervous sleep), but he pointed out certain important differences between natural sleep and the hypnotic state and tended more and more to explain hypnosis as a state of *monoideism.* In addition to these men there were innumerable others who thought of hypnosis as sleep; among them were Liébeault, Binet, Féré, and Bernheim.

The second origin of the theory relating hypnosis and sleep came from the work of Pavlov on the conditioned reflexes of dogs. He noticed that the repetition of a conditioned stimulus, without any presentation of the unconditioned stimulus (that is, without *reinforcement*), caused a lethargic or drowsy state in his animals. They slumped in their harness, and the muscles in some cases became rigid. Some of them slept. These observations led to the theory that the part of the brain which was most directly affected by the conditioned stimulus became the center of an inhibitory process which radiated to other parts of the brain so long as the stimulus was presented monotonously and without reinforcement. The final stage of the process of inhibition was sleep. The stages prior to sleep were called *hypnosis*. "Inhibition is partial sleep or sleep distributed in localized parts, forced into narrow limits; true sleep is a diffused and continuous inhibition of the whole of the hemispheres." (20)

Against the sleep theory is the preponderance of the evidence obtained from a long series of experiments comparing the state of the patellar reflex, respiration, cardiac activity, cerebral circulation, the encephalogram, the electrical resistance of the skin, and the basal metabolic rate in sleep and in hypnosis. Surveys of this literature are given by Jenness (14), Gorton (11), and Weitzenhoffer (27). The results in general show that in these respects hypnosis is like the waking state and not like sleep.

In the experiments of Barker and Burgwin (2, 3) it has been shown that when subjects are hypnotized by means of visual fixation and eye closure, the electroencephalogram remains the same as it is in the normal state, but when specific suggestions for the production of sleep are given, actual sleep, with its characteristic encephalogram, is produced. These experimenters suggest that *hypnotic suggestibility* and *hypnotic sleep* be carefully distinguished. Their work gives plausibility to the criticism (14, 11) made of some of the experiments in which hypnosis was reported to be physiologically akin to sleep, namely that the subjects were made so passive and quiet in their trances that they were actually asleep for part of the time.

The question of the relationship between sleep and hypnosis never seems to become finally settled. Just when one thinks the relationship is disproved, experiments appear showing similarities between the two states. Darrow and others (7, 8) have published two abstracts, in which phase relations between brain waves obtained from different areas were studied in hypnosis, drowsiness, and sleep. This work was highly quantitative, whereas previous studies were not, and the conclusions reached could not, we believe, have been even suggested by mere inspection of the records. An increase of "average in-phase peak to peak correspondence between waves in occipital and motor areas" was reported for ten out of eleven subjects; the increase was from an average of 33 per cent in waking to an average of 42 per cent in hypnosis, and it was greatest for the expiratory phase of the respiratory cycle. The difference was significant at the 1 per cent level. One other major finding was reported; this one is given merely as a sample to show the kind of experimentation involved. The general conclusion was that, with respect to these measurements, hypnosis is like light sleep and unlike both deep sleep and the waking state.

Koster of Amsterdam (15), who accepts the theory that hypnosis is a partial sleep, has recently repeated the well-known experiment of Bass (4) on the knee jerk and reports that he finds this reflex to be diminished both in sleep and in hypnosis. Bass had found it to be of normal strength in hypnosis and diminished in sleep, and his finding was confirmed by Brown (5) and True and Stephenson (25).

The theory of Pavlov that hypnosis is due to the radiation of internal inhibition from a spot in the brain which is repeatedly and monotonously stimulated is held by some authorities outside of Russia. Among them is Völgyesi (26) of Budapest, who states that the parts of the brain which are thrown out of action are deprived of the normal supply of blood by a process of *vasomotor decerebration;* for this addition to the theory he gives no evidence.

Hull (12) has criticized Pavlov's theory effectively. The theory is so vague that he found it hard to determine how the theory might be tested experimentally. If Pavlov meant that in human subjects the lower centers of the brain are inhibited, as he thought was the case in animals, then conditioned reflexes should be established during the hypnotic trance either with difficulty or not at all. But experiments show that conditioning is accomplished in the trance as easily as in the normal state. If, on the other hand, Pavlov believed that in human subjects the higher cortical centers are inhibited, then the facts go against the theory very decisively, as hypnotized subjects can think, calculate, learn, and solve problems with normal facility.

In spite of recent publications in this field, the preponderance of evidence is against the sleep theory of hypnosis.

The dissociation theory

Another theory, which at one time was dominant but now has few, if any, supporters is the dissociation theory. Its historical affiliations are with the views of Pierre Janet and Morton Prince. The fact that many phenomena of hysteria and multiple personality can be duplicated or imitated by means of hypnosis made this theory especially attractive, as it brought all of these phenomena under the single concept of dissociation which had been set up in the French school of psychopathology in the late 19th and early 20th centuries.

William McDougall's exposition of his version will be presented as an example of this kind of theorizing. He used the concept of dissociation very freely, in fact lavishly, in explaining hypnosis. In discussing the subject's inability to make a certain movement when in the trance, he writes:

> *The patient will fail to achieve a forbidden movement, not merely because he cannot or will not, or has not sufficient motive to, make the necessary effort; but because, when he tries to make the movement and succeeds in innervating the proper muscles, the antagonistic muscles come into play and prevent the movement. At this stage, then, there is manifested a certain splitting of the personality, a conflict of one part against another: the muscles of one set obey the one part, the conscious willing subject; the antagonistic muscles obey some other part of the personality, which understands and is subservient to the commands and suggestions of the operator. (18, p. 87)*

McDougall believed that the motor and sensory phenomena of hypnosis implied some functional dissociation within the nervous system. When an arm is made anesthetic and paralyzed, we are justified in inferring that the sensory and motor neurones in the arm are somehow shut off or isolated. But there are perplexing problems. He says:

> *Where, at what level, this rupture of continuity occurs is a difficult question. We may, I think feel sure that the rupture occurs at synaptic junctions: but whether at those of the spinal, the subcortical, or the cortical level it is difficult to say. Perhaps it is sometimes at one level, sometimes at another. But there are facts indicating that in some cases the dissociating rupture occurs in the cerebrum and involves a considerable system of neurones. These are the facts of negative hallucinations. (18, p. 90)*

Negative hallucinations are evidence of a splitting of the personality. The objects which the subject is told not to see are both seen and not seen. If five cards are given the subject, and he is not to see two of them, in some sense these cards must be seen;

they must be discriminated from the others, otherwise the subject would not know which cards he is to ignore. Just how some of the dissociations are neurologically possible McDougall admitted was a very obscure problem; he cherished obscure problems.

McDougall believed that these dissociations were produced by conative factors, the chief one being in this connection the instinct of submission. He thought that the symptoms produced by hypnotic suggestion (especially uniocular blindness, in which he believed even after the present writer's experiments had given negative results) were "the clearest possible instances of the role of conation in producting dissociation" (19). Through his hormic psychology and his own explicit statements on the role of conation in hypnosis he is linked with present motivational theories and deserves much credit for his pioneer theorizing, which still lives in its general form although the details of his presentation are open to criticism. That part of his theory which emphasizes neural dissociation seems dead or moribund in the English-speaking countries.

The dissociation theory has been ably criticized by White and Shevach (29, 30). In the first place, they assert that the functions which are supposed to be dissociated are "biologically implausible, arbitrary, and changeable." They concede that, if a subject can be made deaf by suggestion, the statement that the auditory centers in the brain are dissociated might have some plausibility. But this appearance of truth ceases when we find that the subject can easily be made deaf to the sound of one particular voice, while he hears all other sounds normally. In cases of amnesia, the subject may be made to remember one or more incidents in a trance and forget the rest. He may be made unable to write one letter of the alphabet, while he can form all the others. McDougall recognized a fundamental difficulty in explaining such cases by dissociation, saying that the question as to how verbal suggestion can determine the location of a line of cleavage that separates two systems remains a "very obscure problem."

The second major criticism by White and Shevach is that the systems which are supposed to be dissociated, or isolated, actively participate in the determination of behavior. For instance, in McDougall's example of negative hallucination, the subject must discriminate certain cards from the others in order to ignore them. There is no real dissociation of systems here; in fact, McDougall acknowledged this fact when he says that the cards must be "in some sense perceived." The reports of subjects in referring to posthypnotic amnesia support, not a dissociation theory, but rather a motivational theory, a theory that such amnesia is due to an unwillingness to remember, an attempt to occupy oneself with other things than an effort to recall. When measured by the method of recall, amnesia may seem to be complete; but when measured by the method of relearning, it does not, since the subject may require only half the usual number of repetitions to relearn what he has allegedly forgotten. Also, practice effects acquired in the trance (for example, in sorting cards into pigeonholes, in tasks involving continuous addition, etc.) are fully retained in the posthypnotic period in spite of amnesia for the doing of the tasks.

Ideomotor and conditioned-response theories

The theory of ideomotor action was an early attempt to explain voluntary action. It is still considered valid by many psychologists, but with the advent of objective psychology and the study of conditioned responses the terminology in which it is clothed has been changed. William James stated the principle thus: "Every representation [idea] of a movement awakens in some degree the actual movement which is its object; and awakens it in a maximum degree whenever it is not kept from doing so by an antagonistic representation present simultaneously to the mind." At another place he said that "the determining condition of the unhesitating and resistless sequence of the act seems to be *the absence of any conflicting notion in the mind.* Either there is nothing else at all in the mind, or what is there does not conflict. The hypnotic subject realizes the former condition. Ask him what he is thinking about, and ten to one he will reply 'nothing.' The consequence is that he both believes everything he is told, and performs every act that is suggested." (13, II, pp. 526, 523)

The modern equivalent of the ideomotor theory emphasizes the principle that any frequently repeated antecedent of an act can become a conditioned stimulus for that act. Words and other symbols are conditioned stimuli for actions; their meanings are products of a process of conditioning. What is characteristic of the responses to the verbal stimuli of a hypnotist is the promptness and dependability with which they are evoked and the absence of any interfering or inhibiting symbolic or verbal responses in the subject.

The ideomotor theory of action in its modern form is implied in the theory of hypnosis published by Hull in 1933. Since he defined hypnosis as a state of generalized hypersuggestibility, all that he had to explain was the origin of this hypersuggestibility. He writes:

> *A true suggestion response is one in which the subject's own symbolic processes, instead of becoming active either in facilitating or in resisting the tendency to action naturally arising from the experimenter's words, remain passive so far as the particular act suggested is concerned. It seems reasonable to assume that this passivity is facilitated by the suggestions usually given for the subject to relax and not to think of anything but sleep. This withdrawal of the subject's symbolic activities would naturally leave his muscles relatively susceptible to the symbolic stimulation emanating continuously from the experimenter. (12, p. 397)*

Individual differences in susceptibility are due to the fact that persons differ in their ability to suppress their own symbolic processes. When these processes are inhibited, the subject's movements are controlled by the symbolic stimuli coming from the experimenter, his words being, like all words, conditioned stimuli for actions.

There are certain difficulties with this theory. First, Hull does not explain why the experimenter's symbolic stimuli are so much more effective than the subject's own symbolic stimulation of himself. Why, for example, is the subject (even the subject who can be put into a deep trance) less able when he is in the waking state to inhibit the bodily changes which are responses to painful stimulation than when he is in the trance? An experiment by Sears (23) showed this difference of abilities.

A second difficulty arises in that Hull's theory fails to explain not amnesia but the remembering of the events of the trance. He does not specificially set out a theory of memory; but if, as behaviorists usually do, he assumes that memory is simply the reinstatement of previous verbal responses, a difficulty arises. If hypnosis occurs only when the subject's verbal responses are absent, how could the subject ever recall the events of the trance period? Hull gives no light on this point. At one place he gives us reason to think that our account of his theory of memory is correct; in a very philosophical mood, indicated by his use of the terms *in essence* and *really,* he sets forth his monistic belief that "experiences in essence are really actions" (12, p. 401). No verbal action, no memory. Yet, though the subject may remember nothing after a deep trance, these lost memories may be restored by putting him back into the trance.

A third difficulty which is very serious is that Hull's theory requires the subject to be a complete automaton while he is in the trance. He has inhibited all symbolic processes which might prevent his responding to the experimenter's commands. Yet it is a fact that subjects often fail to respond to suggestions exactly as they are given; the reaction is often a compromise between the suggestion and the tendencies of the subject which oppose the suggestion. This fact is so well known that it needs no illustration. In cases where a suggestion like that of a blindness in one eye cannot be carried out, the subject may cleverly outwit the experimenter by devising a trick which will give the appearance of blindness. Also, in cases where a suggestion is given that is contrary to the subject's moral code, the subject may come out of the trance. Hull does not tell us how this comes about. In this connection R. W. White calls our attention to the cases in which posthypnotic suggestions are stated in very general terms (such as "Make a speech on the tariff") with the details of the execution left to the subject, who may do a great deal of thinking and show a considerable amount of ingenuity in the work, although his efforts may be less wide-ranging than those of a person in a waking state. Hull's theory is difficult to accept if one does not believe that experiences are essentially actions; there are too many profound alterations produced in the subject's perceptions and there is too much intelligent, motivated, and discriminative behavior by the subject which does not seem to fit such a theory.

Livingston Welch's theory of hypnosis is a conditioned-response theory, but it is one of a new kind, involving as its central principle a new variety of conditioning which he has discovered and called *abstract conditioning* (28, 6). What he means by this term may be conveyed by an account of the process by which hypnosis is usually induced. The operator tells the subject to fixate a bright object and then tells him that his eyes are becoming tired. The eyes then become tired as a result of the fixation. The subject is now told that his eyes will commence to blink, and they do blink. In each case, the operator gives a conditioned verbal stimulus to the subject, and the stimulus is then followed by the fact symbolized by the words. The verbal stimulus is given and then followed by reinforcement. When this process has been repeated a sufficient number of times, abstract conditioning occurs; the subject will now respond by giving the appropriate action to a symbolic stimulus which has never been reinforced. If the operator says that the subject will feel a slight electric shock, the subject will respond by feeling a shock. In this way, the generalized hypersuggestibility characteristic of the trance is built up.

The existence of abstract conditioning has been proved by an experiment by Corn-Becker, Welch, and Fisichelli (6). Subjects were told that they were to participate in an experiment on palmar skin resistance, and electrodes were applied to their hands. Then words were projected one at a time on a screen. The word *red* was shown, and immediately thereafter a red light was turned on; the projected word *music* was followed by actual music. Seven words were presented in random order, each reinforced by the actual event which it represented. On the eighth, twelfth, or sixteenth trial the words *electric shock* appeared. This stimulus was never reinforced. In a group of naive subjects 73 per cent gave psychogalvanic responses to this stimulus which were either greater or of longer duration than the same response given to any of the other stimuli. In a control group, in which no verbal stimuli were reinforced, the corresponding percentage was 13. The results illustrate the principle of abstract conditioning, in which a stimulus which has never been reinforced in the experiment produces a response because other stimuli which are quite different from it have been reinforced. One might object that the results were due to the subject's expectation of a shock, but this objection is met by the fact that there was no correlation between the subjects' expectation or nonexpectation and the size and duration of the galvanic response.

It might be expected, Welch wrote, that good hypnotic subjects would show abstract conditioning sooner than difficult subjects in this experiment. However, neither Welch nor anyone else has tested the hypnotic susceptibility of any of the many subjects used in the conditioning experiment. This important gap in the theory should be filled.

Sarbin criticizes Welch's theory thus:

> *If a subject comes into hypnotic experiment with certain self-perceptions and role-taking skills, it is possible for him to become hypnotized without the usual monotonous delivery and so-called reinforcement. In an unpublished study the present author has shown that some subjects can be hypnotized with these instructions: "Make yourself comfortable in this easy chair. I'll step out of the room for a few minutes so you can relax. When I come back, I will count to ten, you will close your eyes and go into a hypnotic sleep." (21, p. 258)*

Welch has a reply to this objection. He would say that the abstract-conditioning process in such subjects took place in the past. He writes:

> *In the past, indeed throughout his life, when he was told that a certain person was an expert in mathematics, Latin, golf, boxing, or other skill he has usually discovered that this person* was *a good mathematician . . . or whatever he was said to be. Since such statements have proven true in the past, he generalizes and takes the experimenter or hypnotist at his word. (28, p. 359)*

A second objection is that in many cases in which the operator follows the procedure that Welch takes as typical of hypnotic induction, hypnosis often occurs and the deeper stages are reached after a patchwork of successes and failures on individual suggestions. One subject, an excellent somnambulist who was hypnotized without suggestions of eye closure or sleep, said, "You said that I couldn't unclasp my hands, but I did. Then you told me a second time, and I unclasped them. But the third time it worked, much to my surprise, and the hands were stuck." Also, if the whole process depends upon conditioning, how is it possible to make a person who has proved on several occasions to be a good subject, unhypnotizable in the future by merely telling him that all efforts in the future will be unsuccessful?

Hypnosis as goal-directed behavior in an altered state of the person

In 1941 R. W. White of the Harvard Psychological Clinic published an important article in which he expounded a motivational theory of hypnosis (29). Previous to this time articles by various writers had shown that the hypnotized person was highly motivated to act as he thought a hypnotized person should act. He would do everything possible to give the results desired by the experimenter, using all available knowledge to give the appearance desired by the hypnotist. White used these experimental findings and added to the conclusions which they suggested a very keen criticism of other theories. He defined hypnotic behavior as "meaningful, goal-directed striving, its most general goal being to behave like a hypnotized person as this is continuously defined by the operator and understood by the subject."

This statement is not the whole of White's theory. To account for some of the more impressive features of the hypnotic state, such as the transcendance of normal abilities and certain physiological phenomena, he adds that this goal-directed behavior occurs while the subject is in an altered state. It is easy to overlook this second part. Needless to say, the more vague part of his theory is the part which attempts to say in what the alteration of the person consists.

Let us return to the first part of the theory, which defines hypnosis as goal-directed striving to behave like a hypnotized person. When a hypnotized person cannot separate his clasped hands, there is no dissociation, as McDougall would have us to believe. According to White, the subject is doing exactly what the operator told him to do; he tries to pull the hands apart and at the same time to clasp them. Posthypnotic amnesia is not a case of two dissociated systems either. The person simply makes no effort to recall the events of the trance. The brain traces are laid down as usual, as is proved by the fact that the subject can recall them when he is again hypnotized. The reports of the subjects bear out this theory of amnesia. They state that they can't make the effort to remember, that they don't want to think, or that they "partly know and partly don't." The suggestion that the subject will have posthypnotic amnesia is a relatively difficult one to obey, as an attitude of ignoring the memories of the trance must be maintained for a considerable period of time. Very often a posthypnotic amnesia is temporary; the memories come back because the subject abandons his attitude of ignoring or turning away from them.

But the high degree of motivation of hypnotic behavior will not explain everything. If we go to a dentist and try as hard as we can to ignore pain, we do not succeed, although a hypnotized subject gives no evidence of pain. The explanation of the difference, according to White, is that the hypnotized person is an altered personality. His theory is a double one. "There is," he says, "no law of nature which declared that hypnosis may not be at one and the same time a goal-directed striving and an altered state of the organism."

To discover the nature of the change, White says we must (*a*) study the abilities shown by the subjects in the trance and (*b*) examine the process by which hypnosis is induced.

In the trance there are certain losses as well as gains. Since the gains are more impressive, the losses are little discussed. The subject loses alertness except to those things to which the operator directs his attention. He responds only to those stimuli and ideas which are connected with the goals set by the operator. If the goal demands ideation, as is the case in which a problem is to be solved or a speech made on a topic supplied by the operator, ideation occurs, but even then there are limitations beyond which the subject does not wander. This concentration of the subject, this limiting of his activity to the task at hand, is to be seen in his lack of spontaneity, his literal-mindedness, and his lack of humor or perception of humorous situations.

The ability of the subject to transcend the normal limitations of functions is difficult to explain on any theory. White points out that, in Sears's well-known experiment on analgesia of the skin, those bodily changes which occur during painful stimulation and are subject to some voluntary control (verbal report, facial flinch, respiratory changes) showed the greatest decrement as a result of suggested anesthesia. Those changes which are not voluntarily controllable, the cardiac and galvanic skin reactions, showed a smaller decrement. The results indicated, moreover, that the ability of the organism to suppress the bodily reactions to pain are far greater in the trance than they are in the normal state. The greatest effect is on the changes which are wholly or partially subject to voluntary control.

Similar results are found in the experiments on posthypnotic amnesia; that which is most subject to voluntary control shows the greatest effect. Recall of words learned in the trance may be entirely inhibited, but amnesia for them as measured by the method of relearning may average only 50 per cent. The retention of manual habits learned in the stylus maze, measured by the relearning method, shows also only 50 per cent amnesia, while the practice effect resulting from the mental addition of digits in the trance shows no posthypnotic decrement at all. "As one passes from specific learned content to the more remote effects of practice, the effectiveness of hypnotic suggestion declines," White concludes, and he states that the chief characteristic of the altered state of the person is a "change in the success achieved by certain kinds of striving." How is the change brought about when hypnosis is induced?

The necessary conditions for induction of a trance are, according to White, (*a*) relaxation, (*b*) reduction of sensory input, (*c*) the presence of an operator. Of these prerequisites, we doubt very much the first. Subjects can be hypnotized for the first time while they are standing and without any mention of drowsiness, sleep, or relaxation. White takes notice of this fact and says that Hull suggests relaxation even to the subjects who are standing: "I direct him to look steadily into my eyes and think of nothing but sleep, to relax his muscles all over, even so much that his knees bend a little and his legs scarcely hold him up." But if Hull's subjects had relaxed their muscles, they would have fallen on the floor.

The "reduction of sensory input" that White mentions should be replaced, in the present writer's opinion, by the words "concentration of attention." That is to say, it is not necessary, though it may be helpful, to darken the room or have the subject relax in a comfortable chair, but the subject's attention must be concentrated. The end result of both procedures may be the same, so far as the subject's conscious experience is concerned, as concentration makes the perceptions of objects other than the one attended to very vague and unclear or even eliminates them from the field of consciousness entirely.

The operator is necessary at least on the first occasion of induction, but White's statements on the function of the operator seem to be open to question. White states that there is "a continuum from the wide awake state through drowsiness to sound sleep." Then he says that the operator, if he is successful, "must bring his subject a short distance along this continuum to a light drowsiness, but must stop him there and prevent him from getting more sleepy; otherwise he will go into the passive trance or drop off to sleep altogether." By keeping up a continuous stream of auditory stimulation while the other senses are relatively closed he holds the drowsiness at a light stage and prevents a lapse into sleep. "The dual function of the operator is to prevent the deepening of drowsiness and to keep regnant the wish to behave like a hypnotized person." The peculiarities of hypnotic behavior—the feeling that movements are produced without volition, the literal and humorless manner, and the subsequent poor memory—can all be viewed as results that are related to drowsiness. In drowsiness our images become "more vivid, more concrete, and more absolute."

Because of the weakness of the evidence which tends to link hypnosis and sleep and because of my experience in hypnotizing persons in a standing position without suggesting sleep, drowsiness, or relaxation, I would regard drowsiness as having nothing to do with hypnosis. For White's "reduction of sensory input," which is too objectively stated, I would substitute "reduction of sensory input to which the subject attends," and I would omit relaxation. While one would hardly pick a boiler factory as a place for successful hypnotizing, one could no doubt hypnotize there those persons who had worked in the factory long enough to be able to pay no attention to the very noisy sensory input. The essential thing is not the amount of the objective sensory input but the concentration of attention or narrowing of the field of awareness; this is facilitated by the operator's words which continually and repetitiously confine the subject's attention to a very limited field.

In discussing the nature of the changes brought about in the organism, White mentions a possible functional decortication, consisting in a lowering of some levels of activity. He says that it has been shown that unconscious strivings may affect the autonomic nervous system and produce psychosomatic disorders. "It may well be that hypnotic behavior lies somewhere between the level of volition and the level of unconscious strivings, enjoying some of the privileges of the latter in the way of extended control." In this part of his theorizing, White is necessarily vague, and his speculations are as good as anyone's. The nature of the change in the organism which leads to the various physiological manifestations in hypnosis remains unknown.

Hypnosis as role-taking behavior

The theory of goal-directed striving has recently been narrowed down somewhat by Theodore Sarbin (21), who calls his view of hypnosis the theory of role-taking. "Hypnosis is one form of a more generalized kind of social psychological behavior, namely, role-taking."

Sarbin believes that White's theory has a gap in it, in that it "fails to provide an explanation for differential susceptibility beyond that due to motivational factors, such as need for submissiveness and deference." To the motivational factors Sarbin adds role-taking perception and aptitude for role-taking. The actor must first perceive the role he is to play, and some actors can take a role more completely than others. Sarbin compares hypnosis to drama. Some actors on the stage report that they lose themselves and become relatively unaware of the audience or other environmental objects. Sarbin states that there is a continuum of different degrees of absorption in one's role ranging from ordinary acting, in which self and role are differentiated, "heated" acting, hypnosis, hysterias, and states of ecstasy or mystical experiences.

Sarbin points out numerous facts which support his ideas on the importance of motivation, role-taking aptitude, and role-perception. If there is a lack of harmony between the subject's perception of himself and his perception of the role he is to play, motivation is not favorable for hypnosis. If a subject is hypnotized today and is told later that he has acted foolishly while in the trance, he will probably prove not to be hypnotizable tomorrow. Also with respect to role-perception, the behavior of the subject in the trance is consistent with his understanding of hypnosis; for example, if he believes that subjects under hypnosis must keep their eyes closed, then a command to open the eyes will cause him to awaken. With respect to role-taking aptitude, Sarbin cites experiments by Lewis and himself (17) on the inhibition of gastric contractions by suggesting to hypnotized persons that they were eating. A correlation was found between the depth of hypnosis and the ability to inhibit these hunger contractions. Sarbin gets some help from the triadic hypothesis of Rosenzweig and Sarason, which states that susceptibility to hypnosis is associated with repression as an ego-defense and with impunitiveness. Sarbin says that all three of these traits are *as-if* behavior, that is, role-taking behavior in a general way; the subject behaves as if the repressed experience did not exist (repression), and he acts as if a frustrating experience had really not been frustrating (impunitiveness).

Sarbin assimilates to this theory a recently published theory of Magda Arnold (1) that the effects of hypnosis are due to imagination. "Hypnosis," she writes, "essentially consists in concentrating and therefore intensifying the subjects' imaginative processes." Arnold's theory is based upon experimental work in which the vividness of subjects' imaginal processes was correlated with their behavior in the body-sway test. Arnold admits, with White, that the hypnotic subject is engaged in goal-directed activity, but she doubts that he is motivated by a desire to submit to the operator and behave like a hypnotized subject. Rather he is trying to imagine vividly the situation described by the operator and to imagine himself in it. Sarbin very readily accepts her ideas and states that imagining is *as-if* behavior, role-taking, and that the hypnotizable are, other things being equal, those who can vividly perceive or imagine a role.

The bodily changes which can be produced in the trance, such as the Babinski reflex in regressed conditions and the complete absence or the diminution of reactions to loud sounds or pain, are difficult to explain on the basis of any theory. White mentions some possibility of inhibition of some of the higher cortical centers as a result of focalization of activity in other centers. Sarbin passes over the question very lightly; he states that role-taking is organic and that any act involves the whole organism, as Goldstein has asserted. Since this is true, "the extension of the limits of behavior involving the autonomic functions is understood in terms of the organism as a whole." Although he wrote these words in 1950, he mentions only autonomic changes, which are much more plausibly explained by a psychological theory than such changes as the production of the Babinski reflex in age-regression which was reported by Gidro-Frank and Buch in 1948 (10) and confirmed by True and Stephenson in 1951 (25).

A three-factor theory

Weitzenhoffer's theory (27) cannot be classified as a conditioned-response theory, although it invokes abstract conditioning; it is certainly not a motivational theory. Perhaps it might be called an eclectic theory. At any rate, the name *three-factor theory* is adequate. According to its author, three factors explain hypnotic suggestibility: homoaction, which is a simple form of learning; heteroaction, which is an effect similar to transfer of training; and dissociation, the narrowing of the field of awareness.

Homoaction means the effect that is produced by a response to suggestion upon the response to a later suggestion of the same kind. Homoaction is shown by the postural-sway experiments; if a subject responds to the suggestion that he is swaying, his next response to the same suggestion will be more prompt. *Heteroaction* means the effect upon a later response to a suggestion of a different kind. Homoaction accounts for some of the increase in suggestibility in the early stages of hypnotic induction, but there occurs also, overlapping the homoaction and eventually masking it because of its increasing quantity, a process of generalization of suggestibility, heteroaction.

Weitzenhoffer makes a valiant attempt to base his theory upon physiological principles. Homoaction he explains by certain properties of nerves and muscles, such as summation effects, physiological reinforcement, the effect of tonus on the strength of muscular responses, and other properties. "Homoaction appears to be merely a form of neuromotor enhancement combined with ideomotor action," and ideomotor action is "a complex conditioned response or habit phenomenon." (27, p. 249)

The generalization of suggestibility, heteroaction, he thinks is at present to be identified with abstract conditioning. The reader of Weitzenhoffer may be disturbed by the fact that Hull's studies (12, p. 319) showed no heteroactive effect between suggestions to move the head or arm and a later suggestion of a different kind, and thus failed to substantiate his hypothesis that the hypersuggestibility of the trance might be due to heteroactive effects. In a personal communication Weitzenhoffer points out that in Hull's work the amount of heteroaction present—and there is no reason to expect that an appreciable amount would be present, since a sequence of only two suggestions was used—was masked by the much larger amount of homoaction present. Hence he tentatively turns to abstract conditioning as expounded by Welch as the paradigm for the production of generalization of suggestibility.

These two principles do not completely explain hypnosis in its most fully developed form. Alone, they could account only for the lighter stages. The deeper stages involve dissociation. The phenomena not explained by the first two factors are "a very extensive and powerful generalization" sometimes occurring under conditions which seem to preclude any conditioning, the complexity of some of the phenomena, and the individuality of behavior and the independent mentation of the subject. It is clear that hypnosis involves the activity of the higher centers of the brain, since it is dependent upon the use of language. The third factor invoked is "a constriction of consciousness, which in essence involves a *dissociation of awareness from* the majority of sensory and even strictly neural events that are taking place" (27, p. 254). Through this constriction the subject's perception of the world may be profoundly altered. Antisocial behavior can be produced by an alteration of the subject's perceptions. White's and Sarbin's theorizing is dismissed with the statement that there is an alternative interpretation, namely, that "the subject behaves the way he does because it is the only pattern of behavior consistent with his present perception of the environment" (27, p. 253).

Weitzenhoffer's theory has some strong points. One which impresses me is its ability to account for the performance of subjects who respond to some waking suggestions and not to others and fail to go into a trance (this might be called *abortive hypnosis*); that the effects produced result from ideomotor action, homoaction, and a little generalization is an attractive hypothesis.

The theory has its weak points. Involving three factors which act in different degrees in different subjects and which overlap, the theory would be difficult to test experimentally.

The principle of abstract conditioning needs further quantitative investigation. At present it is a frail reed to lean on. In the experiment by Corn-Becker and associates two criteria were adopted: the galvanic skin response could be either greater in milliamperes or longer in duration to qualify as the largest response in a series. A breakdown of the data as to these two criteria would be welcome. The effect must be slight, since 56 per cent of the control subjects showed a galvanic response which was among the three largest when the words *electric shock* were exhibited on the first trial, and 60 per cent of those of another group of control subjects did the same when it was presented on the twelfth and sixteenth trials in the series in which no word was reinforced by presentation of the thing which it signified. Weitzenhoffer has, however, only tentatively accepted abstract conditioning.

Weitzenhoffer should make a better answer to the motivational theorists. It seems fair, when the context is considered, to take the sentence quoted above as a definitive statement of his argument against them. Certainly he would admit the inadequacy of explaining the behavior mentioned as due to a change in the perception of the *environment* alone.

Theories of psychoanalytic origin

Before he abandoned hypnosis as a therapeutic method, Freud had recognized its erotic relationships. He describes in his autobiography a scene in which a young female patient embraced him as she was coming out of the trance. Psychoanalytic theory of hypnosis was not crystallized, however, until 1909, when Ferenczi stated that there are two kinds of hypnosis, father-hypnosis and mother-hypnosis. The hypnotizer is an image of either the father or the mother, and hypnosis is an evocation of infantile erotic masochistic relationships toward the parents. Freud (9) approved of Ferenczi's theory and his distinction between paternal and maternal hypnosis. He believed that in hypnosis the subject withdraws all of his interest in the external world and concentrates it on the person of the hypnotizer. The operator calls out in the subject a portion of his archaic inheritance, the idea of a powerful and dangerous person toward whom one can adopt only a passive and masochistic attitude. Freud not only connected hypnosis with the attitude of the *primal horde* toward the father but also compared it with being in love with sexual satisfaction excluded, the libidinal ties between subject and hypnotist being like those between child and parent, *goal-inhibited.*

Schilder and Kauders state that hypnosis and suggestibility have an erotic origin (22). "If one hypnotizes women, the hypnotizer often has occasion to observe, just before the hypnotic sleep and just after the awakening, the glance of surrender which is characteristic of sexual excitement." Other similarities between the hypnotic state and love are pointed out. It might be objected that, if this is the case, hypnosis would be most easily performed when subject and operator are of different sex. But there is a ready answer from Schilder and Kauders: "We have been taught by psychoanalysis that homosexual inclinations are present in all persons, and it may be that hypnosis between persons of the same sex may operate through these inclinations." (The concept of bisexuality is, like that of reaction formation, a very present help in explaining facts that at first might appear to be inconsistent with a theory.) In addition, hypnosis has a second root, subordination to the authority of another. Officers are harder to hypnotize than privates; children are more susceptible than adults. Hypnosis is an attitude of subjection, of subordination, of masochism. The subject subordinates himself to the hypnotizer masochistically in order to have a share in the greatness and power of the hypnotizer, the power to produce alterations in the world when he merely wishes them.

There have been some attempts to gather data which would prove the psychoanalytic theory. Ferenczi investigated the meaning of hypnosis for some of his patients who had been hypnotized and later analyzed. He wrote that these cases confirmed Freud's theory that hypnosis arises from the masochistic component of the sexual instinct. Speyer and Stokvis (24) analyzed the fantasies of a male subject who was hypnotized by a woman and later by a man. They conclude that during hypnosis a regression of the erotic instinctive life occurs, usually reaching the level of the Oedipus situation.

That at certain times and places subjects indulge in highly colored fantasies about being hypnotized no one will doubt. Domination through hypnosis and libidinal domination are associated in the popular mind; in certain songs *hypnotize* has a sexual meaning. However, the theory that hypnosis is to be explained as of libidinal origin has not yet been furnished with anything like adequate evidence.

In 1944 an article by two analysts, Kubie and Margolin, appeared (16). There is little about this carefully written work which will arouse the *odium psychoanalyticum,* since it bases hypnosis only on the libidinal ties between parent and child and since it cites much work by persons outside the analytic group. The authors distinguish the hypnotic process and the hypnotic state, stating at the outset that the process of induction can best be studied in the novice, since the subject who has been hypnotized several times develops short-cuts into the trance, such as responding to mere signals. They recognize three stages in hypnosis which shade into each other. In the first stage there is a progressive elimination of channels of communication with the environment, only those channels of communication between operator and subject being left. The condition is one of partial sleep. The hypnotist becomes the sole representative of the outside world; this phase is similar to the sensorimotor relationships of the infant to the world, in which the parents play a role like that of the hypnotist.

In the second phase the ego boundaries of the subject are eliminated or constricted as a result of the reduction of sensorimotor channels, and a psychological fusion occurs between operator and subject. The operator's words become indistinguishable from the subject's thoughts, and states of nypnagogic revery with vivid sensory images may be released. Physiologically the process is an extension of the processes of normal attention, "the result of the creation in the central nervous system of a concentrated focus of excitation with the surrounding areas of inhibition (in the descriptive Pavlovian sense)." Immobilization, monotony, sensory adaptation, and rhythm are discussed as contributing factors. Psychologically, the induction of hypnosis depends upon a reduction of alertness through the quieting of anxiety and other defenses.

The final, fully developed stage involves a partial reexpansion of the ego boundaries, the subject now being able to communicate freely with the outside world, and the incorporation of a fragmentary image of the hypnotist within these boundaries. The hypnotist's voice has become a part of the subject's ego, and the compliance of the subject with the hypnotist's orders is therefore more apparent than real. The operator "becomes something which the subject carries around inside of him—a secret 'will,' or purpose—a 'still, small voice of conscience'—an unconscious component of the new personality which has emerged." This final phase parallels that phase in the development of the infant's ego in which its boundaries expand and parental images are retained as unconscious components of the ego. Hypnosis is thus a reproduction of a natural process of development.

The article is a careful working-out, with some novel features and with more consideration of various views of the subject, of ideas previously adumbrated in the psychoanalytic school. The authors admit that the evidence for their theory is fragmentary. Ten years after publication of this work, the outlines sketched remain worthy of serious consideration, but in the interim they have received no filling-in or supplementation.

Conclusions

Thus ends our review of theories. In a condensed account, it is likely that some distortion may occur; authors' qualifying statements are often omitted, and certain things may be emphasized at the expense of others. We hope that such distortion has not been serious.

It must be concluded that there is as yet no adequate theory of hypnosis; we cannot adopt as our own any theory without shutting our eyes to facts which are left unexplained or which seem to call for a different kind of theory. This conclusion will be unpleasant to some; there are others, however, more interested in searching for answers to small questions than in making formulations which are all-inclusive, who agree with Robert Louis Stevenson that "to travel hopefully is a better thing than to arrive."

There are many facts which speak in favor of a motivational theory: the eagerness with which subjects try to produce the results desired, the facts of amnesia, and others. There are many facts which speak for role-taking. But such theories cannot explain those changes that take place over which the subject has no control and about which he has no knowledge, such as the Babinski reflex in regression or the spontaneous and self-terminating trance often occurring during performance of a posthypnotic suggestion. That not all of behavior in the trance can be role-taking—doing something which in our society is defined as the behavior of a hypnotized person—seems true when we consider that all of the phenomena had to have a beginning, and on the first occasion they were entirely unexpected. De Jussieu, the botanist who was a member of the King's commission in 1784, poked around among the patients receiving treatment at the baquets and discovered postmagnetic amnesia. This amnesia, previously unknown, could not have been part of a role at the time.

The theory of Hull leaves no room for cases in which the subject is not an automaton. Welch's abstract conditioning is unable to explain some of the effects listed above, and it has yet to be shown that there is a correlation between the ability to be hypnotized and the ability to be conditioned abstractly. Moreover, there is reason to suspect the adequacy of such a simple, molecular mechanism as the key to the problem; to accept it, it seems, would be like trying to explain accident-proneness as a function of reaction time. Weitzenhoffer's theory will appeal to those who look to mechanisms rather than motivations as the starting point; it is a carefully constructed fabric, but it has its difficulties.

The psychoanalytic school's final product up to the present time, the theory of Kubie and Margolin, which sees hypnosis as a recapitulation of childhood development, is in need of additional evidence.

The present writer inclines toward the motivational theory of White with his own modifications dissociating it from sleep or drowsiness. This theory is a theory of "motivation plus." The plus is an altered state of the nervous system, a structure containing about 10^{10} parts. What exactly is that altered state? "The rest is silence."

REFERENCES

1. Arnold, M. B.: "On the Mechanism of Suggestion and Hypnosis," *J. Abnormal & Soc. Psychology* **41**:107–128 (1946).
2. Barker, W., and S. Burgwin: "Brain Wave Patterns During Hypnosis, Hypnotic Sleep, and Normal Sleep," *Arch. Neurol. & Psychiat.* **62**:412–420 (1949).
3. ———: "Brain Wave Patterns Accompanying Changes in Sleep and Wakefulness During Hypnosis," *Psychosomat. Med.* **10**:317–326 (1948).
4. Bass, M. J.: "Differentiation of the Hypnotic Trance from Normal Sleep," *J. Exp. Psychol.* **14**: 382–399 (1931).
5. Brown, W.: "Sleep, Hypnosis, and Mediumistic Trance," *Character and Pers.* **3**:112–126 (1935).
6. Corn-Becker, F., L. Welch, and V. Fisichelli: "Conditioning Factors Underlying Hypnosis," *J. Abnormal & Soc. Psychology* **44**:212–222 (1949).
7. Darrow, C. W., E. C. Henry, M. Gill, M. Brenman: "Inter-area Electro-encephalographic Relationships Affected by Hypnosis: Preliminary Report," *EEG. clin. Neurophysiol.* **2**:231 (1950).
8. ——— and M. Converse: "Frontal-motor Parallelism and Motor-occipital In-phase Activity in Hypnosis, Drowsiness, and Sleep," *EEG. clin. Neurophysiol.* **2**:355 (1950).
9. Freud, S.: *Group Psychology and Analysis of the Ego*, London, International Psychoanalytical Press, 1922.
10. Gidro-Frank, L., and M. K. B. Buch: "A Study of the Plantar Response in Hypnotic Age Regression," *J. Nervous Mental Disease* **107**:443–458 (1948).
11. Gorton, B. E.: "The Physiology of Hypnosis," *Psychiat. Quart.* **23**:317–343, 457–485 (1949).
12. Hull, C. L.: *Hypnosis and Suggestibility*, New York, D. Appleton-Century Company, Inc., 1933.
13. James, W.: *Principles of Psychology*, New York, Henry Holt and Company, Inc., 1890.
14. Jenness, A.: "Hypnotism," in J. McV. Hunt, *Personality and the Behavior Disorders*, I, 466–502, New York, The Ronald Press Company, 1944.
15. Koster, S.: "Experimental Investigation of the Character of Hypnosis," *J. Clin. Exp. Hypnosis* **2**:42–55 (1954).
16. Kubie, L. S., and S. Margolin: "The Process of Hypnotism and the Nature of the Hypnotic State," *Am. J. Psychiat.* **100**:611–622 (1944).
17. Lewis, J. H., and T. R. Sarbin: "Studies in Psychosomatics: The Influence of Hypnotic Stimulation on Gastric Hunger Contractions," *Psychosomat. Med.* **5**:125–131 (1943).
18. McDougall, W.: *Outline of Abnormal Psychology*, New York, Charles Scribner's Sons, 1926.
19. ———: "The Relations between Dissociation and Repression," *Brit. J. Med. Psychol.* **17**:141–157 (1938).
20. Pavlov, I. P.: "The Identity of Inhibition with Sleep and Hypnosis," *Sci. Monthly* **17**:603–608 (1923).
21. Sarbin, T. R.: "Contributions to

Role-taking Theory. I. Hypnotic Behavior," *Psychol. Rev.* **57**:255–270 (1950).
22. Schilder, P., and O. Kauders: *Hypnosis* (*Nervous Mental Disease* Monogr. Ser.) Washington, 1927.
23. Sears, R. R.: "An Experimental Study of Hypnotic Anesthesia," *J. Exp. Psychol.* **15**:1–22 (1932).
24. Speyer, N., and B. Stokvis: "The Psychoanalytical Factor in Hypnosis," *Brit. J. Med. Psychol.* **17**:217–222 (1938).
25. True, R. M., and C. W. Stephenson: "Controlled Experiments Correlating Electroencephalogram, Pulse, and Plantar Reflexes with Hypnotic Age Regression and Induced Emotional States," *Personality* **1**:252–263 (1951).
26. Völgyesi, F.: *L'Hypnose et le Mystère Cérébral*, Paris, Vigot Frères, 1944.
27. Weitzenhoffer, A.: *Hypnotism*, New York, John Wiley & Sons, Inc., 1953.
28. Welch, L.: "A Behavioristic Explanation of the Mechanism of Suggestion and Hypnosis," *J. Abnormal & Soc. Psychology* **42**:359–364 (1947).
29. White, R. W.: "A Preface to a Theory of Hypnotism," *J. Abnormal & Soc. Psychology* **36**: 477–506 (1941).
30. ——— and S. Shevach: "Hypnosis and the Concept of Dissociation," *J. Abnormal & Soc. Psychology* **37**:309–328 (1942).

Frank A. Pattie, Ph.D.

2

METHODS OF INDUCTION, SUSCEPTIBILITY OF SUBJECTS, AND CRITERIA OF HYPNOSIS

IN REVIEWING THE HISTORY of methods of inducing hypnosis one is impressed with the great variety of methods. Mesmer (1734–1815) produced convulsive seizures and subjective phenomena by putting his hands on the shoulders of the patient, then bringing them down the arms to the finger tips and, after holding the thumbs for a moment, repeating the process. In cases in which he wished to alleviate pain, he touched the painful spot with his fingers, making passes which followed the direction of the nerves. Some later workers made passes without contact. Mesmer's methods are still used by a few cultists, books on *animal magnetism* occasionally appear in France, and a practicing magnetopath of Switzerland (27) has recently published a history of animal magnetism.*

* In 1946 I had a visit from a young man who had learned to hypnotize while he was in the U. S. Navy. He wanted to demonstrate his work, and some of my students volunteered. He attempted to hypnotize by making passes, saying nothing during the induction. How successful his method was I do not know, as my students later told me they had simulated. In 1952 I found that this man had migrated to Los Angeles and was entertaining

Esdaile (1808–1859), who performed many surgical operations with hypnosis, put the patient to bed in a darkened room and directed him to close his eyes and try to go to sleep. "He then made passes without contact over the entire body, and from time to time breathed gently on the head and eyes. This process was continued for an hour and at the end of it many of the patients were sufficiently influenced to undergo painless operations." (5)

The induction procedure which uses visual fixation is so familiar that it is hard to realize that it was not used until 1842. James Braid (1795–1860) was the first to use it. His method was nearly the same as those that employ fixation today. In the last years of his career he did not insist upon prolonged fixation but had the subject close his eyes after a short time. The fact that he could hypnotize the blind and that seeing subjects could be hypnotized in the dark led him to believe in the essentially subjective nature of hypnosis and to hold that direct verbal suggestion was the best method. Physical methods he regarded as indirect suggestions and as having no effect in themselves; their efficacy depended on the mental processes which they excited.

A feature that is common to all methods in which the subject knows that he is to be hypnotized is a preliminary interview, in which fears are allayed and misconceptions about hypnosis removed. In this talk the subject is asked to tell what he knows about hypnosis, whether he has ever seen anybody hypnotized, and whether he has any fears about unpleasant consequences. The operator assures the subject that susceptibility to hypnosis is no sign of weakness of mind or of will, that there will be no difficulty in bringing him out of the trance, and that he will not be made to do anything foolish or harmful. He tells the subject that most people can be hypnotized to some extent but no one can be hypnotized if he resists the operator's suggestions. The subject is instructed to listen attentively to what the operator says

luncheon clubs, billing himself as "the world's greatest hypnotist." Probably he had by then modernized his methods.

without either resisting or too actively or eagerly striving to be hypnotized, since both of these conditions will work against hypnosis. If a method involving suggestions of sleep is to be used, the operator may compare hypnosis to a sleep in which the sleeper keeps in communication with the operator and is responsive to him. Brenman and Gill (6) in their excellent chapter on induction suggest that hypnosis be compared to the sleep of a mother who remains responsive to the slightest sounds of her child while undisturbed by louder sounds from other sources. The amnesias, hallucinations, and other experiences of the deep trance may be explained by stating that hypnosis is similar to sleep, in which dream images of hallucinatory vividness occur, for which an amnesia often develops after waking like the quick forgetting of dreams.

From the subject's expressions about his understanding of hypnosis the operator may obtain information which will be incorporated into the suggestions given while inducing the trance. Mayer's book, *Die Technik der Hypnose* (17), gives several cases in which the subject's conception, correct or incorrect, of hypnosis was utilized in the induction process.

As a further aid in getting the subject into the proper frame of mind and to increase his belief that he can be hypnotized, the operator may demonstrate ideomotor action by means of a Chevreul pendulum (named for a long-lived French chemist, 1786–1889). A finger ring is suspended by a thread held between the subject's thumb and index finger. The subject's elbow rests on the table; the hand is held as high as possible above the surface of the table. The subject is now told to imagine the ring swinging back and forth over a straight line drawn on the table. He is told not to swing the ring voluntarily, but just to hold it. The ring, with the great majority of subjects, will swing in the imagined direction. The experimenter explains that this experiment demonstrates that all thoughts tend to express themselves in action; similarly, in hypnosis all one has to do is to think vividly of an action suggested, such as going to sleep, and then the action will take place.

The sleeping method

In this method the subject is placed in a comfortable chair with a support for the head or on a couch in a reclining position. He is instructed to relax as much as possible. His relaxation may be tested by lifting an arm and then dropping it; if he is properly relaxed, his arm will be entirely passive and he will not participate either in the lifting or in the return to its original position. The subject is then asked to fixate a small object, such as a thumbtack stuck in the end of a pencil. The operator now begins a continuous and monotonous stream of talk, telling the subject that he is relaxed and feels fatigued, that he feels just as he does before he drops off to sleep at night, that his eyes are especially tired and that they will soon begin to blink more rapidly, that finally they will be unable to stay open any longer and will close, whereupon he will not be able to reopen them until told to do so. Detailed and practically verbatim records of the process are available in Volume 1 of Wolberg's *Medical Hypnosis* (34) and in other books. In my own procedure, when the eyes begin to blink frequently and there are signs that the subject is responding, I place the palm of my hand on the subject's forehead, saying that when I put the hand there the subject will feel much more tired and his eyes will feel so very tired that they will close. In some cases the eyes close of themselves; in others I have the subject follow the fixated object as it moves up and down, the eyes close as the subject looks down, and I then place my finger tips on the lids. I then say, "You will not be able now to open your eyes; when you try to open them you will only raise your brows," and at this point I lift the subject's brows. In this way I attempt to divert any effort to open the lids into another channel, the lifting of the brows. Whether this little trick does any good I do not know. It seems to be helpful. If the subject cannot open his eyes, I then produce catalepsy of the clasped hands, telling him he cannot separate them and that the greater effort he makes, the tighter they will cling to each other. Then other suggestions are tried, such as not being able to lift the hand from the lap or to separate the palms of the hands after they are firmly pressed together. Then an attempt may be made to produce hallucinations; first I try to make the subject feel an ant on his arm and to brush it away, and then I grasp his hand and tell him that he will feel an electric current in his hand. If the subject responds to these suggestions, I may then tell him that he will be able to open his eyes, but he will still be asleep and responsive to my suggestions.

In case the subject cannot open his eyes but does separate his hands, I keep patiently working on the subject with a continuous stream of talk and often find that after a few trials he becomes unable to separate the hands. I have learned in the past few years the value of not giving up too soon and of continuing to work with a subject who fails to respond to certain suggestions. My work with hypnosis has been almost wholly for experimental purposes; this fact somewhat works against the acquisition of a good technique of induction, since no particular person must necessarily be used for experimental work. In therapeutic work, where it is necessary to hypnotize a particular patient, an artful technique must be acquired.

The most reliable sign that the subject is hypnotized is the disinclination to talk which appears in the earlier stages of induction. After eye catalepsy has been produced, the subject will nod or shake his head in answering questions. In my subjects, this is an almost universally present phenomenon. After this reluctance to talk has been dispelled and a conversation begun, the subject will never spontaneously change the topic of conversation. In all my experience, I have seen only one subject, an excellent somnambulist who had been hypnotized several times previously, who introduced a new topic. I suspected that he might be simulating a trance, but I convinced myself that he was not.

The hand-levitation method

In the field of methods of induction, which has been worked over for 150 years, it would seem difficult to be original. However, Dr. Milton Erickson developed in 1928 a method which certainly deserves to be called original.

In this method the subject is seated in a comfortable chair in a relaxed condition. He lays his hands, palms down, on his thighs and is instructed to keep watching them closely. The operator directs the subject's attention to the sensations he is receiving from his hands. Soon, he says, he will notice a small movement in one of the fingers or in the hand. When some movement appears, the operator calls the subject's attention to it, and from now on this hand is the center of the subject's observation. Then it is suggested that the spaces between the fingers will widen, that the fingers will arch up from the thigh, as if they want to lift the hand. Then sensations of lightness in the hand are suggested, and that the hand and arm are slowly rising. As they rise, it is suggested that the subject will feel more and more drowsy and sleepy and that he will want to feel more relaxed and sleepy. As the hand approaches the face, these suggestions are made stronger, but it is stated that the subject will not and must not go to sleep until the hand touches the face. As the hand gets nearer to the face, the suggestions given refer to the eyes, and closure is suggested.

Wolberg (34) gives a verbatim report of the use of this method, which he considers the best of all procedures. The advantages are: (*a*) the patient participates in the induction, and this fact is helpful in certain therapeutic procedures; (*b*) the subject sets his own pace in entering the trance and there are no challenges such as, "You can't open your eyes," with the ensuing embarrassment if the subject does open his eyes. The disadvantage of this method is that it is more time-consuming and requires more effort and endurance on the part of the operator.

My own preference is decidedly for the hand-levitation method over the eye-fixation method. In the latter method the challenges to the subject are difficult to handle; if the subject is able to carry out the act of opening his eyes or unclasping his hands, the process of hypnotization is hindered. I have, however, on a few occasions not been able to produce results with the hand-levitation method and have then hypnotized the subject by using the fixation method.

The method of waking suggestion

The hypnotic state can be induced while the subject is standing erect and without closure of the eyes or any suggestions of relaxation or drowsiness, and without any reduction of sensory input except that which is incident to ocular fixation and concentration of attention.

Here is my own version of the method: The subject stands in front of me and is asked to look steadily into my eyes. I am also standing. I then tell him that he will sway back and forth in response to my suggestions, but he is merely to listen attentively to what I say; he is not to help the swaying along by voluntarily moving back and forth, neither is he to resist swaying. Next I ask him to clasp his hands tightly and hold them in front of his face at the level of his nose. Then I sway toward him with the palms of my hands directed toward him at the level of his shoulders. Then I sway backward. My forward movement toward the subject tends to make him sway backward, since that is a natural reaction in order to get out of my way. The holding of the clasped hands in front of his face impairs somewhat his freedom of movement and perhaps in this way facilitates the swaying. If the swaying appears I then tell him the response will increase in extent each time my hands approach him. I tell him that the next time he sways he will have to take a step backward in order to keep his balance. If he does take the step, I call up an onlooker and tell him to stand behind the subject and catch him if he falls backward. I now tell the subject that he will sway backward but this time he will not be able to bend his knees to take a step and will fall, but the person behind him will catch him.

I next proceed to other suggestions, such as catalepsy of the hands, inability to speak his name, inability to lift a foot from the floor, etc. If the subject has responded to all or most of these suggestions, I then demonstrate amnesia. I take the subject by the hand and say that after I slowly release the hand he will perform an act which will be named at that time and then he will take my hand again. I now release the hand and tell the subject that he will give me his ring or wrist watch. If he does so, I then take his hand and tell him that as I slowly release the hand the memory of what he has just done will gradually leave his mind. Meanwhile I have pocketed the ring or watch. The onlookers later ask the subject the time or where his ring is.

I have on many occasions conducted a full-scale class demonstration of hypnosis with positive and negative hallucinations, amnesia, age-regression, and other standard phenomena by this method of induction in subjects who had never been hypnotized before.

In some subjects I have found that if they disobey instructions and no longer look into my eyes, the spell is broken, and they can unclasp their hands or perform other forbidden acts. I call their attention to the fact that they looked away and in some cases I am able to obtain more complete control of them by the suggestion, "I will be able to control your actions even when you are not looking into my eyes."

This method is a domineering, authoritarian procedure which is useful as an experiment for instructional purposes. It is certainly not a method to be chosen for subjects who are to be given therapy.

Methods making no use of the word hypnosis

Recently papers by Adler and Secunda (1), Conn (9), and Schneck (26) have described methods of induction which avoid the use of the word *hypnosis*.

Adler and Secunda use this method because of objections that patients might have to being hypnotized; many react with fear and misgivings. These physicians make use of two frequent complaints—inability to relax and to concentrate—and tell their patients they will be taught to do both. The patient is given suggestions to relax while he concentrates on looking steadily at his own thumb and forefinger. A greater degree of relaxation will be achieved, the patient is told, when his thumb and forefinger come together. When they do come together, the suggestion is given that a hand will move without effort from the arm-rest to the chair beside the patient. To bridge the gap between the light trance, which by now has been reached, and the deeper trance state, Erickson's hand-levitation technique is used, but without mention of *sleep* or *trance,* for which the word *relaxation* is substituted. ("Touching of your face will be the signal that you are in the deepest stage of relaxation.") The authors state that at this point the patient can be tested for depth of trance if that is desirable. They indicate, as many other therapists do, that deep hypnosis is not necessary for therapeutic results. When the patient is brought out of this state by suggestions of awakening, he usually asks whether he has been asleep or has been hypnotized. Whichever term he uses is accepted. No amnesia is suggested, and it does not appear. The method of Conn is very similar to that of Adler and Secunda.

Schneck's method was developed under conditions in the Army which made it necessary to economize time as much as possible. To save the time required for a preliminary discussion with the patient, in the induction procedure only "relaxation, drowsiness, and possibly sleep" were mentioned. While the reader may have some doubt as to whether the patients of Adler and Secunda and Conn were actually hypnotized or were merely complying with the physicians' directions, he can have little doubt as to the genuineness of Schneck's hypnotism, because he states that he produced motor and sensory phenomena, dreams, automatic writing and drawing, and experimental conflicts. The state was, he says, the same as hypnosis except for the patient's lack of awareness that it was hypnosis. Four out of twenty-two patients inquired if it was hypnosis. Schneck does not state that amnesia occurred.

In Harold Rosen's sensorimotor technique (22) the words *hypnosis* and *sleep* are never used, and subjects are frequently hypnotized without their knowledge. The patient is told to attend to the symptom of which he complains; if he has pain in the lumbar region, he is told to think of his back; if he has trouble relaxing, he is told that his ability to relax is being tested. Every observable reaction, autonomic or motor, is utilized; the reactions are minutely described and commented upon by the therapist, often before the patient is aware of them, "as though they were physiologically based and not about to manifest themselves as a result of suggestions made by the therapist." The whole procedure is nonauthoritarian and permissive, the suggestions are phrased nondirectively, and whether or not amnesia is to occur after disturbing material is recalled or acted out is left to the choice of the patient. The method is called by Rosen a modification of the hand-levitation technique, but raising the hand is not necessarily one of the motor phenomena produced during the process of induction.

The beginner should start by learning the two standard methods, those of eye fixation and hand levitation. After he has obtained some experience in these methods, he may then learn to vary these methods to fit individual cases. Much help in acquiring this ability and in the induction of deep trances may be obtained from a close reading of an article by Erickson (12) in the book edited by LeCron. One of the most remarkable features of his induction procedure is his utilization of the subject's resistances. The suggestions are so worded that a positive or a negative reaction or an absence of reaction are all responses to his suggestion and thus facilitate the process of induction. While his definition of the deep trance given in this article presents a semantic difficulty, since it is stated in terms of a theory rather than descriptively—"a level of hypnosis that permits the subject to function adequately and directly at an unconscious level of awareness without interference by the conscious mind"—the reader can learn by reading further how he describes the deep trance in behavioral terms.

Dehypnotization

The hypnotist can bring the subject out of the trance merely by telling him that he will waken when a signal, such as tapping three times on the table or counting up to five, is given. The subject can himself give the signal.

In my experience, I have never had any trouble with dehypnotization. On one occasion I had to repeat the command to awake three or four times because the subject did not want to perform a posthypnotic suggestion. Several of my colleagues have been troubled by subjects who relapsed into the trance; therefore as a precaution I give, in addition to the usual suggestion of feeling well after the trance, the suggestion, "You will never go back into the trance on your own; you will have to be put back into it by a competent person," before dehypnotization. Whether this has protected me from this trouble or I have only been lucky I do not know.

Williams (33) has collected twelve cases in which subjects did not come out of the trance when the signal was given. The striking fact about these cases is that they were all clearly explainable by reference to the subjects' motives or by their failure to understand instructions. In some cases waking up would have meant a return to unpleasant conditions or the performing of a disagreeable post-hypnotic suggestion. In one case the trance served needs, aggressive and attention-getting, of the subject and was therefore continued after the signal for waking was given. In other cases the subject refused to terminate the trance because of unfinished business; one wanted to see a hallucinated movie through to its end, and another wanted to have the operator try to interpret a dream he had had. One person failed to dehypnotize because the rather complicated instructions regarding the signal were not understood. Another thought that hypnosis was like an Amytal Sodium interview which he had experienced, after which he was supposed to sleep for an hour; because of this self-instruction, he did not awaken from the trance when directed to do so. Williams gives additional cases involving incomplete dehypnotization; in two of them unpleasant emotional reactions originating during the trance persisted into the waking state. The other was a case in which a subject could not open his eyes in the waking state. He had, prior to trance-induction, been asked to choose one suggestion out of a list of ten as one that he would resist in a trance. He chose catalepsy of the eyelids; in the trance he could not resist eye catalepsy, and it persisted afterwards. There is no obvious motivational explanation of these three cases of perseveration.

Rosen (22) describes five cases which have occurred in six years of practice; he presents each case in which the patient refused to come out of the trance with a parallel case of a patient not treated by hypnosis who refused to leave the office when the therapeutic interview was ended. The dynamics are the same in these parallel cases and not hard to uncover; a desire to spend a longer time with the therapist, a wish to finish an hallucination of shooting the therapist are examples. The problem, Rosen states, is not one of hypnosis but of psychotherapy.

A curious case was reported by Raimy (21). A student hypnotized his wife. When he awakened her, she was completely mute as a result of a tonic contracture in and around the throat which prevented her from making sounds or moving the lips. Her husband had tried to dehypnotize her by having her count up to ten in unison with him. While mute she wrote out, "The number seven is hardest to get out; it gets stuck." Speech was partially restored in an hour by relaxation procedures and casual suggestions. On the next day, the subject remembered that several months before she had had Pentothal Sodium given intravenously as an anesthetic for minor surgery. The anesthetist had followed the standard procedure of having her count aloud while the drug was being injected to gauge the depth of anesthesia. She had struggled to count past six and had been unable to pronounce seven. In this case counting served as a stimulus for two conflicting responses—in a past situation it had resulted in an inability to speak, in the present one it was supposed to result in arousal. Raimy recommends that this method of dehypnotization not be used, since the use of Pentothal Sodium is increasing and its use involves counting aloud by the patient. Since so many of Williams' cases were clearly explained by the subject's motivation, the question arises whether Raimy's was also due to motivation or was a rare case in which the subject was the victim of an uncontrollable process of redintegration.

Susceptibility of subjects

One of the most frustrating features of hypnosis is the fact that not all persons are susceptible to it. When the hypnotist fails to induce a trance, his feelings of omnipotence are threatened, and he feels depressed. The psychology of the hypnotist has recently been discussed by Pardell (19), and LeCron (16) has studied the hypnotizability of hypnotists and confirmed Pardell's statement that few hypnotists have themselves been hypnotized.

For many years attempts have been made to determine what kind of person is susceptible to hypnosis. The Abbé Faria in 1819 thought that the "liquidity of the blood" had something to do with it. Today we know hardly more than he knew about the question. Susceptibility is not a sign of low intelligence; there is probably a sex difference in favor of the females but so small as to be of merely academic interest; and older persons are not as susceptible as younger ones. Beyond these facts there is no certainty, one man's findings not being confirmed by the next investigator.

The percentage of persons who are susceptible. Bramwell (5), one of the older authorities, after surveying the literature of the 19th century, stated that the following figures had been established by many independent workers: (*a*) from 78 to 97 per cent of persons are affected to some extent; (*b*) from 10 to 20 per cent of young adults can reach the deepest stage of hypnosis; (*c*) the factor of age is important, since 55 per cent of children can be hypnotized to the deepest stage, but only 7 per cent of persons with ages from fifty-six to sixty-three.

The percentage of normal subjects who can be put with relative ease into the deepest stage, somnambulism with posthypnotic amnesia, is at the present time stated as 20 or 25 per cent when fixation methods are used. W. R. Wells (30) gives even lower figures: "If enough time were spent, up to 20 or 25 per cent of college students could be developed sufficiently for such experiments, but this would call for an immense amount of work . . . Even the great masters, Liébeault and Bernheim, were not able to develop more than 20 per cent of subjects to the somnambulistic stage marked by complete amnesia."

Christenson (8) states his results with Erickson's hand-levitation method. Out of eighty-five volunteers at a soldiers' lounge, about half went into deep somnambulistic trances during the first session; 13 per cent were failures, 21 per cent light trances, 14 per cent borderline cases showing some signs of deep hypnosis but failing to perform posthypnotic acts or to show amnesia. These figures show 52 per cent were somnambulistic subjects; 22 per cent were difficult somnambulisms achieved only after a delay or some struggle, and 30 per cent were easily produced somnambulisms without much dependence on the method. The subjects were about equally divided between soldiers and college girls. About half of the onlookers at the demonstrations volunteered to be subjects. Even if we were to assume that the ones who refused to volunteer were completely refractory to hypnosis, that assumption would merely halve this figure of 52 per cent and make it 26 per cent for the general unselected population.

Sex differences. Women are generally thought to be somewhat more susceptible than men to hypnotic suggestion. No experiment has ever been conducted to determine the influence of the sex of the hypnotist on the susceptibility of his subjects, and this impression may be true only when hypnotists are of the male sex.

When one goes through the long list of articles usually cited on this sex difference (for example, those given by Weitzenhoffer) and omits those which do not report on actual tests of hypnotizability or postural sway, not many are left. Hull (15) reported that women were somewhat more responsive to postural sway than men when the experimenter was a woman, but the difference lacked statistical significance. He combined results from Barry et al. (3) and Davis and Husband (10) and found that women made somewhat higher scores on a scale of hypnotic susceptibility, but again the difference was not significant. He concluded that the average sex difference is comparable, in statistical terms, to about one-fifteenth of the average sex difference in height. Friedlander and Sarbin (14) reported slight but consistent differences in favor of women. Aveling and Hargreaves (2) stated that girls responded more than boys to waking suggestions of hand levitation and hand rigidity. The slight difference which we may conclude probably exists might be of theoretical interest if the relationship of susceptibility to the sex of the hypnotist were determined; clinically whatever difference exists is insignificant.

Differences in intelligence and traits of personality. Attempts to discover what differences exist between good subjects and refractory ones have been very unproductive. One reason for lack of certainty is the fact that existing measures of personality, especially those involving self-description, are of doubtful validity. Intelligence has been found in some studies not to be correlated with susceptibility, while in others a small positive correlation has been obtained. M. M. White (31) obtained a coefficient of .33, and Davis and Husband (10) one of .34 for 22 and 55 college students, respectively, while Hull et al. and Barry et al. (3) obtained zero coefficients. No negative coefficients have been found; one can tell his subjects that to be hypnotizable is not a sign of inferior intelligence. Future investigations should include a wider range of intelligence than is found among college students. Hull (15) and Weitzenhoffer (29) summarize the unsuccessful attempts to establish correlations between susceptibility and intelligence, neurotic traits, extraversion-introversion, and a variety of other traits including such vague ones as "sympathy" and "readiness to confide." To their citations may be added a reference to Sarbin (24), who reports that the hysteria scale on the Minnesota multiphasic personality inventory differentiates somnabulistic subjects from light-trance subjects at the .01 level of confidence. If this finding should be confirmed by others, it will be the first uncontroverted conclusion that can be drawn from the literature on personality differences between susceptible and nonsusceptible subjects.

Some light on susceptibility of normal persons was thrown by the work of H. A. Murray (18) and his collaborators at the Harvard Psychological Clinic, especially by R. W. White. Two kinds of trance were distinguished, the active and the passive. Those persons who go into the latter kind of trance, which is one of drowsiness and sluggishness, have high ratings on the variables of personality which indicate passivity. On the other hand, those who go into the active and alert kind of trance have high ratings on the "need for deference" and "need for affiliation" and low ones on the "need for autonomy." The trance, according to White, can be entered as a result of two different sets of motives. "It can be achieved because the subject is so deferent, so eager to fall in with and please the hypnotist, in which case the trance is of the alert type, or it can be attained for itself as a state of welcome passivity, in which case it is of the sluggish or drowsy type. There are, it would seem, two distinct types of people who can be hypnotized under such circumstances as ours." (32) It should be noted that White's subjects reclined on a couch while relaxation, sleep, and drowsiness were suggested, and the arms were occasionally stroked lightly.

An important study by Rosenzweig and Sarason (23) led to their triadic hypothesis: "Hypnotizability as a personality trait is to be found in positive association with repression as a preferred mechanism of defense and with impunitiveness as a characteristic type of immediate reaction to frustration." By *impunitiveness* is meant the tendency to blame neither others or oneself for a frustration but to gloss the matter over and act as if there had been no frustration. This trait and the coordinate traits of *extrapunitiveness* (blaming others or external things) and *intropunitiveness* (blaming oneself) were measured with the Rosenzweig picture-frustration test. Repression was measured by putting the subject through a test with twelve jigsaw puzzles, in which he was made to fail six times and to succeed six times. If the subject remembered a preponderance of puzzles on which he succeeded, repression was supposed to be demonstrated. The multiple coefficient of correlation of hypnotizability with repression index and impunitiveness was .83.

An abbreviated thematic apperception test was given, including the "hypnosis card" (showing a hypnotist with a subject on a couch). The good and poor subjects could be differentiated to a statistically significant degree by the stories told in response to this card. The verbal and adverbial phrases used in the stories told by the poor subjects were typically extrapunitive in their expression of fear, aggression, and suspicion. The stories of hypnotizable subjects were typically impunitive in conveying cooperativeness, conciliation, and acceptance of the presence and success of hypnosis. Analysis of the stories in terms of needs "shows deference, affiliation, and abasement to be characteristic of the hypnotizable subjects, and autonomy and anxiety of the nonhypnotizable subjects." The results of the study confirm not only White's previous finding with respect to the "hypnosis card" but also something we have known for a long time, namely, that if a person is afraid or suspicious of hypnosis or of the hypnotist, he will very likely prove to be a poor subject.

While Rosenzweig and Sarason's study was well planned and executed, they suggest that further corroborative and elaborative work should be done. Their hypothesis was partially corroborated by the work of Petrie (20). He used seventy-two neurotic patients as subjects and furnished evidence that persons who repress (that is, forget tests after which they were discouraged by comments about their poor work and remember those after which they received praise) tend to be more suggestible than those who do not repress. The coefficient of correlation was small, .32±.16, indicating a very weak linkage of these two traits.

It might be expected that the Rorschach test would show differences between suggestible and nonsuggestible subjects. Sarbin and Madow (25) found that the whole-large detail ratio, W/D, differentiated the good from the poor subjects, those with a ratio above .40 being good subjects. A later study by Brenman and Reichard (7) did not confirm this finding but stated that the differentiation could be made by the amount of the shading response given by the subjects, those whose records showed a large amount of this kind of response being good subjects. The shading response is believed by the experts, or at least some of them, to indicate free-floating anxiety. In a recent doctoral dissertation by Steisel (28) twelve hypotheses relating to possible Rorschach indicators of suggestibility were taken from the writings of the experts and tested. In no case was any relationship demonstrated between a particular Rorschach variable and any test of suggestibility. The postural-sway test, which is highly correlated with hypnotic susceptibility, was included among the tests. Unfortunately Steisel did not refer to the work of Sarbin et al. and Brenman et al. and did not test their conclusions.

Variations in susceptibility. While usually a subject improves in his ability to go into the trance on successive occasions, there are some whose susceptibility shows considerable variability. There is, for example, what is known as *second-session resistance.* A subject who performed well on the first induction either refuses to be hypnotized again or is hypnotized only after a certain period of resistance. The reasons for this change may be that the subject has talked the matter over with someone else who has commented on the silliness of his behavior, or he may have changed his attitude as a result of his own thinking. I recently lost two excellent subjects. Each one watched the other one perform in the trance and was greatly amused, but when each one found out that her own behavior had been of the same kind, she did not keep her appointment for a second induction. This relationship may be reversed: Sarbin (24) tells of a subject who was refractory on the first attempt but on the second trial performed all of the classical tests. The explanation was found in a description of hypnosis that the subject had been asked to write in class. He had written, "It takes time to learn to be hypnotized. Most people can't be hypnotized the first time."

Another cause of decreased hypnotizability in therapeutic cases is an improvement in the patient's condition. The patient may feel, as one put it, that the matter can now be handled "on a more mature basis." A striking case of varying susceptibility was reported by Bird (4) in a patient who was treated with hypnosis for parkinsonism, the tremor being abolished and muscular rigidity diminished for periods up to half an hour in length, while the same control could be effected in the normal state for only 15 seconds at a time. The symptoms having been allayed by pyramidotomy, the patient was refractory to hypnosis, stating he had never been hypnotized and that "weak-mindedness" causes susceptibility to hypnosis. Prior to the surgical operation he had shown some remarkable variations in hypnotizability, which Dr. Bird attempts to explain in psychodynamic terms.

Variability in responsiveness to suggestions in the trance. Now and then a subject is found who is a good somnambulist but who fails to respond to certain suggestions which on the conscious level seem to be entirely free of any emotional complications. One of my good subjects could not be made to experience a visual hallucination; when I would tell her to look at a clock on the wall and tell the time, she would say that she saw no clock and begin to tremble. I never discovered the cause of her anxiety and the failure to produce a visual hallucination, and the subject could throw no light on it herself. An interesting case is described by Ehrenreich (11). A normal girl was able to unclasp her hands in the trance, although she responded to all other suggestions. The hand clasping had no conscious emotional meaning to her. The author hypnotized her thirteen times over a period of several months and tried to discover what hand catalepsy meant to her and why she resisted it. He uncovered some material relating to the subject's childhood, but no clear explanation of the case was found, nor of the change in her behavior which occurred in the eleventh and subsequent sessions, in which she finally was unable to separate the hands. The results of this prolonged probing into the subject's unconscious were essentially negative. The last sentence in Ehrenreich's article shows that this outcome did not weaken the faith that he had at the beginning: "The major missing links in our understanding of hypnotizability are probably to be found in the unconscious needs, wishes, prohibitions, etc., which influence so greatly all of the person's behavior, as well as his response to hypnosis."

Criteria of Hypnosis

The term *criteria* has two meanings in hypnosis. It refers to signs of hypnosis in the individual by which he may be differentiated from a simulator, and it also refers to certain inherent characteristics of the trance which occur without being suggested by the operator.

There are no infallible indicators of the presence of the hypnotic state. The experienced hypnotist, the authorities tell us, can determine whether a subject is hypnotized or not by taking into account all of the symptoms. The absence of any somatic or psychological indicator is somewhat embarrassing; in science one does not like to depend upon the opinions of authorities. Persons who have just entered the trance show a great degree of passivity, a disinclination to talk, and a tendency to reply to questions by movements of the head. After the hypnotist has encouraged the subject to talk, he shows a great degree of literal-mindedness and a lack of spontaneity and initiative. He may participate in ridiculous situations without showing any sign of amusement. Deafness to the voices of the onlookers may be suggested—it sometimes appears to arise spontaneously—and disparaging or humorous remarks made about the subject produce no sign of reaction on his part. When anesthesia of the skin is produced, the subject's insensitivity to strong stimulation may be considered good evidence, but I have seen some excellent simulations of such anesthesia by college students. Even when a somnambulistic subject is given an instruction which produces a certain amount of self-initiated activity, such as making a talk before the class on a topic of his own choice, there is nevertheless a certain narrowness of the subject's scope of awareness and of his actions which can be recognized; his activities are always confined to a field which is more restricted than it would be under normal conditions.

One of the most infallible indicators that a trance was genuine is afforded by some characteristics of posthypnotic behavior. One of my subjects, hypnotized on only two occasions, experienced tingling sensations in her thighs when the trance was being induced; subjective sensations are not uncommonly reported. The subject was given a posthypnotic suggestion of writing her name on the blackboard. After she came out of the trance and the signal was given for the posthypnotic act, she began to feel the tingling sensations, performed the act, and returned to her seat. Later she was questioned about what she had done since she was brought out of the trance; she named several things, but she failed to report the posthypnotic act. Not one person in a thousand knows that a spontaneous and self-terminating trance often occurs during the performance of a posthypnotic suggestion and there is amnesia for the act performed; there is thus no knowledge available which can be used for simulation. In this case the recurrence of the queer sensations at the beginning of this spontaneous trance was especially interesting.

In the past it was believed that there were three inherent characteristics of hypnosis—criteria in the second sense stated above. This triad, amnesia, rapport, catalepsy, was considered not to be produced by suggestion.

An article by Young (35) in 1926 contributed much to dispel this belief. Young showed that *rapport*, the dependence of subject on operator, could be abolished for certain suggestions. One of his colleagues who was not a hypnotist told Young's subjects to determine to resist certain suggestions which were liable to be given in the next hypnotic session. They successfully resisted the suggestions which they had previously chosen to resist. *Catalepsy* (waxy flexibility) is the result of suggestion, since no spontaneous tendency to it is observed, and the mere lifting of a subject's arm may be considered a suggestion. Also *amnesia* is not an inherent feature of the trance, since the hypnotist can make the subject remember some, all, or none of the events of the trance. With these three alleged criteria gone, hypnosis became simpler; Hull defined it as a state of generalized hypersuggestibility.

While no one of this triad can be considered a *sine qua non* of hypnosis, a spontaneous tendency toward amnesia may occur. Eysenck and Furneaux (13) report an experiment in which they hypnotized subjects by a relaxation method. The subjects fixated a bright object while a continuous low sound was made, and suggestions of fatigue and closure of the eyelids, arm catalepsy, etc., were given. No subject seemed to suspect that he had been hypnotized when he was questioned a few days later by a colleague. A considerable amount of amnesia appeared after the hypnosis. The subjects were questioned about the twenty-two suggestions that had been given. The amnesia was greater in the subjects who had responded to the largest number of the suggestions, a smaller number of suggestions being recalled. This amnesia occurring without suggestion of amnesia is worthy of additional investigation.

REFERENCES

1. Adler, M. H., and L. Secunda: "An Indirect Technique to Induce Hypnosis," *J. Nervous Mental Disease* **106**:190–193 (1947).
2. Aveling, F., and H. L. Hargreaves: "Suggestibility with and without Prestige in Children," *Brit. J. Psychol.* **12**:53–75 1921–1922).
3. Barry, H., Jr., D. W. Mackinnon, and H. A. Murray, Jr.: "Studies in Personality: A. Hypnotizability as a Personality Trait and Its Typological Relations," *Hum. Biol.* 3:1–36 (1931).
4. Bird, H. W.: "Varying Hypnotizability in a Case of Parkinsonism," *Bull. Menninger Clin.* **12**:210–217 (1948).
5. Bramwell, J. M.: *Hypnotism, its History, Practice, and Theory,* 3d ed. London, Rider & Co., 1913.
6. Brenman, M., and M. Gill: *Hypnotherapy,* New York, International Universities Press, 1947.
7. Brenman, M., and S. Reichard: "Use of the Rorschach Test in the Prediction of Hypnotizability." *Bull. Menninger Clin.* **7**: 183–187 (1943).
8. Christenson, J. A.: "Dynamics in Hypnotic Induction," *Psychiatry* **12**:37–54 (1949).
9. Conn, J. H.: "Hypno-synthesis," *J. Nervous Mental Disease* **109**: 9–24 (1949).
10. Davis, L. W., and R. W. Husband: "A study of Hypnotic Susceptibility in Relation to Personality Traits," *J. Abnormal & Soc.*

Psychology **26**:175–182 (1931).

11. Ehrenreich, G. A.: "The Influence of Unconscious Factors on Hypnotizability," *Bull. Menninger Clin.* **15**:45–57 (1951).
12. Erickson, M. H.: "Deep Hypnosis and Its Induction," in LeCron, L., ed., *Experimental Hypnosis*, New York, The Macmillan Company, 1952.
13. Eysenck, H. J., and W. D. Furneaux: "Primary and Secondary Suggestibility: An Experimental and Statistical Study," *J. Exp. Psychol.* **35**:485–503 (1945).
14. Friedlander, J. W., and T. R. Sarbin: "The Depth of Hypnosis," *J. Abnormal & Soc. Psychology* 33:453–475 (1938).
15. Hull, C. L.: *Hypnosis and Suggestibility*, New York, D. Appleton-Century Company, Inc., 1933.
16. LeCron, L.: "A Study of the Hypnotizability of Hypnotists," *Personality* **1**:300–306 (1951).
17. Mayer, L.: *Die Technik der Hypnose*, Munich, J. F. Lehmann, 1934.
18. Murray, H. A., Jr.: *Explorations in Personality*, New York, Oxford University Press, 1938.
19. Pardell, S. S.: "The Psychology of the Hypnotist," *Psychiat. Quart.* **24**:483–491 (1950).
20. Petrie, A.: "Repression and Suggestibility as Related to Temperament," *J. Personality* **16**:445–458 (1948).
21. Raimy, V.: "A Note on Hypnotic Technique," *J. Clin. Psychol.* **5**:423–424 (1949).
22. Rosen, H.: *Hypnotherapy in Clinical Psychiatry*, New York, Julian Press, Inc., 1953.
23. Rosenzweig, S., and S. Sarason: "An Experimental Study of the Triadic Hypothesis in Relation to Frustration, Ego-defense, and Hypnotic Ability," *Character and Pers.* **11**:1–14, 150–165 (1942).
24. Sarbin, T. R.: "Contributions to Role-taking Theory. I. Hypnotic Behavior," *Psychol. Rev.* **57**:255–270 (1950).
25. ——— and L. W. Madow: Predicting the Depth of Hypnosis by Means of the Rorschach Test," *Am. J. Orthopsychiat.* **12**:268–271 (1942).
26. Schneck, J. M.: "Modified Technique for the Induction of Hypnosis," *J. Nervous Mental Disease* **106**:77–79 (1947).
27. Schneider, E.: *Der animale Magnetismus: seine Geschichte und seine Beziehungen zur Heilkunst*, Zurich, Konrad Lampert Verlag, 1950.
28. Steisel, I. M.: "The Rorschach Test and Suggestibility," *J. Abnormal & Soc. Psychology* **47**:608–614 (1952).
29. Weitzenhoffer, A.: *Hypnotism*, New York, John Wiley & Sons, Inc., 1953.
30. Wells, W. R.: "Expectancy versus Performance in Hypnosis," *J. Gen. Psychol.* **35**:99–119 (1946)
31. White, M. M.: "The Physical and Mental Traits of Individuals Susceptible to Hypnosis," *J. Abnorm. Soc. Psychol.* **25**:293–298 (1930).
32. White, R. W.: "An Analysis of Motivation in Hypnosis," *J. Gen. Psychol.* **24**:145–162 (1941).
33. Williams, G. W.: "Difficulty in Dehypnotizing," *J. Clin. Exp. Hypnosis* **1**:3–12 (1953).
34. Wolberg, L. R.: *Medical Hypnosis*, 2 vols. New York, Grune & Stratton, Inc., 1945.
35. Young, P. C.: "Hypnotism," *Psychol. Bull.* **23**:504–523 (1926).

Frank J. Kirkner, Ph.D.

3

CONTROL OF SENSORY AND PERCEPTIVE FUNCTIONS BY HYPNOSIS

SENSORY AND PERCEPTIVE functions are subject to error and modification. The degree of their accuracy or error may be judged by accepted reality criteria. Error as well as accuracy of these functions is determined by natural processes. The locus of error may be in the stimulus object, stimulus energy, sense organ, afferent pathway, or central processes of sensing and perceiving.

Sense data are usually at variance with the physical world and are corrected in the process of perceiving by memory. The stimulus object may be misleading and the result is a faulty perception or illusion. Common examples of such stimulus objects are shown in Figures 1 and 2 from Dunlap (14).

Figure 1 is Zöller's figure. While the long vertical lines appear as if they would converge if extended, they are actually parallel. Figure 2 is Müller-Lyer's figure. The vertex of the middle angle divides the horizontal line into two equal parts. These are optical illusions of spatial relations.

The physical stimulus may be misleading. For instance, light energy passing from one medium to another of different density at an angle changes its direction. This refraction of light reflected from a submerged object as viewed from above the surface of the water gives a false impression of the actual position of the object.

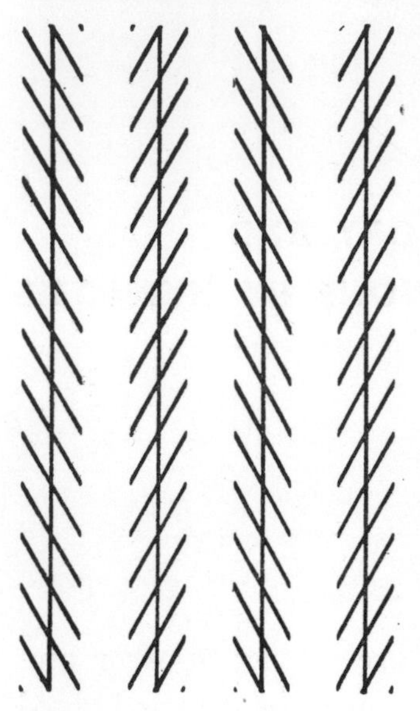

Figure 1. Zöller's figure.

The sense organ may be the locus of some errors. The illusion of movement occurring in postrotational nystagmus is the result of a complicated vestibular reflex and the retinal image shifts.

In certain pathological conditions the afferent pathway is the locus. The hallucinatory experiences of the phantom limb may be attributed to the activation of impulses by a neuroma. This is discussed by Dorcus and Shaffer (13). Figure 3 is from the same source. Pain is frequently a most troublesome sensation. As shown in this figure, it is perceived as if it were emanating in the manner in which it was learned. The impulses previously originating at *A* and *B* are transmitted over trunk *C*. Impulses activated by pressure at points where they now terminate by amputation are centrally interpreted as if originating at *A* and *B*.

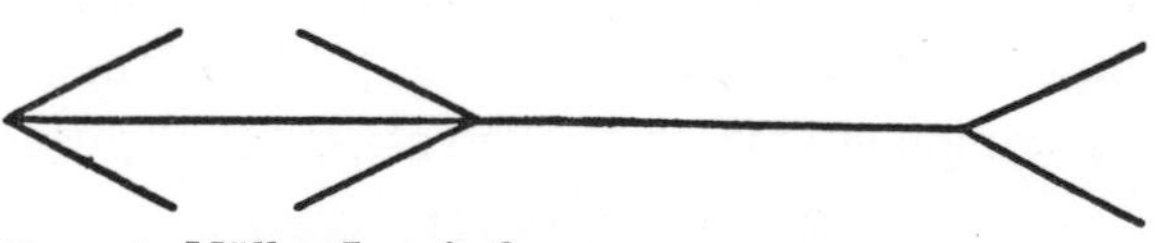

Figure 2. Müller-Lyer's figure.

When something is perceived it takes on meaning by association. The sense data are integrated with the associations and perception occurs. Perception, then, is dependent upon sense data and learning. Learning determines attitude or what is selected for perceiving and what is done about it. According to Boring,

Langfeld, and Weld (2), attitudes are formed by suggestion, generalization of personal experiences, and emotional trauma.

By suggestion is meant the acceptance of norms of society as they impinge upon the individual. This is uncritical acceptance.

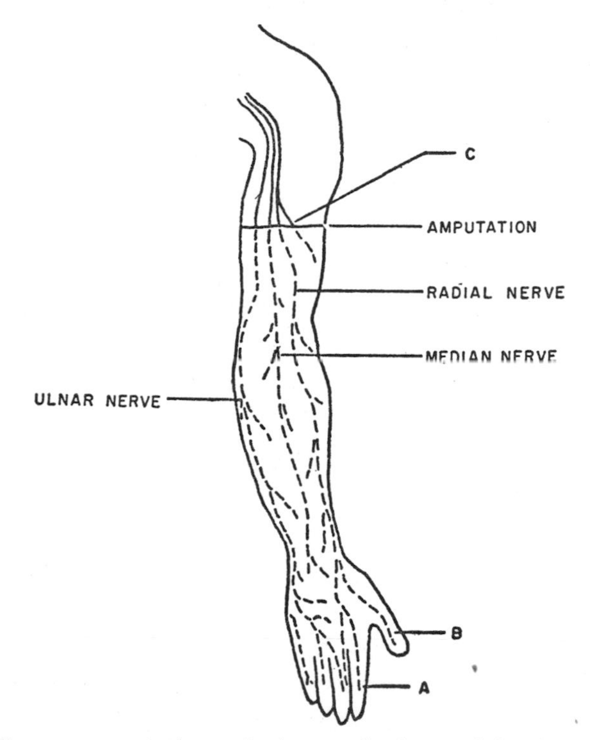

Figure 3. After an amputation pain is perceived as originating at *A* and *B* where it was first learned.

As experience and training increases, there is less dependence upon suggestion. There are times of emotional stress, when critical thinking is interfered with, at which times there is an increased susceptibility to suggestion.

Personal experiences, past and present, are evaluated and generalized. This involves acceptance and rejection and serves as a background for future experiences.

Traumatic events may shatter previously accepted values and

result in rejection and substitution. As these factors modify behavior they represent a learning process.

The literature on waking suggestibility has been reviewed by Dorcus and Shaffer (13) under the heading of Susceptibility to Nonprestige Waking Suggestion. Illusions of smell, taste, spatial relations, movement, warmth, weights, etc., following suggestions to children and adults in the waking state are reported by Small (48), Brown (4), Triplett (53), Guidi (24), Heron (29), and others.

Hypnosis as a state of hypersuggestibility provides an excellent means of influencing sensory and perceptive functions. The readiness with which these changes occur has resulted in fantastic beliefs of the potency of hypnosis. Many of these earlier beliefs have been converted into hypotheses and subjected to rigorous testing in the laboratory. These experiments include investigations of the effectiveness of suggestion in the trance state for the control of functions of sight, hearing, taste, touch, pain, warmth, vertigo, fatigue, and time.

Sight

Studies on the influence of hypnotic control of visual functions include visual acuity, size perception, uniocular anesthesia, negative hallucinations, and positive hallucinations.

Sterling and Miller, Young, Eysenck, and Weitzenhoffer have explored the effects of hypnosis on visual acuity.

Sterling and Miller (50) compared visual perceptual acuity and visual sensory acuity in the trance and waking states, in well-controlled experiments. In the comparison of *visual perceptual acuity,* the circle, square, plus, and star on four of Rhine's ESP cards were used as stimuli. The depth of hypnotism ranged from "very light" to "deep." Of the nine subjects, five performed better and four worse in the trance. As a group the performance was slightly better in the waking state. There was no apparent relation with the depth of hypnosis. *Visual sensory acuity* was found to average out about the same in trance and waking states.

Young, Eysenck, and Weitzenhoffer investigated the effect of hypnosis on the *discriminatory recognition* of visual patterns. The testing of this function usually consists of the exposure of a stimulus such as an ink blot, postage stamp, or playing card. The stimulus pattern is exposed later for recognition among other similar stimuli. Young (59) tested visual acuity in the waking state and in hypnosis with ink blots. The ratio for the two states averaged 100 with five subjects above 100 or doing better, three below 100 or worse, and three the same in the hypnotic state. Later, Young (60) reported another study in which he used postage stamps as stimulus material with similar results. He concluded that "in the past the hypnotic performances were marvelous mainly because the normal waking ability, not having been adequately tested, was considered inconsequential, or else because of the peculiar constitution of the hypnotic subject." Eysenck (22), using the same comparative method, got similar results for one or two subjects when he used stimulus cards with geometrical drawings and the reverse side of playing cards. However, his data show a significant improvement in the hypnotic state with the Müller-Lyer figure and the color-equation test, with critical ratios of 4.1 and 3.5, respectively. This variability suggests that unknown variables are operating which may be intrinsic in the stimuli or the subject.

The above studies were critically evaluated by Weitzenhoffer (55) and then repeated. His experimental design was formulated to avoid previous weaknesses. He took the following precautions: (*a*) to make suggestions of improving visual perception and memory rather than just urge the subjects to do their best; (*b*) to determine carefully the depth of trance; (*c*) to allow time for a *mental set* and reorientation of the subject, according to Erickson (19); (*d*) to differentiate between *active* and *passive* subjects, as reported by White (56); and (*e*) to pre-test and adjust the difficulty of the task.

His subjects were undergraduate volunteers at the University of Oklahoma. Twenty-three were selected for further screening. As criteria for the depth of hypnosis, he used the David-Husband (11) scale as shown in Table 1. The description of *depth* is in

Table 1. Scoring System for Hypnotic Susceptibility

Depth	Score	Objective symptoms
Insusceptible	0	
Hypnoidal	1	
	2	Relaxation
	3	Fluttering of lids
	4	Closing of eyes
	5	Complete physical relaxation
Light trance	6	Catalepsy of eyes
	7	Limb catalepsies
	10	Rigid catalepsy
	11	Anesthesia (glove)
Medium trance	13	Partial amnesia
	15	Posthypnotic anesthesia
	17	Personality changes
	18	Simple posthypnotic suggestions
	20	Kinesthetic delusions; complete amnesia
Somnambulistic trance	21	Ability to open eyes without affecting trance
	23	Bizarre posthypnotic suggestions
	25	Complete somnambulism
	26	Positive visual hallucinations, posthypnotic
	27	Positive auditory hallucinations, posthypnotic
	28	Systematized posthypnotic amnesias
	29	Negative auditory hallucinations
	30	Negative visual hallucinations; hyperesthesias

the first column, *score value* of each in the second, and criteria or *objective symptoms* in the third. Of the twenty-three subjects, two were unsusceptible; the depth of fourteen subjects ranged from hypnoidal with "complete physical relaxation" to medium light trance with "limb catalepsies," and six ranged from the lower to the upper limits of the state of somnabulistic trance.

The trance characteristics of the subjects selected to complete the experiment are shown in Table 2. The score is cumulative and ranges from 28 to 341 in the table.

Table 2. Characteristics of Ss Completing the Experiment

N	Trance depth	Score	Type
1	Medium-light	28	Moderately active
1	Medium	59	Moderately active
1	Deep	112	Passive
3	Deep	138	Moderately active
1	Very deep	341	Very active

Using the inverse side, he arranged ten series of playing cards. The card-recognition limit for each subject was ranked on a scale from 0 to 10. The mean difficulty score of the twenty-three subjects was 4.5 as compared with 6.0 for the trance group.

The testing was systematically carried out with a maximum of five sessions. It was found that all but one of the seven subjects in the trance group had scores which were practically identical for the pre-trance, trance, and post-trance tests. The subject with the greatest depth and "very active" type was superior. He is referred to as L. G. In waking he had a score of 7.0. In the trance his score was perfect on recognition and without hesitation.

L. G. was tested further. A more complex pattern of the back of playing cards was used, color was hallucinated on blank white cards, and distance was tested. He was able to pass the first color-hallucination test, but as the tests became more complicated, response time increased and confusion was manifested. An optimal distance for the best performance was found to exist.

As well as in the waking state, individual differences appear to exist in hypnosis. L. G. was superior in both states. In addition, he differed from the others in acquiring the "very deep" state and being "very active." However, unless this is an "all-or-none" phenomenon, one would anticipate some correlations with these hypnotic characteristics. Another possibility is that some subjects were motivated to perform this function to their maximum ability in the waking state while others were not.

Inasmuch as these results show that visual acuity may be increased, the same, or decreased in hypnosis, apparently hypnosis per se as a single variable cannot be depended upon to lower thresholds.

Ashley, Harper, and Runyon (1) investigated the effects of hypnotically induced economic states on the visually *perceived size* of coins and metals in our value system. The subjects were fourteen students of about the middle socioeconomic status. After the subjects were hypnotized, amnesia was suggested for their life histories with the exception of their names. Prepared "rich" and "poor" histories were substituted according to the experimental situation the investigators wanted to establish. In the main part of the experiment a penny, nickel, dime, and quarter were used to serve as the stimulus values, either present or remembered. In the supplementary part of the experiment, a gray slug was used. The subjects were told it was made of either lead, silver, white gold, or platinum. In all cases, the subjects were instructed to adjust a spot of light to the size of the object. The difference in the perceived size of the coins in the "rich" and "poor" was found to be significant to better than the 5 per cent level of confidence for all of the coins with the exception of the nickel which was significant between the 5 per cent and 10 per cent level. In the judgments of the metals, the "poor" perceived them larger than the "rich" but in either situation the slug increased with the cost of the metal. This cost-value difference was found to be significant to less than the 1 per cent level of confidence. The authors conclude that "the psychological organization (which is responsible for the wants, needs, interest, attitudes, and values) of a person contributes to the figural organization of his perceptions."

A single case was reported (35, 36) in which the activity of the alpha rhythm (EEG) was observed in relation to the periodic suggestion of *blindness* in the hypnotic state. The eyelids were taped open and the subject was hypnotized. It was found that whether the experiment was in a light room or dark room trains appeared with the suggestion of blindness and discontinued with the suggestion of seeing. These results were not completely reproducible with a nonhypnotized subject. In a dark room the alpha rhythm would stop when it was suggested that the subject saw something, but it would not start in a light room when it was suggested that the subject saw nothing. These researchers and others (5, 33, 51, 52) report the transitory nature of the alpha rhythm in the waking state associated with a variety of stimuli, and conscious processes not traced to detectable stimuli.

Experiments on hypnotically induced *colorblindness* are reported by Erickson and by Harriman.

In his study Erickson (20) selected six subjects. There were two nurses, two occupational therapists, one medical student, and one hospital attendant. Four were female and two male. None of them had had any acquaintance with the Ishihara test. As the experimental design was conceived, there was no preliminary test of their color vision, although later they were found to have normal color vision. To acquaint the subjects with the task, calendar numbers were presented under test conditions on cards similar to the plates. The subjects were required to read them to the experimenter.

Suggestions of total red, green, and red-green colorblindness were given in a prearranged order, resulting in a different pattern for each subject. In general the hypnotic procedure was to induce gradually a somnambulistic state. Then hypnotic blindness was induced by degrees to carry over posthypnotically. Part of the vision was restored, with blindness retained for a color or colors. For the color inhibited, instructions given included "amnesia of all connotations and associations for that color, thereby rendering the name of the color either a nonsense syllable or a totally unfamiliar word."

All sixteen plates of the Ishihara test were used with a total of thirteen administrations. A comparison of normal color-vision and defective color-vision responses as abstracted from Erickson's detailed data, based on the six subjects, is shown in Table 3. The headings of vertical columns indicate the types of suggested blindness, normal color-vision responses, defective color-vision responses, and total responses. The key indicates the meaning of the symbols in the subcolumns. The numbers in parentheses under the symbols are the expectancy responses for these categories. The order of increasing response to suggestion from low to high is green, red, red-green, and total.

Table 3. Results of Ishihara Test in Hypnotically Induced Colorblindness

	Normal			Defective					
Suggested	N (60)	N/T (18)	N/RG (12)	T (60)	RG (48)	R (12)	G (12)	D or N/T	Total
Green	30			19	23	1	1	16	90
Red	17			20	26	8	0	19	90
Red-green	6			42	32	8	2	0	90
Total colorblindness	4			51	13	4	5	13	90

KEY: N normal; T total colorblindness; RG red-green; R red; G green; D uncertain

Noting the differences of opinion between Erickson and Grether as to what actually occurred in Erickson's colorblindness experiment, Harriman (25, 26) set out to discover whether the alterations in color vision induced during hypnosis were comparable in degree and character with actual colorblindness (as Erickson concluded) or differed from color-vision deficiency as found among the population with this deficiency (as believed by Grether). Sixteen subjects participated in the two experiments. All subjects met the depth requirements of 28 on the Davis scale. Red-green blindness was hypnotically induced with timing, lighting, and other relative factors carefully taken into consideration. Harriman drew the following conclusions:

1. Color-vision anomalies can be induced by hypnotic procedures.
2. These alterations in the responses of normal subjects resemble attitudinal changes more closely than they resemble profound change in sensory content.
3. There are, in general, wide differences between color-vision anomalies induced by hypnosis and those which occur naturally.
4. Hypnotic colorblindness is characterized by negative type of behavior, but the subjects do not interpret the usual tests for colorblindness in the positive manner which is a distinctive feature of true colorblindness.
5. Parsimoniously interpreted, these investigations indicate that by a hypnotic technique the subjects were given an appropriate mental set, for which amnesia was then induced; and that their responses depended upon the nature of the suggestions.

The relation of the projection of the *afterimage* following the hypnotic induction of hallucinated color was explored by Erickson and Erickson, Rosenthal and Mele, and Hibler and Dorcus.

Erickson and Erickson (21) report the hypnotic hallucination of the psychological primary colors, followed by their negative afterimages. The experiment was conducted with five university freshmen in commerce and engineering. They were trained and responded to hypnosis with a very deep trance. Word-association tests were administered before and after trance induction as controls to check the associations with the primary colors.

The colors were hallucinated on sixteen sheets of plain white typing paper. The instructions went as follows: "I am going to show you, one at a time, sheets of colored paper. Each sheet is entirely of one solid color. I will name the color of the first sheet, and you will name the color of the next sheet. You will continue in this alternate fashion. As I name the color of the first sheet, you will look at it carefully until you see it plainly and clearly, just exactly as I have described it. Nod your head as soon as you see it plainly, and I will then put it out of sight in the left hand-drawer of the desk and take a new one from the right-hand drawer. As I show this next sheet, you are to look at it carefully and tell me what color it is. It, too, will be of a single bright color, but a color different from the one I named. After you have named the color of your sheet, it will then be my turn. . . ." As each color was suggested, it was accompanied by the adjective *bright*.

Of the five subjects, one was unable to hallucinate color. The other four responded every time with the appropriate complementary color, although the colors were duller than those suggested. When the second word-association test was administered, nine color associations were revealed, two of which were complementary colors. Of these two, one was given by the subject who did not respond to color suggestion. In the final step of the experiment the subjects were questioned. They were "unable to define or to name complementary colors when asked directly." Even after a definition was given, the tendency was to contrast dimensions other than quality.

Without going into detail, Rosenthal and Mele (43) obtained similar results to those under discussion. They found knowledge of afterimages in one of their four subjects in the waking state. They raise a doubt as to the extent of this knowledge in the other three subjects when they say, "Since our Ss were quizzed in the waking state and not in the hypnotic state, it might be possible that they were not as naive about knowledge of after-images, i.e., unconsciously, as the test of conscious knowledge would indicate."

Taking into consideration the improbability that these results could be obtained in the waking state, Erickson and Erickson offer two hypotheses to account for them. The first one is based on association and unconscious experiencing of the afterimage in everyday life. The implication is that a central process of unconscious association is attained in the hypnotic state. The second includes the concept of the first. It is based on the mental set and the tension created by the task, which leads to psychophysiological processes resulting in readjustment or a response to relieve the tension. The limitations of this response are determined both by the experimental situation and the residua of previous color experiences and associations.

Using laboratory equipment, Hibler (30) repeated the above experiment with some variations which will be discussed later.

Table 4. Experimental Results

	Trance hallucination of colors on blank cards			Trance hallucination involving color changes		
Subject	Color hallucinated as stimulus	Afterimage reported in trance	Afterimage reported in waking state	Suggested hallucination	Afterimage reported in trance	Afterimage reported in waking state
A		Blue	None		Blue	Green
B	Blue	Orange	None	Red as	Green	Green
C		Yellow	None	blue	Yellow	Green
D		Yellow	None		Green	Green
A		Red	None		Red	Orange
B	Red	Green	None	Blue as	Orange	Orange
C		Green	None	red	Green	Yellow
D		Green	None		Yellow	Yellow
A		Yellow	None		Yellow	Pink
B	Yellow	Purple	None	Green as	Red	Red
C		Blue-gray	None	yellow	Blue	Pink
D		Blue	None		Pink	Pink
A		Green	None		Green	Purple
B	Green	Red	None	Yellow as	Blue	Blue
C		Red	None	green	Red	Purple
D		Dark red	None		Blue	Blue

His results are shown in Table 4. The hallucinated color was followed by the complementary color or an approximation to it by subjects *B, C,* and *D,* while subject *A* reported the same color for the afterimage. Subjects *A* and *C* remained true to form for the hallucinated color when it was suggested in the presence of a physical stimulus of another color. Under these conditions, *B* and *D* reported the afterimage of the physical stimulus. No afterimage to the gray disk was reported in the waking state. Complementary colors or close approximations following physical stimuli were reported by all subjects in the waking state.

Hibler agrees with Erickson and Erickson on the prerequisite of the association of the afterimage with the hallucinated color, but evidently would disagree on the level of consciousness at which this occurs. Among the criticisms of Hibler's investigation, Erickson (16) questions the depth of trance in which subjects "may not experience visual hallucinations when so instructed, but may, at a level of verbalized agreement, give the expected answer," and the failure to utilize a "period of time directly proportional to the complexity of the alterations desired" in the establishment of the hypnotic trance.

Dorcus (12) investigated the afterimage phenomenon prior to the above experiments. His test was more complicated than those reported above. Five subjects were tested, after one was disqualified because of red-green colorblindness. He used cards 3b, 4a, and 6c of the Wallin set made by Stoelting. Card 3b was used to check color vision and the other two were used in the experiment proper. The complexity of the test is obvious in Dorcus's explanation in which he states, "Card 6c contains a blue disc, the after-image of which is normally projected on blue and produces gray. The hypnotic Ss received suggestions to the effect that the original blue was green. The after-image of the suggested color green when combined with blue would produce a red-blue mixture instead of the usual gray." The results show that the physical stimulus was dominant.

Considering the findings of these experimenters it appears that (*a*) positive color hallucinations have been demonstrated, and (*b*) pseudo-negative afterimages may follow, if the task is not too complicated. Also, there is disagreement on the level of consciousness at which these responses occur.

Pattie (39) used five subjects to test the effectiveness of suggested *uniocular blindness* in the hypnotic trance. One of the subjects responded sufficiently to indicate by her reports the loss of vision. Pattie later proved the eye was functioning.

Lundholm (37) induced *negative* and *positive hallucinatory conditioned stimuli.* A reflex was conditioned to the lighting of a lamp. It failed to appear when hypnotic blindness for the lamp was induced. He then suggested to a hypnotized subject that a lamp would light up every time he received a shock. The subject hallucinated the lighting of the lamp. It was then found that the subject would withdraw his hand when the electric lamp was actually turned on. Lundholm contributes this failure to respond overtly to inhibition.

Erickson (19) reports *negative hallucinations* involving members of a group of people. His demonstration was made before a medically trained group with a female subject. He made certain that she recognized every member of the group by name before he gradually step by step rationalized the absence of Dr. A from the room. A similar procedure was used to psychologically absent Dr. B. The subject was then requested to identify those present. She performed the task without apparent hesitation by omitting Dr. A and Dr. B. The group, with the exception of A and B, was then told quietly to challenge her statements. She behaved differently in regard to A and B. She had no trouble in explaining A's absence as a matter of fact. When challenged on B, she showed avoidance and confusion.

The demonstrations show overt evidence of the hypnotic induction of negative and positive hallucinations. Some behavior is suggestive of inhibition and conflict.

Hearing

Hypnotic suggestion has been applied to audition to test acuity by Sterling and Miller, Schneck and Bergman, and Schneck and to induce total deafness and selective deafness by Pattie, Erickson, Lundholm, and Dynes.

Sterling and Miller (50) found no significant difference for *auditory acuity* for a pure tone frequency of 925 v/s in the hypnotic and waking states. Schneck and Bergman (47) tested eight subjects for auditory acuity in the waking state and in hypnosis. Frequencies ranged from 128 to 8,191 v/s. Among the subjects were two with normal hearing, four with defective hearing, and two suspected of psychiatric difficulties. Of the sixteen ears, there was no response for one ear, five ears showed greater acuity in hypnosis, and ten in the waking state. In another report, Schneck (46) presented data which show that the aid of hypnosis was ineffective in significantly changing sensitivity for three non-psychiatric cases, but there was a marked increase in sensitivity for three psychiatric cases with histories of hearing interferences. Of these latter three cases, two demonstrated amnesia for the test situation. The author raises the question of the importance of depth in effecting a difference in the audiograms for the hypnotic and waking states. The writer hypothesizes that these three psychiatric cases have a functional overlay that is circumvented through hypnosis.

Pattie (40) induced hypnotic *unilateral deafness* in four subjects and presented evidence that binaural hearing was operating.

Erickson (17) performed an elaborate investigation of *hypnotic deafness*. He remained flexible and as events occurred he utilized them. In his introduction he states, ". . . significant questions centering about this manifestation concern first of all, its comparability with organic deafness, and secondly, the nature of the processes entering into its production, whether as an actual or only an apparent condition, together with the systematic problems that arise in distinguishing between 'apparent' and 'actual.' "

The subjects for the experiment were screened. Starting with more than 100 normal college students who had training as hypnotic subjects, about 70 were selected. Later this number was reduced to 30 by further screening. These were classified in three groups on the basis of the depth of the trance. Of these 30, 10 more were eliminated when they gave no evidence of induced deafness. Apparent anacusia was induced in 6, and the remaining 14 showed various degrees of auditory impairment.

As some of the unexpected hypnotic behavior seems to be related to induction suggestions, part of his instructions and suggestions for induction will be quoted:

1. *A clear concise emphatic statement that it was proposed "to hypnotize" him into a state of absolute deafness.*
2. *The statement that, as this was done, hypnotic suggestions would be given which would cause slight difficulty and then more and more difficulty in hearing until finally all sounds, including the hypnotist's voice "would fade into nothingness."*
3. *The statement that, as all sounds faded away, he would receive a sharp slap on the shoulder which would cause "the utter silence of absolute deafness," and that* ever afterwards whenever he was in a deep trance *merely a blow on the shoulder would produce "instant and absolute deafness."*
4. *The statement that the deafness would persist* unchanged and complete *until his right wrist was squeezed, or until he was informed definitely in some way to recover his hearing, whereupon his hearing would return "instantly and completely."*
5. *The induction of a state of amnesia for all commands and instruction, the amnesia to be present continuously for all future trance, post-hypnotic and waking states.*

Erickson classified the clinical findings of his experimental group as follows:

1. *Impairment of auditory functioning*
   a. *Fluctuation of auditory threshold*

1. *Progressive increase in deafness*
2. *Progressive decrease in deafness*

b. *Impairment of spatial localization and time relationships*

c. *Impairment of sound discrimination*

2. *Selective deafness*
3. *Hallucinatory phenomena and dependence on visual cues*
4. *Associated sensory changes and motor disturbances*
5. *Apparently total hypnotic deafness*

Auditory threshold fluctuations either progressively increased or decreased. The behavior of two subgroups are discussed on this basis.

For those in which the threshold progressively increased, it became necessary for the experimenter to keep elevating his voice. The subject seemed to hear clearly for a while and then observed that the experimenter's voice was gradually becoming a "mumble." This process continued until a subjective experience of "complete silence" came over the subject. To check this phenomenon further, the subject was blindfolded. Then he was spoken to with increasing loudness followed by silence for a short period. When speech was resumed, a minute or so would elapse before the subject would again hear "mumbling" which would then fade out. This pattern continued with the repetition of the voice following silence. The lag in the response seems to Erickson to be a result of a summation in the nervous system. Another possible explanation is that inhibition became lax during the silence and strengthened with the voice stimulus.

The reverse happened with some of the other subjects. They showed the pattern of gradually regaining hearing when talked to and losing it during silence. Generally speaking, the amount of threshold increase bore a direct relation with the duration of silence. The elimination of visual cues slowed up the process.

Similar results were obtained with the decreased and increased auditory threshold changes when various sounds such as buzzers, bells, tuning forks, and alarm clocks were used.

Another group of subjects had difficulty in locating the source of sounds and in determining spatial relations. For example, a subject was instructed to listen to and identify a noise. A concealed, ringing alarm clock was used. There appeared to be a prolonged period of time before the sound was perceived which was followed by a period of perseveration of ringing after the ringing ceased. On inquiry the subject wrote, "I couldn't tell. It was just a faint noise," followed with, "And what's more, I can't even tell you where it came from." Then, the stimulus object was placed in another position and a second alarm clock added. At this point, the subject seemed to have picked up the direction of one of them, but his behavior indicated considerable confusion. In the comparison of the subjects in this phase of the experiment, Erickson observed that the poorer somnambulistic ones showed less perseveration and localized the source of the sound more readily.

In testing sound-discrimination impairment, continuous passages were read in sequence by three different persons, of whom one was a woman. As the readers changed, one would pick up where the other left off. This change of voices was not detected, but there was recognition of changes in loudness. An electric buzzer and tuning fork were differentiated, but only after a time lag. However, with this and subsequent sounds, it was found that the differentiation was reported entirely on the basis of loudness or volume.

Some of the subjects showed selected deafness. Two characteristics were prominent. They readily heard extraneous noise on the street, outside voices, etc., but they seemed to have a convenient disregard or deafness for sounds connected with the experiment. For instance, the intensity of an electric buzzer was increased while one subject was reading. He did not raise his voice or give any observable evidence of hearing it. However, he responded to sounds on the street such as an automobile horn and a streetcar.

When he was blindfolded, he responded to laboratory auditory stimuli but when the blindfold was removed, he reverted to his previous behavior. Another subject had a prejudice against being seen by a third party while he was in a trance. He remained aware of any sounds in or around the laboratory that threatened him in this respect. A third subject showed practically total deafness to every auditory stimulus with the exception of the experimenter's voice. In their selective deafness, these subjects evidently perceived quality as well as loudness.

The reactions of the few totally deaf subjects indicated panic and shock. They insisted upon hearing some single sound. A clicking pendulum satisfied this requirement, but when it was stopped, hearing was restored regardless of instructions to the contrary. Two pendulums were arranged with one visible and one concealed. The visible one was quietly in motion and the concealed one was clicking. With the subject watching the pendulum, hypnotic deafness was induced. He was given written information and instructions to the effect that his ears would be stopped up, and when he could no longer hear the pendulum he was to convey this information to the experimenter. When the obstruction was complete, the clicking pendulum was stopped. The subject's attention was directed to the visible moving pendulum. He was instructed to let the examiner know when he heard the first faint sound. The visual perception of the swinging pendulum resulted in the hallucination of its sound. The starting of the concealed pendulum had no effect on the subject. The stopping of the silent pendulum had no effect when he did not see it. However, when it was stopped while he was looking at it, hearing was immediately restored.

Some of the subjects showed sensory and motor disturbances associated with hypnotic deafness. One subject gave evidence of decreased visual acuity by having difficulty in reading, etc. Dilatation of the pupils, a focusing disturbance, and irregular jerking of the eyeballs were discovered upon examination. Another subject reported a general anesthesia with the greatest loss in the arms and legs. There were other subjects with disturbances of lesser degree. Erickson found it was necessary to let them keep their associated disturbance to maintain hypnotic deafness.

Following this experiment, Erickson (18) selected two of his male subjects with hypnotic total deafness for a conditioned-response experiment. The equipment consisted of an electric buzzer, shock apparatus, and a kymograph which recorded currently the shock, response, and buzzer. After the subject was conditioned, hypnotic anacusia was induced. As shown in Figure 4, the conditioned response consistently occurred during the hearing period and just as consistently dropped out during hypnotic deafness. Employing the conditioned patellar reflex response,

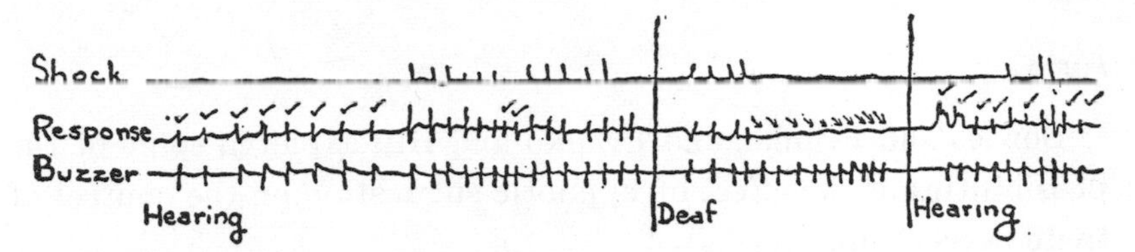

Figure 4. A conditioned response to sound during periods of hearing and hypnotically induced deafness.

Fisher (23) got similar results with posthypnotic auditory anesthesia. The ringing of the bell, used as the conditioned stimulus, was heard as a clicking sound. When selective deafness for the bell was suggested, the "singing of birds" was reported. The kymographic record shows a slight tendency toward the conditioned response.

After inducing posthypnotic deafness, Lundholm (37) was unable to condition a sound tick to an electric shock. When conditioning was attempted in the waking state, a tendency toward establishing it appeared. This was followed by a complete disappearance. Distraction and direction of attention to the sound had no effect. Further efforts of contrasuggestion resulted in behavior characteristic of conflict.

Using a pistol report as a stimulus, Dynes (15) compared the respiratory rate, cardiac rate, and psychogalvanic reflex activity of seven subjects in waking and hypnosis. He found the startle to be absent during hypnosis, and little or no discernible effect on the rate and rhythm of respiratory and cardiac activity occurred, but the trance had only slight influence on the psychogalvanic reflex.

The results of these investigations indicate that increase in auditory acuity is questionable, and other auditory sensory and perceptive functions can be controlled for practical purposes by hypnosis. On the psychophysiological axis, the degree of control seems to be related to the integrative levels at which normal responses become more involuntary.

Taste

Bowles and Pronko, and Pronko and Hill explored some of the possibilities of the effect of hypnotic suggestion on the control of taste perception.

Twenty subjects were reported for each experiment. Bowles and Pronko (3) tested the depth of hypnosis thusly: "If he lift it [arm] readily, the condition was termed very light; if he lifted it with difficulty, it was termed light; and if S was unable to move his arm the hypnosis was termed medium. . . ." The experiment proceeded with eye closure. A cotton-roll technique was used to absorb the salivary content for comparison. Lemon juice was suggested as maple syrup, maple syrup as maple syrup, maple syrup as lemon juice, and lemon juice as lemon juice. In all cases secretions were greater for the stimulus of lemon juice than maple syrup. "When maple syrup was presented as maple syrup in contrast to maple syrup as lemon juice, the ratios varied from 1.00 to 0.26." The ratios were higher for the hypnotic than for the waking state. The verbal reports indicating the acceptance of the suggestion coincided roughly with the anticipated saliva output.

In a sequel, Pronko and Hill (41) used a drop of water on the tongue as the only physical stimulus. The suggested substances were lemon juice, maple syrup, and water. The findings were comparable to those of the previous experiment.

Touch

Young (59) compared the tactual threshold in waking and hypnosis. He used two hairs of measured diameter and strength glued to skewers for hand application. There were 6,670 stimulations, half in each state. The stimulus was applied to each hand in the region of the knuckle between the middle and index finger. In the hypnotic state the hand was "sensitized" and all the subjects reported a feeling of hyperesthesia. The results are in ratios. A ratio below 100 means a decrease and above 100 an increase of sensitivity in the hypnotic state. The average ratio is 93, but there is a wide variability as shown in Table 5, compiled by Hull (31).

Table 5. Summary of Young's Experimental Results on the Power of Hypnotic Suggestion to Heighten Sensitivity to Weak Tactual Stimuli

Hypnotic group (Each entry represents one subject)		Control group (nonhypnotic) (Each entry represents one subject)
Hypnotic state of subject	Score	
Lethargic	91	85
Lethargic	72	121
Lethargic	69	—
Light trance	103	—
Light trance	87	—
Light trance	117	—
Light trance	86	—
Deep alert	91	—
Deep alert	97	—
Somnambulist	97	—
Somnambulist	108	—
Somnambulist	95	—
Somnambulist	101	—
Mean	93.4	103
$P.E._M$	2.36	—

This variability led Young to suspect a relationship between the depth of hypnosis and sensitivity. The data, however, do not seem to support this hypothesis. It seems rather to be more of an individual matter, possibly what the hypnotic state means to the subject.

Pain

Studies of hypnotic control of pain that are primarily designed for experimental purposes have been reported by Wolff and Goodell, Levine, Dynes, and Sears.

Wolff and Goodell (58) applied several techniques to a single subject to effect an increased threshold to pain. The results are shown in Figure 5. Among these techniques was *shallow hypnosis* which raised the threshold 40 per cent.

Levine (34) used two hysterical female subjects. He checked

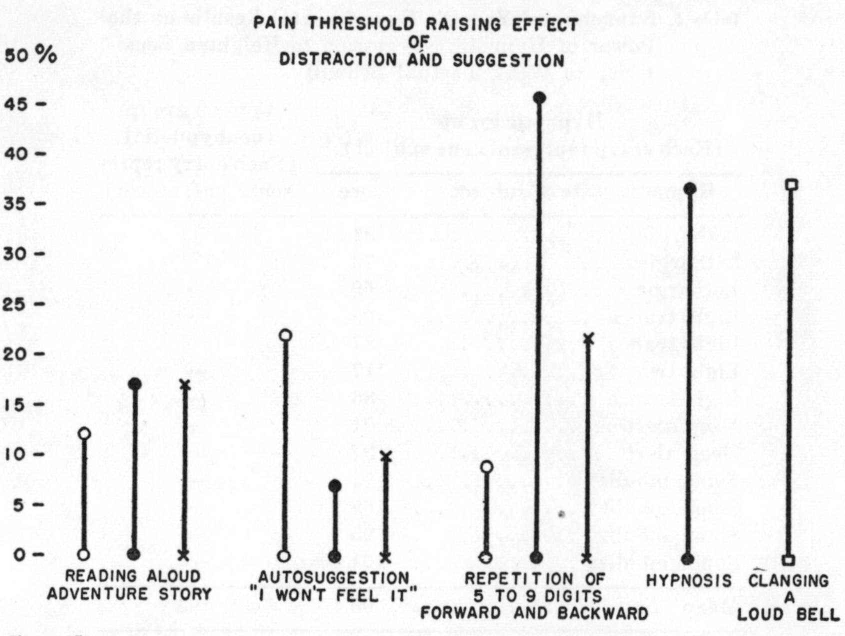

Figure 5.

the overt, subjective, and psychogalvanic reactions to pain under three conditions. These conditions were hypnosis, hypnotic anesthesia, and waking hysterical anesthesia. A venipuncture needle was employed as a stimulus. The results are shown in Table 6.

Table 6. Reactions to Painful Stimuli in Specified Settings

Setting and stimulus			Response		
State	Type of anesthesia	Stimulus	Overt response	Report on perception of pain	Psychogalvanic response
Hypnosis	None	Stuck with needle	Present	Present	Present
Hypnosis	Produced by suggestion, i.e., hypnotic anesthesia	Stuck with needle	Absent	Absent	Present
Waking state	Present without suggestion, i.e., hysterical anesthesia	Stuck with needle	Absent	Absent	Present
Hypnosis	None	Hallucination of being stuck with needle	Present	Present	Present

In the investigation of the effect of hypnotic analgesia on respiratory rate, heart rate, and psychogalvanic response, Dynes (15) used a pinprick to elicit pain in seven subjects. On the basis of his comparative data during trance and waking, he concluded: (*a*) Contrary to the waking state, there was "little or no disturbance" in the normal rate and rhythm of respiratory and cardiac activity during and following pain stimulation in the hypnotic trance, and (*b*) the psychogalvanic reflex showed only a "slight decrease" in the hypnotic trance.

In a well-controlled and rather elaborate experiment, Sears (45) investigated selected physiological reactivity to a painful stimulus applied during hypnotic anesthesia and the waking state. Approximating "psychophysiological levels" of voluntary and involuntary control, the responses measured were changes in facial grimace, respiration activity, pulse activity, and the psychogalvanic reflex. Seven trained somnambule subjects were employed in the experiment. A recording pain stimulator was designed to elicit pain but not break the skin. It was applied to a circumscribed area on the calf of each leg. A standardized pattern of stimulation and recording was set up as shown in Figure 6.

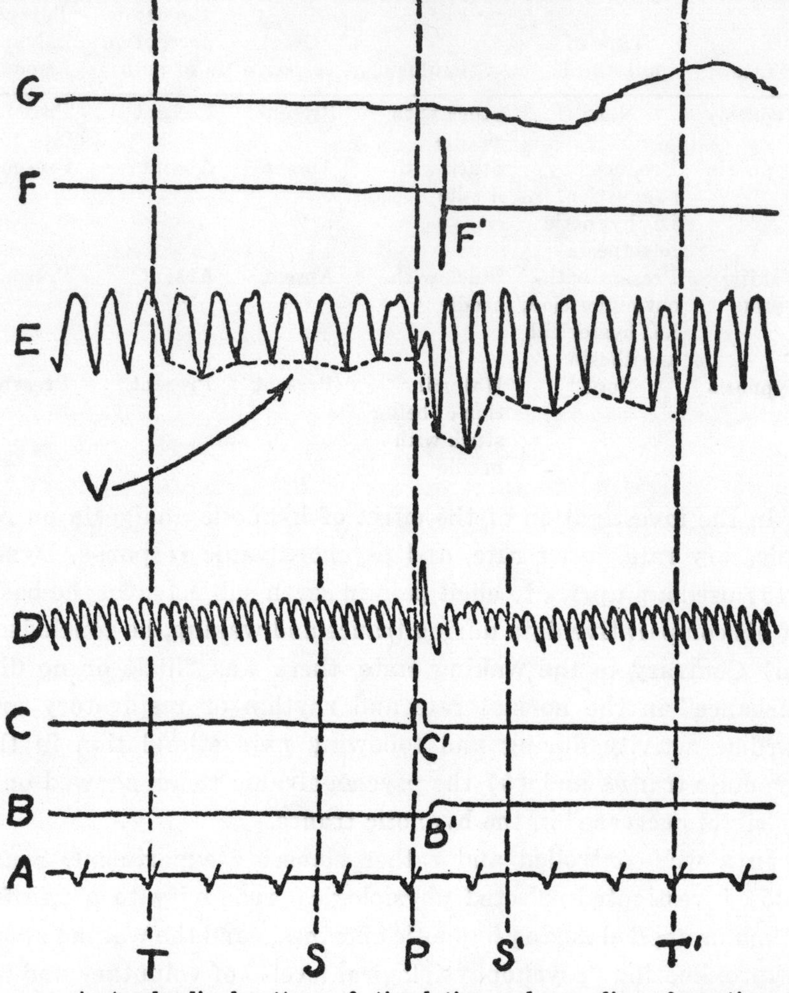

Figure 6. A standardized pattern of stimulation and recording of reactions to pain.

In this typical record, time is recorded at *A*, at 5-second intervals; *T* shows the beginning of the 20-second pre-stimulus period; *S*, the beginning of the 7½-second pre-stimulus period; *P*, the time of the application of the pain stimulus; *S′*, the end of the 7½-second post-stimulus period; and *T′*, the end of the 20-second post-stimulus period. The facial grimace tracing is indicated by *B* with *B′* showing the record of a flinch. The pain-stimulus tracing is shown at *C* with the stimulus record at *C′*. The pulse tracing is at *D* and the respiratory tracing at *E*, with *V* showing the broken line followed by the oscillometer for measuring variability. The leg-withdrawal reflex tracing is at *F* with leg flinch at *F′*; and *G* shows the galvanic skin-reaction tracing.

Sears ran a waking, trance, and control series. In the waking series each leg was stimulated. In the trance series the right leg was stimulated without the suggestion of anesthesia, and the left leg with hypnotic anesthesia. The control series differed from the trance series in that the subjects were in the waking state but instructed to apply voluntary inhibition to the left leg. The comparative data are the medians of the differences following stimulation. Table 7 shows the critical ratios abstracted from Sears's six tables. A critical ratio of three or better is considered reliable, with values of two to three showing trends. Using three as the minimal criterion of significance, three or better appears in the

Table 7. Critical Ratios of Sears's Waking, Trance, and Control Series

Reactivity	Waking series R. L. L. L.	Trance series N. L. A. L.	Control series N. L. V. I.
Facial grimace	1.13	3.87	.61
Respiratory oscillation	.79	5.20	.10
Respiratory variability	.42	3.62	.18
Pulse oscillation	1.37	1.74	2.33
Pulse variability	1.90	3.04	1.08
Galvanic skin oscillations	.14	2.95	.41

KEY: R. L. right leg
L. L. left leg
N. L. normal leg
A. L. anesthetic leg
V. I. voluntary inhibition

trance series for facial grimace, respiratory oscillation, respiratory variability, and pulse variability. Speaking of the results in another way, facial grimace, and respiratory oscillation and variability, and pulse oscillation were greatly reduced, and galvanic skin reaction was reduced 20 per cent in the trance series for the anesthetic leg.

The findings indicate: (*a*) Hypnotic suggestion is superior to waking inhibition in reducing selected reactivities to pain; (*b*) influence exerted by the trance state for specific reactivities is related to their degree of controllability in the waking state; and (*c*) individual differences occur in both states as shown in Sears's detailed data.

Warmth

Sears (45) reports a single subject to whom a posthypnotic suggestion of anesthesia to burning heat was given with no change of normal acuity to cold. When a piece of ice shielded from sight was applied to his leg he reported "something cold, like ice." But when a "burning hot piece of metal" was applied to the same spot, the subject reported he felt nothing, even after he witnessed the metal being heated.

In a rather elaborate experiment, von Eiff (54) investigated the influence of hypnosis on temperature perception and warmth regulation. Men and women dressed in bathing apparel were subjected to temperatures ranging from 0 degrees centigrade to 10 degrees centigrade. Experimental and control series were compared. With the suggestion of warmth in the trance state of stage two of Forel, the subjects reported they felt quite warm or warm and pleasant.

The findings for the hypnotic series showed lesser increases in ventilation and oxygen consumption, a lesser loss of skin temperature, and a greater loss of subcutaneous (sublingual and rectal) temperature than those for the control series. The author concluded: (*a*) the general feeling tone and temperature perception can be physically influenced even when temperatures of 10 degrees centigrade and 0 degrees centigrade are acting on an unclothed body. Among the conditions necessary for temperature perception there is, in addition to material factors, a certain psychic reaction to the temperature stimulus. (*b*) The chemical warmth regulation can to a large extent be eliminated (blocked out) through hypnosis. (*c*) The view that increased oxygen consumption under conditions of coldness may be related to the rise in reflex muscle tonus was made more probably through hypnotic research. A chemical warmth regulation in the narrower sense probably does not exist under physiological conditions. (*d*) The physical warmth regulation can be influenced by means of warmth suggestions in the presence of cold but cannot be eliminated.

Vertigo sense

Dorcus (12) compared postrotational nystagmus following actual rotation and following hypnotically suggested rotation. There were four subjects. Actual or suggested rotation was in the Dunlap chair. Observations were direct and with motion pictures. Hypnotic suggestion of rotation followed actual rotation. "Voluntary" nystagmus differed from true nystagmus.

Dorcus had six subjects in the postrotational reaction phase of the experiment. Prior to the experience of actual rotation, none of the subjects showed imbalance following hypnotic suggestion of rotation in the Dunlap rotator. Following the experience of rotation and imbalance, the subjects were hypnotized and received suggestions of rotation. This produced postrotational imbalance, but the direction of falling did not conform to the direction of the true postrotational falling reaction.

The author emphasizes the importance of memory for eliciting the correct response. The response is voluntary to the extent that, if it is known, it is carried out when suggested by the hypnotist.

Fatigue sense

Reports on the hypnotic and waking abilities to withstand muscular fatigue under a constant load have been made by Nicholson, Williams, and Roush.

In order to get objective findings, Nicholson (38) used a Mosso ergograph, an instrument commonly used to measure finger-flexor work capacity. The contractions were recorded on a drum. The middle finger lifted a known weight, with each contraction timed by a metronome.

The results are shown in Figure 7. In the upper tracing fatigue is markedly offset by hypnosis. The lower tracing shows little if

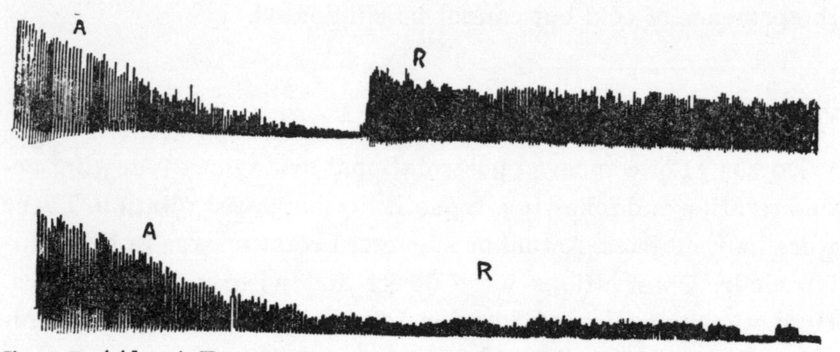

Figure 7. (*Above*) Ergograph tracing of fatigue offset by hypnosis. (*Below*) A tracing of fatigue following suggestions in the waking state.

any change following suggestions in the waking state. There were complaints and reports of subjective fatigue following the waking work period, but there were none following the hypnotic work period.

Williams (57) critically reviewed Nicholson's report and repeated the experiment with certain modifications. The changes in the apparatus consisted of measures to eliminate or minimize arm and finger pain caused by contact with the apparatus and the development of a new type of ring to prevent slippage from the finger. Rhythm was established at 80 beats per minute by a metronome. In addition to the ergograph, he used an apparatus consisting of "a meter tape set on two revolving wheels one of which was controlled by a ratchet." The ratchet controlled the summation of the tape as the finger flexed. The two records were taken simultaneously. A 5-kg. or a 3-kg. weight was used, as specified in his data, instead of Nicholson's 4½-kg. weight. In addition to making the transition from normal to hypnosis during the work period, he made the transition from hypnosis to normal.

The objective findings are comprised of kymographic records and statistical data based on centimeter and kilogram-meter units. The kymograms are illustrated in Figure 8. In record *A*, the change is shown from trance to normal and from normal to trance; in *B*, from normal to normal and from trance to trance; and in *C*, from normal to trance to normal. The intervening statement was, "Keep on pulling."

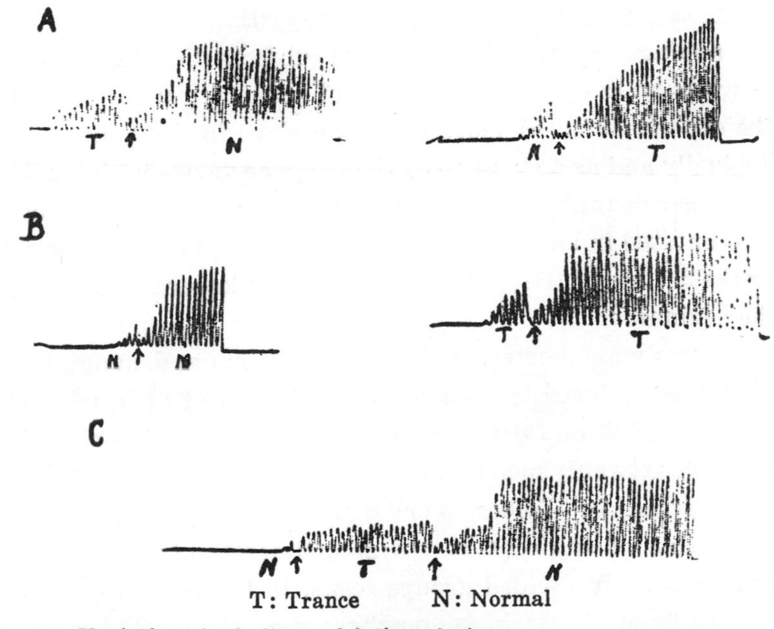

Figure 8. Variations in findings of fatigue tests.

Table 8 shows the cumulated results of five subjects. The per cent of improvement in the trance ranges from 1.6 to 52.9. The average per cent of increase was 16.08.

Table 8. Totals of Kilogram-meter Units of Work in Normal and Trance States

Subject	Normal	Trance	Per cent
A.T.	25.215	27.895	10.6
E.M.	28.825	29.65	2.8
K.W.	44.10	49.625	12.5
R.S.	16.25	24.85	52.9
E.Y.	32.145	32.685	1.6
Totals	146.535	164.705	12.39
Average per cent increase			16.08

The subjects gave reports of their reactions to their changing work capacities. "The weight became heavier" in the normal state and "the finger became weaker and would not come up" in the trance state. The instructions "against fatigue" may have accounted for its complete avoidance in reporting.

The findings show: (*a*) Two of the subjects did more work in the normal state by a total of three of seventeen units or cycles of the experiment; (*b*) more work was done in the trance state individually and as a group; (*c*) the increase varies with individuals under constant experimental conditions; and (*d*) fatigue is not elimintated in either state, as the author reports the recovery after the decline of the work curve to be at a lower capacity than in the beginning.

The arm dynamometer, hand dynamometer, and hanging-by-hands were employed by Roush (44) as means of measuring the affect of hypnosis on fatigue with endurance as the criterion. The subjects were twenty men and women students. Depth of hypnosis was determined by Wolberg's criteria. Two series were run with some overlap of subjects. In the second series of fifteen, there were three evenly divided groups tested in the following order: Group I—hypnotic, waking, posthypnotic; Group II—waking, posthypnotic, hypnotic; Group III—posthypnotic, hypnotic, waking. When the subjects were instructed to disregard pain, performance favored hypnosis in all three tests. These comparisons were significant to the .05 per cent level of confidence or less: hypnotic and waking states for all three tests; and posthypnotic and waking states for the arm dynamometer and hand dynamometer. In the order of the degree of significance the ranking of the tests is: arm dynamometer, hand dynamometer, and hanging-by-hands. This order suggests some muscle groups are favored over others.

Sense of time

Dunlap (14) says to perceive time is to perceive change. On this basis, whatever is experienced as a criterion of change in one's life experiences should have a bearing on the time perceived. Stalnaker and Richardson (49) investigated time estimation with nine "commonly called well-trained trance subjects." They used short periods of time ranging from one to three minutes. They found no reliable differences for the group in the number of mean numbers of errors or magnitude of deviations. Subject G had a tendency to make estimates too large in trance and too small in waking. No attempt was made to explore mental activity during these periods.

Cooper (6) experimented with a different approach. He suggested hallucinatory activities during the trance state and compared "subjective" time with "world" time. For instance a subject hallucinated the counting of 664 cows in an estimated personal time of 30 minutes while the world or solar time was 65 seconds.

The technique employed by Cooper is expanded in a second article on the subject by Cooper and Erickson (8). There were several different activities suggested to each subject. Table 9 is representative of activities and results. In the table, *B1* stands for completed activity with no mention of the duration of the activity; *A3*, for an incomplete activity with definite suggestion of personal time assignment; and *B3*, for completed activity with definite suggestion of personal time assignment. These results coincide with those of Klein (32) where his report touches on this subject.

Table 9. Sample of Suggested Activities and Experimental Results

Subject	Code	Activity	W.T.	A.T.	S.P.T.	E.P.T.	Count	D.R.
C	A.T. + B1	Counseling		20″		10′		
C	A.T. + B1	Counseling		10″		10′		
D	A.T. + B1	Listening to music (piece)		20″		5′		
D	A.T. + B1	Watching ballet (scene)		20″		10′		
D	A.T. + B1	Problem		1′		15′		
A	A.T. + A3	Watching football game		10″	10′	10′		
A	A.T. + A3	Counting candies		10″	10′	8′	402	60
B	A.T. + A3	Visiting friends		10″	10′	5–10′		
C	A.T. + A3	Counting candies		10″	10′	10′	127	
D	A.T. + A3	Watching races		10″	10′	10′		
D	A.T. + A3	Swimming		10″	10′	8′		
D	A.T. + A3	Dancing		10″	10′	10′		
A	A.T. + B3	Counting pennies (50) #		10″	10′	3′	28	19
A	A.T. + B3	Considering a decision		30″	1 hr.	1 hr.		
C	A.T. + B3	Counting flowers (150) #		10″	10′	10′	145	
C	A.T. + B3	Counting pearls (200) #		10″	10′	10′	100	

KEY: W.T. world time
A.T. allotted time
S.P.T. suggested personal time
E.P.T. estimated personal time
D.R. demonstrated rate, in terms of items counted per minute
(# subject to count at least this number)

Cooper and Erickson conclude: (*a*) The subjective experience determines the estimate of time; (*b*) thought "can take place with extreme rapidity relative to world time"; (*c*) there is no retrospective falsification; and (*d*) in some respects the hallucinatory thought was superior to that of the waking state.

Motor and monmotor learning and the semantics of these interesting phenomena are discussed by Cooper and Tuthill (10), Cooper and Rodgin (9), and Cooper (8).

During the investigation by Erickson (17) of hypnotic deafness, one of the subjects during an inquiry reported a total loss of time. He expressed it this way: "Well, take last Saturday's session. When I sat down for you to hypnotize me I pulled out my watch and it said 6 o'clock. I started to put it back, and then I took a second look at it and it said 10 o'clock. But before I could figure that out, I noticed that it was dark outside, my coat and tie were off, my sleeves rolled up, and I was just about exhausted, and it was really 10 o'clock."

Change is experienced by means of the senses. As the order of events has been learned, they represent criteria for the judgment of the passage of time. Subjective estimates of time are speeded up or slowed down according to sensory experience (18) as projected in the imagination or ideation. These phenomena are demonstrated in hypnotically induced hallucinations and amnesia, and in laboratory waking tasks by Harton (27, 28).

Discussion

Among the variables that are thought to be important by investigators for the hypnotic control of sensory and perceptive functions are depth, activity, ability, transcendence, motivation, and mental set.

Certain phenomena of hypnosis such as hallucinations are criteria for the *depth* of hypnosis. In testing visual, auditory, and tactile acuity, the judged depth of the trance bore no consistent relationship to the effect upon the threshold changes. Perceptual illusions of taste were readily elicited in the light to medium depth trance. It is estimated that the suppression of "experimental" pain approaches an hallucinatory depth. Pain seems to be complicated by fear. For example, there is a reduction of pain in childbirth (42) when associations of fear are replaced with confidence and a positive course of action.

The *activity* of the subjects seems to have made little difference. There appears to be no relation between performance in the acuity tests and the fact that subjects were "active" and "passive" or "alert" and "lethargic." It may be that the activity of the subject is related to his concept of hypnosis. For instance, a patient with auditory hypesthesia was referred for differential diagnosis. When hypnotized, he dropped into a state of rigid catalepsy. He refused to budge from this state or verbalize until he was returned to the waking state with considerable resistance on his part. After he witnessed other patients verbalize in the hypnotic state, he was hypnotized again. This time he answered questions promptly with his hearing aid turned on or off.

As a frame of reference, *ability* is defined as capacity plus learning. As subjects meet the requirements of hypnotic depth criteria, they apparently have these abilities. There are divergent points of view as to whether subjects had a knowledge, conscious or unconscious, of negative afterimages. Learning was found to be a factor in hypnotic postrotational nystagmus response, although the learning was incomplete as judged by the inaccurate response. In the direct suppression of pain, the tested measures in the hypnotic state showed a consistent relationship with the degree of normal voluntary control over these effector systems.

The *transcendence* of normal voluntary abilities in hypnosis is determined by a comparison of these abilities in the waking and hypnotic states. The evidence for lowering the threshold for sensory and perceptive acuity when the sense organs are primarily tested against a physical stimulus is inconsistent. The evidence where the sense organs are secondarily tested by effectors shows that transcendence of normal voluntary abilities occurs. In the latter situations, the central processes become more important than the capacity of the receptor.

Maximal *motivation* would be required to compare maximal

abilities in the waking and hypnotic states. Optimal conditions for motivation would have to be ascertained for each function tested in the waking and hypnotic states.

The importance of *mental set* has been emphasized. It is probable that this process is dependent upon an understanding of the suggestions or instructions and a state of readiness to incorporate them. If this is true, the time interval should vary with different subjects. It has been observed that some subjects will carry out the suggestions as quickly as they are given while other subjects require more persuasion.

To summarize, it has been postulated that normal sensory and perceptive functions are subject to error; suggestion is a common means of modifying attitudes and behavior; and hypnosis increases susceptibility to suggestion. Hypnotic control of functions of sight, hearing, taste, touch, pain, warmth, vertigo, fatigue, and time have been reviewed and evaluated.

The findings indicate:

1. The threshold of visual sensory and perceptual acuity is not consistently altered by hypnosis.
2. The visual perception of size may be altered by the hypnotic induction of attitudes associated with socioeconomic states.
3. Positive and negative visual hallucinations and negative afterimages are demonstrable.
4. There may be a rather consistent relationship between the hypnotic control of visual perception and the alpha rhythm.
5. The auditory threshold is not consistently altered by hypnosis.
6. Positive and negative auditory hallucinations are demonstrable. The results of physiological and psychophysiological techniques show comparative differences in the waking and trance states.
7. Illusions of taste are demonstrable.
8. The threshold for pain perception is raised in the hypnotic

state. The tests suggest that inhibition plays a role in the direct hypnotic suppression of pain.

9. Warmth is perceived, a general pleasant feeling tone is maintained, and skin temperature remains higher, in conditions of cold, when the suggestion of warmth is made in the hypnotic state.
10. Knowledge about vertigo is required to respond to the hypnotic suggestion of vertigo.
11. Fatigue as measured by endurance tests may be reduced in the trance state. There is a greater reduction of fatigue in some muscle groups than in others.
12. The sense of time may be distorted in the trance state.

REFERENCES

1. Ashley, W. R., R. S. Harper, and D. L. Runyon: "The Perceived Size of Coins in Normal and Hypnotically Induced Economic States," *Am. J. Psychol.* 64:564–572 (1951).
2. Boring, E. G., H. S. Langfeld, and H. P. Weld: *Foundations of Psychology*, New York, John Wiley & Sons, Inc., 1948, pp. 562–567.
3. Bowles, J. W., Jr., and N. H. Pronko: "Reversibility of Stimulus Function under Hypnosis," *J. Psychol.* 27:41–47 (1949).
4. Brown, W.: "Individual and Sex Differences in Suggestibility," *U. Calif. Pub. in Psychol.* 2:291–430 (1916).
5. Callahan, A., and F. C. Redlich: "Electroencephalography and Ophthalmology," *Am. J. Ophthalmol.* 29:1527 (1946).
6. Cooper, L. F.: "Time Distortion in Hypnosis," *Bull. Georgetown University Medical Center* 1:214–221 (1948).
7. ———: "Time Distortion in Hypnosis with a Semantic Interpretation of the Mechanism of Certain Hypnotically Induced Phenomena," *J. Psychol.* 34:257–284 (1952).
8. Cooper, L. F., and M. H. Erickson: "Time Distortion in Hypnosis, II," *Bull. Georgetown University Medical Center* 4: 50–68 (1950).
9. Cooper, L. F., and D. W. Rodgin: "Time Distortion and Non-motor Learning," *Science* 115:500–502 (1952).
10. Cooper, L. F., and C. E. Tuthill: "Time Distortion in Hypnosis and Motor Learning," *J. Psychol.* 34:67–76 (1952).
11. Davis, L. W., and R. W. Husband: "A Study of Hypnotic Susceptibility in Relation to Personality Traits," *J. Abnormal & Soc. Psychology* 26:175–182 (1931).
12. Dorcus, R. M.: "Modification by

Suggestion of Some Vestibular and Visual Responses," *Am. J. Psychol.* 49:82–87 (1937).

13. ——— and G. W. Shaffer: *Textbook of Abnormal Psychology,* 4th ed. Baltimore, The Williams & Wilkins Company, 1950, p. 70.
14. Dunlap, K.: *Elements of Psychology,* St. Louis, The C. V. Mosby Company, 1936, pp. 210–211.
15. Dynes, J. B.: "An Experimental Study in Hypnotic Anaesthesia," *J. Abnormal & Soc. Psychology* 27:79–88 (1932).
16. Erickson, E. M.: "Critical Comments on Hibler's Presentation of his Work on Negative After-images of Hypnotically Induced Hallucinated Colors," *J. Exp. Psychol.* 29:164–170 (1941).
17. Erickson, M. H.: "A Study of Clinical and Experimental Findings on Hypnotic Deafness: I. Clinical Experimentation and Findings," *J. Gen. Psychol.* 19:127–150 (1938).
18. ———: "A Study of Clinical and Experimental Findings on Hypnotic Deafness: II. Experimental Findings with a Conditioned Response Technique," *J. Gen. Psychol.* 19:151–167 (1938).
19. ———: "An Experimental Investigation of the Hypnotic Subject's Apparent Ability to Become Unaware of Stimuli," *J. Gen. Psychol.* 31:191–212 (1944).
20. ———: "The Induction of Color Blindness by a Technique of Hypnotic Suggestion," *J. Gen. Psychol.* 20:61–69 (1939).
21. ——— and E. M. Erickson: "The Hypnotic Induction of Hallucinatory Color Vision Followed by Pseudo Negative After-images," *J. Exp. Psychol.* 22:581–588 (1938).
22. Eysenck, H. J.: "An Experimental Study of the Improvement of Mental and Physical Functions in the Hypnotic State," *Brit. J. Med. Psychol.* 18:304–316 (1939).
23. Fisher, V. E.: "Hypnotic Suggestion and the Conditioned Reflex," *J. Exp. Psychol.* 15:212–217 (1932).
24. Guidi, G.: "Recherches Expérimentales sur la Suggestibilité," *Arch. de Psychol.* 8:49–54 (1908).
25. Harriman, P. L.: "Hypnotic Induction of Color Vision Anomalies: I. The Use of the Ishihara and the Jensen Tests to Verify the Acceptance of Suggested Color Blindness," *J. Gen. Psychol.* 27:289–298 (1942).
26. ———: "Hypnotic Induction of Color Vision Anomalies: II. Results of Two Other Tests of Color Blindness," *J. Gen. Psychol.* 27:81–91 (1942).
27. Harton, J. J.: "An Investigation of the Influence of Success on the Estimation of Time," *J. Gen. Psychol.* 21:51–62 (1939).
28. ———: "The Influence of the Degree of Unity of Organization on the Estimation of Time," *J. Gen. Psychol.* 21:25–49 (1939).
29. Heron, W. T.: "The Group Demonstration of Illusory Warmth as Illustrative of the Phenomenon of Suggestion," *J. Abnormal & Soc. Psychology* 22:341–344 (1927).
30. Hibler, F. W.: "An Experimental Investigation of Negative After-images of Hallucinated Colors in Hypnosis," *J. Exp. Psychol.* 27:45–57 (1940).
31. Hull, C. L.: *Hypnosis and Suggestibility,* New York, D. Appleton-Century Company, Inc., 1933.
32. Klein, D. B.: *The Experimental*

Production of Dreams During Hypnosis (Univ. of Texas Bull. No. 3009) Austin, 1930.

33. Knott, J. R., and C. E. Henry: "The Conditioning of the Blocking of the Alpha Rhythm of the Human Electroencephalogram," *J. Exp. Psychol.* 28:134–144 (1941).
34. Levine, M.: "Psychogalvanic Reaction to Painful Stimuli in Hypnotic and Hysterical Anesthesia," *Bull. Johns Hopkins Hospital* 46:331–339 (1930).
35. Loomis, A. L., E. N. Harvey, and G. Hobart: "Brain Potentials During Hypnosis," *Science* 83: 239–241 (1935).
36. ———: "Electrical Potentials of the Human Brain," *J. Exp. Psychol.* 19:249–279 (1936).
37. Lundholm, H.: "An Experimental Study of Functional Anesthesias as Induced by Suggestions in Hypnosis," *J. Abnormal & Soc. Psychology* 23:337–355 (1928).
38. Nicholson, N. C.: "Notes on Muscular Work During Hypnosis," *Bull. Johns Hopkins Hospital*, No. 31 (1920).
39. Pattie, F. A., Jr.: "A Report on Attempts to Produce Uniocular Blindness by Hypnotic Suggestion," *Brit. J. Med. Psychol.* 15:230–241 (1935).
40. ———: "The Genuineness of Unilateral Deafness Produced by Hypnosis," *Am. J. Psychol.* 63: 84–86 (1950).
41. Pronko, N. H., and Harris Hill: "A Study of Differential Stimulus Function in Hypnosis," *J. Psychol.* 27:49–53 (1949).
42. Read, G. D.: *Childbirth without Fear*, New York, Paul B. Hoeber, Inc., 1949.
43. Rosenthal, V. G., and H. Mele: "The Validity of Hypnotically Induced Color Hallucinations," *J. Abnormal & Soc. Psychology* 47:700–704 (1952).
44. Roush, E. S.: "Strength and Endurance in the Waking and Hypnotic States," *J. Appl. Psychol.* 3:404–410 (1951).
45. Sears, R. R.: "An Experimental Study of Hypnotic Anesthesia," *J. Exp. Psychol.* 15:1–22 (1932).
46. Schneck, J. M.: "Audiometry under Hypnosis," *J. Psychosomat. Med.* 10:361–365 (1948).
47. ——— and M. Bergman: "Auditory Acuity for Pure Tones in the Waking and Hypnotic States," *J. Speech Hearing Disorders* 14:33–36 (1949).
48. Small, W. S.: "The Suggestibility of Children," *Ped. Sem.* 4:176–220 (1896).
49. Stalnaker, J. M., and M. W. Richardson: "Time Estimation in the Hypnotic Trance," *J. Gen. Psychol.* 4:362–366 (1930).
50. Sterling, K., and J. G. Miller: "The Effect of Hypnosis upon Visual and Auditory Acuity," *Am. J. Psychol.* 53:269–276 (1940).
51. Travis, L. E., and J. B. Knott: "Brain Potential Studies: I. Perseveration Time to Light," *J. Psychol.* 3:97–100 (1936).
52. Travis, L. E., and M. Holt: "The Effect of Visual After-sensation upon Brain Potential under Different Degrees of Attention," *J. Exp. Psychol.* 22:472–479 (1938).
53. Triplett, N.: "The Psychology of Conjuring Deceptions," *Am. J. Psychol.* 11:439–510 (1900).
54. von Eiff, A. W.: "Der Einfluss auf Temperatur Empfindung und Wärmeregulation," *Z. Ges. Exptl. Med.* 117:266–269 (1951).
55. Weitzenhoffer, A.: "The Discriminatory Recognition of Visual

Patterns under Hypnosis," *J. Abnormal & Soc. Psychology* **46**: 388–397 (1951).

56. White, R. W.: "Two Types of Hypnotic Trance and Their Personality Correlates," *J. Psychol.* 3:279–289 (1937).
57. Williams, G. W.: "The Effect of Hypnosis on Muscular Fatigue," *J. Abnorm. Psychol.* **24**:318–329 (1929).
58. Wolff, H. G., and H. Goodell: "The Relation of Attitude and Suggestion to the Perception of and Reaction to Pain," in *Proc. Assn. Res. in Nerv. and Ment. Dis.*, Baltimore, The Williams & Wilkins Company, 1943, pp. 434–448.
59. Young, P. C.: "An Experimental Study of Mental and Physical Functions in the Normal and Hypnotic State," *Am. J. Psychol.* **36**:214–232 (1925).
60. ———: "An Experimental Study of Mental and Physical Functions in the Normal and Hypnotic State," *Am. J. Psychol.* **36**:345–356 (1926).

Theodore R. Sarbin, Ph.D.

4

PHYSIOLOGICAL EFFECTS OF HYPNOTIC STIMULATION

IN ORDER TO ANALYZE how physiological functions can be modified by hypnotic stimulation, it is first necessary to illumine some of the dark corners of hypnotism with special reference to psychosomatic medicine. From the time of Mesmer to the present day, scientists and laymen alike have been impressed with reports of bodily changes occurring as the result of an apparently inexplicable mysterious force possessed by hypnotist or subject or both. After the rejection of animal magnetism as an explanatory principle, various other principles were educed in order to explain how psychic stimuli could account for shifts in bodily functions. Implicit to these latter mentalistic hypotheses, which were one step removed from mysterious-force notions, was the intellectual heritage of Cartesian dualism.

Few have escaped being caught up in the mind-body dichotomy as one of the essential ideological givens of our culture. With this as an implicit and often unrecognized background for specula-

I am grateful to Professor Mark R. Rosenzweig and to Wallace B. Hall for a number of invaluable suggestions.

tion and explanation, it is small wonder that until now, few have tried to describe psychosomatic interrelations on a monistic basis. Even the term *psychosomatics* reflects the unsatisfactory theoretical basis for contemporary and sophisticated inquiry. Most writers in the field of psychosomatics pay lip service to a monistic hypothesis but their explanations are drawn from interactionistic dualism.

Through the years, our explanations of certain kinds of bodily reactions have become more sophisticated. For example, febrile states are no longer regarded as demoniacal manifestations. One can be a thoroughgoing monist and assert that the fever is a protective bodily reaction to microbial invasion. Similarly, the introduction of stress can produce gastric hyperacidity, hyperemia, and hypermotility in certain persons (Wolff, 102). If the definition of stress is translatable into physical terms, no violence to theory is effected. Assaults of microbes, climatic, chemical, or physical forces, and the stresses developing out of social-psychological imbalances are not discontinuous insofar as bodily effects are concerned (Wolff, 102). It is when the bodily effects are attributed to the discharge of "psychic energies" or similar constructs that scientific progress is halted. This is no mere polemical matter of choice of metaphysical system. The scientist working within the explicit or implicit ideology of physical monism can ask questions which are not footless and which permit answers framed with maximal attention to Lloyd Morgan's canon.

The second nodal point in this introduction is the failure of most experimentalists and clinicians to define hypnosis in terms which allow for measurement (rough or refined). Merely reporting that "the subject was put into a deep hypnotic trance" is not enough. The inference from such a statement is that deep hypnosis is an invariant state, somewhat equivalent to chemical anesthesia. Failure to account for heterogeneity among subjects in terms of their responses to the hypnotic situation, of course, introduces methodological problems. I believe this failure to specify the significant aspects of the interpersonal hypnotic situation is responsible for many failures to duplicate experiments reported by competent observers. This point must be underscored: hypnosis is *not* a single-dimensioned, invariant "state of mind." Rather, it is a set of responses to social-psychological stimuli, many of which are seldom, if ever, explicitly recorded by the experimenter. The unsatisfactory state of affairs in hypnotic research (as in certain other psychological areas, particularly psychotherapy) is a result of failure to recognize some of the major sources of variation: among them the subject, the hypnotist, the situation, the instructions, and the interactions between and among these factors. One wonders whether the magnitude of the problems engenderd by the implicit recognition of the multiple sources of variation has led to a rejection of careful scientific methodology and reporting. Wolberg (101), for example, has said that "hypnosis contains so many complex interpersonal variables it does not lend itself to measurement."

An excellent example of the failure to account for some of the apparent sources of variation is found in the perennial attempts at discovering the relationship between sleep and hypnosis. The hypothesis is usually stated as an identity between sleep and hypnosis or as a disjunction. Such simplistic statements of the problem immediately present complications in the definition of sleep as well as of hypnosis. Looking upon sleep as an invariant, unidimensional entity or an arbitrarily defined organic state is contrary to the knowledge accumulated by Kleitman (52), Lindsley (60), and others. Measurement by EEG, by electromyography, by tendon reflexes, and by temperature are by no means perfectly correlated with "efficiency" of work, subjective reports of alertness, responsiveness to auditory stimuli, etc. Simple measurements of tendon reflexes cannot, by themselves, be equated with sleep. The tendon reflex is only an indicant of the reactivity of the neuromuscular system. For purposes of pointing up our discussion, however, we can assume for the moment that the tendon reflex can be used to monitor states of sleep and wakefulness. With this assumption, we can quickly review some studies which illustrate the necessity of accounting for multiple sources of variation.

The work of Hull (48), Bass (6), Brown (16), and True and Stephenson (91) point to the inference that hypnosis and sleep as indicated by tendon reflexes are not physiologically related. Tendon reflexes, which characteristically are diminished or absent in sleep, are normal in hypnosis and similar to the waking state. This finding has recently been challenged by Koster (53). His subjects (N = 6) showed patellar reflexes such as are observed in sleep. His conclusion is that hypnosis is a form of sleep (*Teilschlaf*).

This seeming contradiction can be reconciled by an hypothesis which is subject to empirical test: the variation in tendon reflexes is a function of at least three sources, singly and/or in interaction—subjects, situation and instructions. Volunteers, for example, when participating as laboratory subjects, where there is activity, appear to be dominated by the set that they are *to do something* upon command. Patients, on the other hand, may be influenced by the characteristics of the consulting room where the set is to adopt the passive-dependent sleeplike attitude suggested by the therapist. Schematically, this hypothesis could be represented thus:

	Volunteers	*Patients*
Subjects:	implicit role-expectations of performance under various motivations	implicit role-expectations of relief of symptoms by following therapist's advice
	Laboratory	*Consulting room*
Situation:	promotes activity set; alertness; something actively happens	promotes passivity set, no need to be alert
	Direct	*Indirect*
Instructions:	reinforcing laboratory atmosphere	reinforcing therapeutic setting

In the laboratory instruction, the press for activity keeps the afferent influx at a high level with a corresponding high muscular tonicity. In the therapeutic instruction, the afferent influx is decreased and muscular relaxation is observed. The diminution of tendon reflexes shows this relaxation. This is reminiscent of the Davis and Kantor report (27). These investigators were able to discriminate two varieties of hypnotic performance: active and passive. In the first, the instructions were focused around actively performing some task, such as contracture of the arm; in the second, the instructions were centered around "going to sleep." Not only may instructions be given explicitly, as in the Davis and Kantor experiment, but needless to say, they may be given implicitly via the total setting. The brain wave studies of Barker and Burgwin (4) may be interpreted in the same fashion: hypnotic sleep and "normal" sleep are indistinguishable on the EEG. The hypnotic subjects accepted the "sleep" instructions literally.

The emphasis on recognizing social-psychological sources of variation in performance removes hypnotic phenomena from the mysterious, the occult, and the mentalistic.* Furthermore, the naturalistic framework makes it unnecessary to rely on traditional and outworn mentalistic conceptions. All the phenomena which are normally subsumed under the term *hypnosis* can be specified as performances, i.e., as *organismic responses.* With the proper observer attitude such responses will be perceived *qua* responses of the skeletal musculature or as verbal reports of subjects.

Psychophysiological relations in hypnosis

Elsewhere in this volume are listed the behaviors normally subsumed under the term hypnosis. They comprise a large array of

* The use of those terms may appear to be anachronistic or may be interpreted as setting up a straw man. That contemporary writers are guided by theories which are not naturalistic and which smack of the occult and of "influence" may be ascertained by reference to many contemporary books and journal articles.

actions from simple sensorimotor responses to complex conceptual behavior, from overt performances which are not distinguishable from waking behavior to pronounced activity of the visceral organs. Before categorizing these performances, it is important to emphasize that whatever the phenomenon under scrutiny, differential responsiveness is the rule. That is to say, subjects respond differentially to the hypnotic situation. One subject may respond somnambulistically and another not at all to identical induction stimuli. Further, the same subject may respond differently to the same induction presented on different occasions. A second point to bear in mind when considering the categorization of psychosomatic hypnotic behaviors (which point will be dealt with in detail in a later section) is differential mediation. For example, a subject may spontaneously respond to the hypnotic situation with uninhibited emotionality. This may be due to his conception of the role of the hypnotic subject coupled with certain needs for abreaction—the mediation in this case would be somatomuscular. Another subject may show the same behavior but its origin might be traced to certain shifts in cortical conductivity occasioned by the mild anoxia associated with muscular relaxation (see below).

With this background, the shifts in behavior noted by investigators from Braid (13) to the present may be grouped somewhat as follows:

1. Changes in motility: during the induction of hypnosis and during the trance state, there is a diminution in normal patterned motor activity.
2. Shifts in orientation from distal stimuli (outside the organism) to proximal stimuli (inside the organism): the body becomes the focus of self-perception with corresponding decrease in external object perceptions.
3. Disinhibition of affective processes: the normally controlled

emotional responses are more easily emitted and/or exaggerated in duration and intensity.
4. Changes in covert behavior: images are more vivid; primitivation of form and content occurs; access to emotionally toned content is facilitated.

A quick perusal of this list will bring to mind conditions other than hypnosis which can be described in the same terms. The performances mentioned are not exclusive to persons enacting the hypnotic role. Identical phenomena are found in religious conversions, mystical unions, excitement, dreams, reveries, psychotherapeutic situations, and certain schizophrenic reactions. Certain physiologically initiated conditions—organic brain disease, fatigue, fever, debilitating disease processes, etc.—show similar responses.

From these remarks, a pointed question emerges: are the physiological changes observed in hypnosis *direct effects* of the social-psychological stimuli, are they *side effects,* or both? To attempt an answer to this question, the relationships of physiological changes to the behavior changes noted above will have to be considered.

These relationships will be examined in the light of a theory of hypnosis based on a multivariant approach and postulating that the responses of hypnotic subjects—both somatic and visceral responses—are not discontinuous from normal psychological and physiological processes. This formulation, a special derivative of role-theory, allows testable hypotheses to be made and presents us with a structure into which available data may be fitted.

The most sophisticated hypothesis regarding the nature of hypnosis is a conative one. Contributing evidence to support such a theory, Dorcus (29), Lundholm (64), Pattie (71), Rosenow (75), and Sarbin (78, 76) agree in principle with White (96) in his definition of hypnosis as "meaningful, goal-directed striving, its most general goal being to behave like a hypnotized person as this is continuously defined by the operator and understood by the subject." The present author has extended White's theory and presented evidence and argument to support the following definition: hypnosis is a special form of a more general kind of social-psychological behavior known as role-enactment. In the hypnotic experiment the subject strives to enact the role of the hypnotized person. The success of his striving is a function of at least three variables: (*a*) favorable motivation—where the role and self-conceptions are not incongruent; (*b*) accuracy of role-perception; and (*c*) role-aptitude—the ability covertly to shift from one role to another as observed in imagination, play, real-life situations, etc.

The similarity between role-enactment in hypnosis and role-enactment in the theater has been pointed up by Allen (2) and the writer (76). The stage director stands in the same relationship to the actor as the hypnotist to the subject. The social positions are defined beforehand; i.e., the reciprocal rights and obligations are implicitly or explicitly recognized. The performances of both persons in the social interact (either director and actor or hypnotist and subject) are aimed at validating the occupancy of their respective social positions. That is to say, the participants in the social action interbehave with each other in ways that are appropriate to each position—*provided,* of course, that the enactment does not involve conduct contrary to the actor's (or subject's) self-concept, that the actor (or subject) has perceived the role correctly, and that the actor (or subject) has at least minimal ability to behave *as if* he is someone or something else.

Because dramatic acting has not been burdened with the incubus of dissociation theory or suggestion theory, few have become concerned about the marked alterations in skeletal and visceral behavior which occur following the director's verbal instructions to the actor. The analyst of dramatic acting is not bothered by such pseudoproblems as the search for a one-to-one constancy relation between the magnitude of the stimulus (the director's instruction; often a single word) and the magnitude of the response (the complex verbal, motor, and visceral reactions of the actor).* Likening hypnotic role-taking to dramatic role-taking should not lead to the inference that hypnosis is sham behavior. Role-theory deals with sham behavior as with any other behavior segment. It is role-enactment with low-level organismic involvement (see below).

From the foregoing account, it is asserted that hypnotic behavior is the enactment of a social role. Three dimensions of role-enactment have been isolated: (1) number of roles; (2) accessibility to self-report; and (3) organismic involvement. The first of these dimensions we shall not elaborate here. Suffice it to say that, as a person proceeds through the maturation-enculturation sequence, he acquires roles congruent with the positions (real or imagined, actual or potential) which he must occupy. One of these roles is that of the hypnotic subject. Such a role is acquired through such media as novels, comic books, movies, television shows, hearsay, etc. The role-expectations of the hypnotic subject show a fair degree of consistency from person to person in the same subculture (Dorcus, Brintnall, and Case, 30).

Accessibility to self-report is substantially the same as a *conscious-unconscious dimension* as used by other writers. The term, *accessibility to self-report,* however, is more continuous with the actual operations involved and is not tied to psychoanalytic theories which attribute specific dynamic properties to unreportable events. In the role of hypnotic subject, the notion of discontinuity of accessibility to self-report is learned as a property of the hypnotic subject along with other conceptions. Among some subjects, the discontinuity is facilitated by physiological by-products of the hypnotic role-taking. In the studies reported below, of course, reportability is most readily associated with events which can be mediated by the somatomuscular and somatosensory systems.

* For a full account of the theory, the reader is referred to Sarbin (76, 77).

The organismic dimension is the variable most pertinent to our discussion. The enactment of any role may be conceptualized in terms of more or less intensity, or rate of energy transformation. *Intensity* is the descriptive term applied to the molar observed event—it is tied to the increased functioning of the organism as a whole and can be monitored by various physiological assessment procedures. In fact, the change in intensity of the molar act depends in part on changes in the internal physiology. For example, the intense role of "quarterback making an end run" cannot be enacted unless the visceral and somatic organ systems are acting synergically.

The organismic-involvement dimension, of course, applies to any social role, be it shaman, professor, shortstop, or mother. It is a matter of everyday observation that roles are enacted with varying degrees of organismic involvement, although in most roles, of course, it is minimal—otherwise the physiological expenditures would be out of proportion to available reserves. One approach to the assessment of the organismic dimension, commonly used by clinically oriented investigators and reporters, is that of global observation of the role. The investigator observes the patterned activity of visible effector organs and then records his observations, using such qualitative terms as agitated, surprised, anxious, heated, calm, matter-of-fact, apathetic, etc. The investigator may further organize his perceptions into social concepts such as frenzied behavior, passive role, assertive conduct, "little-boy" role, etc. To such observations our knowledge of general physiology can be added and we can predict (and test the predictions) that certain physiological changes will be associated with certain degrees of organismic involvement in a particular role.

As an everyday example, take the husband of a primiparous woman who is in labor in a modern hospital. From a time-sample observation we would say that he is tense, anxious, pacing, restless, etc. We could further organize these qualities on the basis of knowledge of the situation into the role-concept of "expectant father." We could further place his conduct at a high level of organismic involvement and predict elevation in blood pressure, increase in temperature, cessation of gastric function, increased palmar sweating, and other characteristics which are part of the adaptive techniques of the organism to stress. Furthermore, we can predict reversals of the global behavior within a finite time interval following the announcement of the birth of the child and the reassurances of the doctor that all is well. The shift in behavior will be organized around his everyday occupational role, one that is normally enacted with low-level involvement. Associated with the taking up of his everyday role are the reversals of the physiological changes mentioned before. The concept of organismic involvement in role-enactment is, for the present, organized around such global conceptions. That such involvement can be monitored by appropriate psychophysiological and physiological techniques has been amply demonstrated (Lindsley, 60).

For purposes of this exposition, we may illustrate seven levels of organismic involvement in role-taking. Hypnotic subjects may perform with intensities that can be classified at any point on this organismic dimension except at the extremes, Levels I and VII. The dimension is schematized in Figure 1.

Level I. This is everyday casual role-enactment. There is little affect, little involvement of self in role. Performances are more or less automatic, routinized, effortless. The actions of the hypnotic subject cannot be classified at this level: to volunteer for an experiment in hypnosis or to seek hypnotic therapy denotes some greater involvement in the social role than Level I.

Level II. At this level, mechanical acting, we can observe the behavior of hypnotic subjects who score low on depth scales (Friedlander and Sarbin (40), Barry et al. (5), and Davis and Husband, (26). Here the hypnotic subject, like the mechanical actor, performs stereotyped movements in order to validate his occupancy of the social position. Again we see little affect and little effort, although more than in Level I. According to retrospective accounts of "mechanical" actors and of hypnotic subjects classified at this level, there is little involvement of self in role.

Level III. Heated acting ("living the role") shows, of course, more effort, more activity on the part of the subject, such as grimacing, increased rate of respiration, and tension, and more side effects of such voluntarily initiated activity. In order to manifest rage, for instance, an actor may work himself up emotionally by violently shaking a ladder in the wings before appearing on

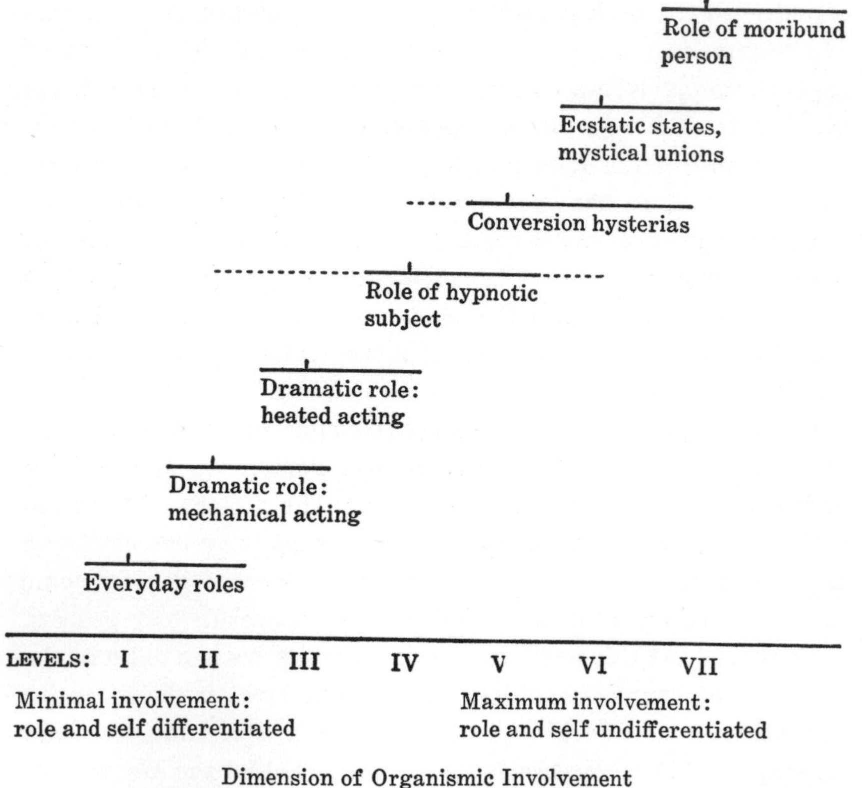

Figure 1. Illustration of organismic involvement dimension showing overlap of levels and particularly range of levels observed with somnambulistic hypnotic subjects.

the stage. Among the easily observed side effects are erythema, rapid pulse, increased sweating, vocal effects, etc. Here we can see much involvement of the self in the role. Many hypnotic subjects behave in ways which allow their being classified at this level.

Level IV. This level is denoted by hypnotic behavior of the somnambulistic type. The classical behavior of the deeply hypnotized subject, the perceptual motor effects, the compulsive posthypnotic behaviors, the amnesias, the hallucinations, all show much involvement of the self in the role. There is apparent effort, a striving to do what the experimenter requests. Here is illustrated most forcefully the operation of the *as-if* mechanism, the influence of covertly taking the role in a relatively complete way, with reduction of possibilities for performing competing roles. The subject performs *as if* he is blind, or deaf, or analgesic, or anosmic, or whatever the role instructions demand.

Level V. The behaviors subsumed under the rubric hysteria are used as a frame of reference on the organismic dimension. The hysteric responds *as if* he suffers some sensory or motoric affliction. The range of intensity overlaps considerably the range of behaviors of the deeply hypnotized person, Level IV. Expression of affect associated with the maintenance of the *as-if* behavior is commonly observed. The involvement of the self in the role of the invalided person is immediately apparent when efforts are made to remove the symptoms. At the same level of intensity are trance states of the Plains Indians (Benedict, 9) and the couvade (Crawley, 23), the primitive custom where the husband lies-in during parturition.

Level VI. Only occasionally are hypnotic performances classified at Level VI. Ecstatic states are usually associated with the suspension of voluntary action. They are seen in socially initiated situations such as religious conversions, mystical states, possession, and religious revivals. In addition to the greater involvement of the skeletal musculature, there is an increased involvement of the organs served by the autonomic nervous system.

Here we see, *in extremis,* affect and effort. The nearly complete submergence of the self in the role is observed. Obviously, such performances cannot be prolonged over time without damage to the organism (Selye, 87). As a general rule, automatic equilibratory controls terminate such intense behaviors through institutionalized rituals, fatigue or exhaustion, and/or autonomic regulation.

Level VII. This level is not applicable to hypnosis. It is an extension of the previous range but is characterized by the failure of equilibratory mechanisms. Well-authenticated cases of voodoo death have been described by Cannon (19) and others. The focus is on role-taking as the initiatory phase of complex and irreversible physiological activity.

With this as a background—the conative hypothesis regarding hypnosis and the organismic-involvement dimension of role-enactment—we can now review the experimental and clinical findings. At the conclusion of this review, we shall offer a sketch of a psychosomatic theory applicable to observed hypnotic events and some implications for therapeutics.

Review of experimental and clinical findings

In the following pages I shall review some studies in which physiological changes have followed social-psychological stimulation. No attempt is made to report all the pertinent literature. The studies reviewed, however, are representative and are grouped more or less according to conventional textbook classifications. At the outset, the criticism of hypnotic research methodology mentioned above should be reiterated: Most reports do not specify what behaviors are subsumed by the term "hypnosis," and further, antecedent and concurrent conditions are seldom specified.

In addition, few studies report whether any notice is given the motoric responses of the subject which may have feedback functions (see below). Another methodological criticism has to do with the small number of subjects and the small number of observations of each subject. Thus the experiments usually fail to meet Brunswik's criteria (17) for representative and systematic design, and generalizations must be made with extreme caution. Furthermore, many of the studies are based upon observation of patients with psychosomatic disease. In such studies, little or no attention is given the excessive lability of psychosomatic symptom formation. (A further discussion of this point is given below.)

Central nervous system.* ANALGESIA. A number of experiments have been reported in which pain is diminished or eliminated as the result of hypnosis. One of the most widely quoted experiments was carried out by Sears (85). Using seven subjects, he recorded various psychophysiological indices: facial flinch, reflex leg withdrawal, respiration, pulse activity, and galvanic skin response. These indices represent a series, graded from most to least voluntary control. The stimulus was a sharp stylus which punctured the leg. His results indicate that the effects could be placed on a gradient: They were greatest for facial flinch and least for the galvanic skin response. The hypnotic trance without the addition of the specific suggestion of anesthesia greatly reduced the facial flinch and slightly reduced the other monitored reactions. In a control (nonhypnotic) series, none of the measured responses were significantly altered. The inference warranted by these findings is that a mechanism other than *voluntary inhibition* is at work.

West, Niell, and Hardy (94), using the Wolff-Hardy apparatus, studied hypnotic response to experimentally induced pain. Among their conclusions are the following: Threshold for pain is raised as the result of hypnotic anesthesia; discrimination of stimuli of different intensities is impaired; the alteration of pain perception is related in degree to the depth of hypnosis. The last-named find-

* Central nervous system functioning involved in auditory and visual perception will not be discussed in this chapter.

ing is particularly interesting in that it suggests variability in depth of hypnosis as a crucial variable in psychophysiological studies.

Dorcus and Kirkner (31) report a systematic study of hypnotic analgesia. They contrast the effects of hypnosis on the suppression of pain in two contrasting groups: male patients suffering from paroxysmal pain associated with spinal cord injury (N = 5) and women suffering from chronic dysmenorrhea (N = 5). The method of treatment was to induce pain hypnotically, then to suppress the pain experience through hypnotic procedures.

The spinal-cord cases reported temporary pain relief but not freedom from pain. The dysmenorrheics, on the other hand, remained relatively pain-free.* The authors' concluding statement is worth reproducing here because it lends support to the role-taking theory sketched on the preceding pages.

> *In the dysmenorrheic, when we break the chain of expectancy and tension, we break down the conditioned processes, whereas in the spinal nerve injury cases we are not destroying a conditioned process, but suppressing the primary pain-arousing mechanism. This is held in abeyance only insofar as the factors that tend to focus the individual's attention on the pain is concerned and in that respect the pain may appear abated. It does not remain inhibited because the source is continually present.* (31, p. 239)

These illustrative studies † help in the clarification of the complex psychophysiological problem of pain perception and pain relief.

The neural mechanisms of pain control are not clearly defined. It is presently believed that impulses initiating at the periphery

* These findings on dysmenorrhea are corroborated in a study by Sarbin and Lewis (79) of 15 dysmenorrheics; 11 remained completely pain-free, two reported partial relief, and two were refractory to hypnotic treatment.

† Other studies are reported by Dynes (34), Levine (58), Lundholm (64), and Pattie (70).

reach the thalamic nuclei and are then projected to the cortex. On this basis it would appear, then, that afferent processes associated with the subject's role-taking behavior block the spread of thalamocortical impulses. To support this interpretation and to imbed hypnotic studies in a more general context, the work of Beecher (7) may be cited. Among the agents of pain relief he lists psychological stimuli. He has analyzed observations of men wounded in battle, reports of athletes injured in games but unaware of pain, freedom from pain of religious martyrs, and accounts of experimental studies of the action of euphoria-producing drugs. From this analysis he concludes that cortical impulses, however produced, can interrupt the perception of pain stimuli. His hypothesis is that analgesia can be a consequent of any large afferent influx, whether produced mechanically, symbolically, or pharmacologically.

VOLUNTARY MUSCLE RESPONSE. The most frequently used test in a formal or informal scale for assessing the depth of hypnosis is induced paralysis or contracture. The subject is given instructions such as, "Your arm feels as if it is tied to a rigid iron bar," or "Imagine a hundred-pound weight suspended from your wrist." In the first instance, the challenge would be "Try to bend your arm"; in the second, "Try to raise your arm." Such suggestions of motoric behavior are, of course, the most readily accepted by volunteer or patient subjects. A problem is immediately evident: Is the behavior any different from normal, but simulated, waking behavior?

Three explanations are possible for the subject's failure to meet the challenge: (*a*) He may simply choose not to move the arm; (*b*) he may be indifferent to the instruction; or (*c*) he may visibly expend effort in the simultaneous contraction of antagonistic muscle groups, the net result being apparent paralysis. Furthermore, phenomenal report as to the effectiveness of hypnotic suggestion on motoric functions cannot be relied upon as support for the appearance of physiological alterations in the neuromuscular apparatus. For these reasons, the study of motoric alterations must be approached through indirect means.

Probably the most effective method of assessing somatomuscular change is by electromyography. Ravitz (72, 73) has reported some experiments in which EMF tracings from electrodes on the head and hand or chest tend to become more regular during hypnosis. At the termination of the trance, a large voltage shift is observed and the tracing returns to the usual waking pattern. The tracings in deep hypnosis appear to resemble sleep records. Stimuli in hypnosis leading to emotional arousal result in shifts in potential differences similar to arousal in the waking state.

A large number of reports have been published which deal in one way or another with the effects of hypnosis on muscular strength, work capacity, motor control, and fatigue. These studies have been adequately reviewed by Weitzenhoffer (93). Because of noncomparable methods of measurement, failure to define the hypnotic situation, and lack of controls the results are difficult to interpret. A safe conclusion is that in the hypnotic induction period, there is a diminution of tonicity (probably related to relaxation). Implied or expressed hypnotic suggestions of increased strength, resistance to fatigue, etc., in appropriately predisposed subjects may result in an extension of the limits of normal waking behavior. This author agrees with Weitzenhoffer, (93, p. 138) that such extensions are "not nearly so spectacular as popular belief would have them."

BRAIN WAVES. Earlier reports on electroencephalographic monitoring of hypnotic states were primarily concerned with EEG differentials between sleep and hypnosis. Loomis, Harvey, and Hobart (62) and Blake and Gerard (11) found EEG patterns for hypnosis to be like those of normal waking behavior. More recently, Ford and Yeager (37) and True and Stephenson (91) have confirmed the earlier studies. Conflicting evidence is offered by Darrow et al. (24) and Barker and Burgwin (4). Darrow et al., using more refined methods, find that EEG's observed in hypnosis are more like those observed in light sleep or drowsy states. Barker and Burgwin's report also conflicts with the earlier studies. Their EEG records for "normal" sleep and hypnotically induced sleep are indistinguishable. These authors specify two conditions, *trance* or hypnotic suggestibility and *hypnotic sleep*. In the first, when the subjects are being given instructions and are responding to such instructions, the brain-wave pattern is essentially the same as in waking behavior. In the second condition, hypnotic sleep, there is a progressive elimination of the alpha pattern as in normal sleep. This investigation, as indicated earlier, emphasizes the importance of specifying the instruction variables. When apt subjects are given sleep instructions, they may perform acts which lead to normal sleep.

In this connection, mention should be made of certain clinical observations made during hypnotic experiments. In the Friedlander and Sarbin experiment (40) I observed two subjects who responded *literally* to the sleep instructions. They were passive and inert, and failed to respond to any stimulation. They had to be awakened by vigorous shaking. A volunteer subject in a demonstration also responded in literal fashion to sleep instruction. Not merely vigorous shaking but the noise of an alarm clock was necessary to restore normal wakefulness. In another instance, hypnosis was being used therapeutically with a hospital in-patient on a medical ward. The patient, among whose symptoms was chronic insomnia, would fall asleep before the hypnotic induction was completed. As in the other examples, the usual dehypnotizing instructions had no effect. Waking could only be achieved by loud noises, tapping on the shoulder, etc.

The implications of the EEG findings and of the examples just cited is that the hypnotic state must be more accurately specified when EEG or other physiological measures are taken. In short, the failure to specify the intensity of response, i.e., the organismic involvement, makes difficult the analysis of measured organic alterations.

REFLEXES. Alteration in reflexes has not been intensively studied. Dorcus (29) reports a carefully controlled study on the effects of hypnotic stimulation on vestibular responses. He studied eye movements and falling reactions after suggested rotation. Subjects who had previously been rotated produced eye movements and falling reactions when they were given the hypnotic suggestion of rotation. The eye movements, however, did not resemble true nystagmus. The falling reaction occurred only with subjects who had been previously rotated; subjects who had not been rotated showed no falling reaction. The obvious conclusion is that one of the important variables in hypnotic research is the prior experience of the subject vis-à-vis the experimental task. The results of experiments involving the central nervous system, such as this study, fit the conative hypothesis that hypnosis is a role-taking enterprise.

Two papers which suggest further analysis of the conative hypothesis regarding spinal reflexes deal with the effect of hypnotic age-regression on the plantar reflex, by Gidro-Frank and Bowersbuch (41) and True and Stephenson (91). In both studies, regression to ages below the first year resulted (in some subjects) in the recovery of the infantile response to plantar stimulation. In the Gidro-Frank and Bowersbuch experiment, chronaxie was also measured. The observable responses to plantar stimulation were accompanied by a complete or partial reversal of the flexor-extensor chronaxie ratio; that is, a return to the infantile condition.* The observed reflex response is similar to, if not identical with, the positive Babinski which is a sign of a lesion of the pyramidal tract or of other interferences in central-nervous-system functioning. The authors regard this neurological effect of the age-regression experiment as equivalent to a functional ablation of certain cortical fields. The mechanism for the functional ablation is not clear. Before accepting this explanation,

* The author observed the positive Babinski but once. It occurred spontaneously in a subject in deep hypnosis.

experimental controls, such as are described in the Dorcus experiment above, should be carefully worked out in order to formulate a more parsimonious explanation. The possibility of foreknowledge on the part of the subjects of what is expected, as well as the possibility of the voluntary performance of the positive Babinski response by some subjects, should be investigated.

Respiratory system. BREATHING RATE. Experimental studies of hypnotic control of respiratory functions do not provide many data for a psychosomatic theory. One would expect some alteration in breathing rate as the result of increased attention to the auditory stimuli emanating from the hypnotist. The author has gathered some preliminary data by taking pneumographic records on eleven subjects. The alterations during the induction were highly variable—although there were some indications that in deep hypnosis there was a slight decrease in rate; at the same time, shallow breathing appeared. Jenness and Wible (50) report that respiratory rhythms in hypnosis and in waking are indistinguishable, but that sleep records show a decrease in rate and amplitude.

Effects are easily noted, however, when direct or indirect suggestions are given. If suggestions of rest, relaxation, and passivity are made to apt subjects, respiratory rate will decrease. When emotional stimuli are introduced, wittingly or unwittingly, respiratory rate increases. The classic study by Feleky (35) demonstrated characteristic respiratory changes in pleasure, pain, fear, disgust, anger, laughter, and hatred. Insofar as these affects are induced by the hypnotic situation, one would expect corresponding alterations in breathing patterns.

Dunbar (33) cites an experiment by Astruck (3) who was able to influence respiratory activity in deep hypnosis by suggesting cardiac acceleration and deceleration. The mechanisms by which the suggestions altered the respiration are not discussed. The question is always open: Is the subject responding to the suggestion with increased effort? with frustration? with anger or annoyance? And is the respiratory change a feedback resultant of such intervening responses?

Therapeutically, hypnosis has been used in the control of respiratory allergies. The work of Laudenheimer (57), Hansen (43), and Brauns (14) has already been reviewed by Dunbar (33). One interpretation of the results would emphasize relaxation as the important factor in allergy control. Laudenheimer, for example, prescribes general muscular relaxation with suggestions of slower and prolonged respiration. In this connection, mention should be made of three cases of asthma treated by the author. The method used was prolonged hypnosis (one to two hours) during which time a variant of Jacobson's cultivated relaxation (49) was taught the patients. Posthypnotic suggestions of inducing relaxation under stressful conditions were given. The hypnotic instructions emphasized a program of action for the patient, thus minimizing the anxiety ordinarily induced by the first signs of a seizure. Uncovering emotional traumata apparently had no immediate effect on the frequency or severity of the asthmatic attacks. The deflection of attention from the incipient seizure (whether initiated by allergens, by affect, or both) to the step-by-step practice of relaxation probably played an important part. The changes in CO_2 tension, in arterial oxygen, and in other blood constituents were not assessed. Their importance as mechanisms in asthma and the manner in which the mechanisms are modified by social-psychological stimulation must be assessed by further experimental and clinical work.

Gastrointestinal system. GASTRIC MOTILITY. Dunbar (33) has reviewed the earlier reported work on the effects of hypnotic stimulation on gastric motility. Using fluoroscopic methods, it was possible to study the influence of hypnotically induced affects on peristalsis, on tonus, and on ptosis. One procedure is to give the subject (patient) a barium meal and then, under hypnosis, give various suggestions, such as "You feel disgusted," or "You will have the same kind of sensations as when you eat a meal for which you have no appetite." Such instructions, in appropriately predisposed subjects, are followed by gastroptosis, atonicity, and lack of peristalsis. When the suggestion is centered around a delicious meal and zestful appetite, the gastroptosis disappears and normal peristalsis and tonicity are observed. (Heyer, 46, and Heilig and Hoff, 45)

In a series of reports, Frick, Scantlebury, and Patterson (39), Scantlebury (80), and Scantlebury and Patterson (81) demonstrated the effect of psychological stimulation on a basic life process—hunger. During periods of hunger contractions, hypnotic suggestions of eating resulted in a cessation of gastric contractions. All these studies were carried out on one or two subjects without attempting to assess the depth of hypnosis. Lewis and Sarbin (59) repeated these experiments on eight subjects, introducing refinements in method. Subjects were hypnotized after fasting fifteen or more hours. The Carlson balloon-manometer method was used. After taking kymographic tracings of hunger and quiescent periods, the experimenter suggested a fictitious meal during the middle of a contractile period. Since each subject participated in the experiment several times, it was possible to derive an index based on the number of times fictitious meals instituted gastric contractions. This index was highly correlated with the depth of hypnosis as measured by the Friedlander-Sarbin scale. In the waking state, imagined feeding did not inhibit the hunger contractions.

It is important to note that, in the deeply hypnotized subjects, mentally working out arithmetic problems produced partial inhibitions. Induced anxiety was also noticed as an antecedent of gastric inhibition. In this connection, Bennett and Venables (10) and Carlson (20) reported observations on the interruption of gastric motility in emotional states. These latter facts must be considered in tracing the mediational routes from social-psychological stimulation to organismic response (see below).

SECRETIONS. Bennett and Venables (10) and Luckhardt and Johnston (63) both found that the imagined ingestion of a meal in hypnosis increases the activity of the stomach. The amount of secretion is similar to that observed when test meals are given. Working primarily with (psychosomatic?) patients, Delhougne and Hansen (28) found specificity of enzyme secretion for specific food substances. "For example, with suggestions of an albuminous food there was an increase in pepsin and trypsin, but not of the other ferments; with suggestion of a fatty food there was increase of lipase, but not of other ferments; with suggestion of a carbohydrate food there was increase of diastase, but not of other ferments . . ." (33, p. 441)

Heyer (46) hypnotized subjects with "healthy gastro-intestinal tracts." Suggestions of specific foods (boullion, bread, milk) were given to subjects with empty stomachs. Samples of gastric contents were obtained with a fine sound. He reported that the *quantity* of secretion corresponded to the *vividness* of the suggestion and that the composition of the juices corresponded to the food suggested. Further to illustrate the apparent autonomic control of gastric functions, he demonstrated the effect of the hedonic tone on the flow of gastric juices. With dysphoric affects, the gastric flow was inhibited more quickly than with euphoric affects. Once the secretion was started, however, the injection of a vagus-paralyzing drug was ineffective. The interpretation is unclear. It is possible that gastric secretion, once started through neural channels, may continue either reflexly on a local basis or through humoral mechanisms.

Other studies on secretory activity have yielded similar results. For example, bile secretion has been found to vary with hypnotically induced affects. Wittkower (100) reported that anxiety, sorrow, and joy appreciably increased bile secretion. The secretion began with the induction of the specific affect and ceased abruptly upon the relief of the affect. The suggested affect of "annoyance," on the other hand, resulted in an inhibition of bile secretion.

These studies on gastric motility and secretion may be summarized briefly: Suggestions given under hypnosis to appropriately predisposed persons are followed by marked changes in functioning. The suggestions are of two kinds: (1) The subject is told to imagine the ingestion of specific foods, and (2) the subject is told to behave *as if* certain affect-producing stimuli were present. Future studies should attempt to assess the contribution of response-produced affective determinants in the gastric response to the first type of hypnotic instruction. Among the problems for psychosomatic theory and research is the tracing of the neural, humoral, and hormonal networks which make such responses possible.

Genitourinary system. A survey of the literature reveals few reports which could be called experiments. There are, however, many reports of hypnotic effects on genitourinary functioning in a clinical or therapeutic setting. Dunbar's review (33) of the older literature supplemented by Kroger's review of more recent studies (56) warrants the inference that practically every form or urological, gynecological, or reproductive function may be ablated or produced through hypnotic procedures.

DYSMENORRHEA. A number of investigators have reported the control of functional menstrual cramps by hypnotic suggestion (Dorcus and Kirkner, 31, Kroger and Freed, 56, Sarbin and Lewis, 79). The learned social and cultural meanings associated with menstruation point to the possibility of strong cortical control of the menstrual process. Kroger (55, p. 62), suggests that "hypnosis and post-hypnotic suggestion may block the painful uterine contractions, thus interrupting the pain pathway from the uterus to the higher brain centers . . . hypnosis may act cortically by either raising the pain threshold or by breaking up the 'pain-pattern' [expectations] conditioned in the cortex as a result of faulty attitudes."

FRIGIDITY AND IMPOTENCE. It is by now well established that nearly all cases of frigidity and impotence are psychogenic in origin. In subjects who are apt role-takers and who are well motivated, suggestions in hypnosis have been therapeutically successful. In the author's experience, extensive depth probing and analytic reconstruction are less effective in eliminating the symptoms than hypnotic suggestions aimed at allaying anxiety and building up appropriate imagery.

FUNCTIONAL AMENORRHEA AND CHANGES IN MENSTRUAL PERIODICITY. The social-psychological factors in amenorrhea have been well described by Dunbar (33). During wartime, for example, the absence of males appears to bear a causal relation to amenorrhea. The extreme lability of the symptom is seen in the rapidity with which it can be eliminated through a single hypnotic session. Dunbar cites several investigators who have successfully treated amenorrhea (or its symptomatic opposite, profuse bleeding) through one or two direct suggestions in hypnosis. As is usually the case, no details are available regarding significant patient variables, situational variables, or instruction variables. Dunbar (33, p. 504) reviews a report of a woman whose menstrual cycle was three weeks (with no other complaints). With a single hypnotic session, the cycle was permanently changed to four weeks. In the series of dysmenorrheas studied by Sarbin and Lewis (79) one young woman, aged twenty-two, besides severe debilitating menstrual cramps also complained of profuse bleeding, a 6- to 7-day period, and a 21- to 22-day cycle. She was a somnabulistic subject. During a 2-month interval hypnosis was used for direct suggestion of freedom from pain; practice of relaxation exercises during the entire cycle was prescribed; and feelings of confidence were emphasized. In several nonhypnotic interviews the origin of social and cultural taboos about menses was discussed. The cycle changed to 26 days, there was no pain, bleeding was reduced, and the period lasted only 4 days. A 2-year follow-up showed that the changes were permanent.

CHILDBIRTH. Clinical accounts of "painless" childbirth through hypnotic analgesia and muscular control have been repeatedly described. Muscular relaxation, although not systematically assessed, is probably one of the important intermediate conditions between the hypnotic suggestion and the painfree response. I have located one study that attempted to evaluate hypnotic childbirth. Abramson (1) reported a study of 100 experimental patients treated by hypnotic conditioning and 100 controls. He found that the experimental group had shorter and less variable labor and required less analgesic drugs. They were also observed to complain less than the controls and were considered more self-controlled.

Cardiovascular system. HEART RATE. It is not uncommon to observe tachycardia during the first part of the induction period. This, of course, cannot be attributed to hypnosis per se, but to unfamiliarity, excitement, anxiety, etc. As a rule the heart rate returns to normal after the subject has accepted the relaxation and trance instructions. Speeding up of the heart rate can be quickly and easily produced in hypnotic subjects through appropriate suggestions. Nearly any instruction aimed at emotional arousal is effective in producing pulse and blood-pressure changes. Whitehorn (97), for example, using such a procedure, reported the acceleration of heart rate by as much as 80 per cent. These results, congruent with the results on alteration of respiration, again raise the question of the intervening mechanism: Does the pulse rate change as the direct result of the symbolic stimuli? or as the feedback resultant of minimal overt (but not monitored) skeletal responses? or both? The only systematic information on this point is that of Jenness and Wible (50) who could not induce cardiac changes directly.

VASOMOTOR CHANGES. White (95) reported an experiment in which unpleasant affective states induced by hypnotic stimulation brought about increases in blood pressure. Heyer (46) found lowered blood-pressure readings for normotensive subjects in hypnosis and higher readings for hypotensives. I have found variable diminution in blood-pressure readings with hypertensives under hypnotic therapeusis focused on cultivated relaxation. (Studies dealing with vasomotor changes reflected in skin conditions are discussed later.)

Clinical reports on the treatment of vasomotor disorders illustrate the effect of social-psychological stimulation on autonomic functions. Lipkin et al. (61) treated nine cases of Raynaud's disease (peripheral vasospasm) by "suggestion." They used impressive apparatus and verbal reassurance. Two-thirds of the cases showed marked subjective and some objective improvement; the other third showed transient relief. The effects of the suggestion included: prolonged vasodilation with hands dripping with perspiration, rapid changes in skin temperature, altered capillary flow, and relief of vasospasm. Weiss (92) published an account of a severe case of Raynaud's disease treated by hypnosis. The patient, a twenty-eight-year-old soldier, had diffuse cyanosis of the hands and feet with complete absence of sweat-gland activity. He complained of severe pain. He had shown no response to conventional medical treatment. In the course of six hypnotic sessions and interviews lasting one week, the vasospastic disorder cleared up completely. Weiss attributed the success of the hypnotic sessions to the uncovering and possible abreaction of repressed hostility toward another soldier who had made improper advances to the patient's wife.

Metabolism. Dunbar (33), among others, has reviewed a large amount of literature which reveals unmistakably the close association of emotional states with metabolic processes. Studies have been reported in which basal metabolic rates, O_2 consumption, acid-base equilibrium, blood sugar levels, glycosuria, blood cell counts, and various metabolites have been assessed before, during, and after emotional behavior.

Many such experiments have been done under hypnosis. Here attention should be focused on the frequently unrecognized possibility that metabolic effects of hypnosis may in reality be effects of unnoticed affective excitants, such excitants being associated with responses to frustration, to indirect suggestion, or to effort. Hypnotic studies in which direct suggestions are utilized to induce anxiety offer no special problems. One such study (Whitehorn, Lundholm, and Gardner, 98) determined metabolic rates for hypnotically suggested moods. Operating under a concurrent suggestion to inhibit all muscular activity, insignificant increases in BMR were associated with elation, irritability, and depression, but a marked increase, 22 per cent, was recorded during anxiety.

SUGAR METABOLISM. Numerous observations have been published about hypnotic effects on sugar metabolism. These observations must be interpreted against the generally accepted fact, based on many laboratory and clinical studies, that hyperglycemia and glycosuria may be consequents of emotional states. One example of these studies will suffice to illustrate the lability of sugar metabolism in excitement. Cannon (18) reported that of the twenty-five members of the Harvard football squad examined after an important game, twelve had glycosuria. Of these positive cases, five were substitutes from the bench who had not actually played. Many other studies could be cited further to illustrate the connection between excitement or anxiety and sugar metabolism. The essential findings culled from the available literature may be summarized somewhat as follows: The trance induction appears to have little or no effect on blood sugar. Slight transient effects can be accounted for by excitement or relaxation. Hypnotic suggestion, in individual cases, of ingesting sugar when sugarfree fluids are taken may produce an increase in blood sugar; conversely, the suggestion that the sugar solution being ingested is sugarfree may produce a decrease in blood sugar (Dunbar, 33). The clinical and experimental reports are not always clear as to whether diabetic patients are the only subjects. It seems safe to assert that glycemic changes under hypnosis are easily effected in diabetic patients whose sugar metabolism is excessively labile and responsive to a wide variety of excitants. It is doubtful whether any reliable glycemic changes can be produced in nondiabetics (Nielson and Geert-Jorgensen, 67) merely by verbal stimulation. The therapeutic possibilities of hypnosis for diabetics, particularly when focused on quieting and on tension reduction, have hardly been explored.

CALCIUM METABOLISM.* Increases in calcium content of the blood have been measured after hypnotic excitation, as well as decrease after hypnotic quieting (Glaser, 42). No information is available, however, on the significant patient variables. Other workers have been able to modify blood calcium *only* in individuals with abnormal or unstable calcium content. In persons with normal Ca levels, it was not possible to alter blood calcium by hypnotic suggestion (Kretschmer and Krüger, 54). This report emphasizes, again, the importance of considering the *lability* of physiological processes in predisposed patients before asserting that hypnosis is the responsible therapeutic agent.

Skin. To conclude this review of clinical and experimental findings, a few typical papers on hypnotic alterations of the skin will be mentioned. As in the case of the other organ systems, little systematic work has been reported. Most of the experiments were done before 1930 and were poorly controlled.

SKIN BLISTERS. In a comprehensive review of all the available studies of blister formation under hypnosis (Pattie, 71) the fact of hypnotic blister formation seems established, although the mechanism is unclear. The methods for producing blisters vary from one investigator to the next. The general procedure is, first, to hypnotize the subject, then to touch the site prescribed with a neutral instrument such as a glass rod, at the same time giving the vivid suggestion that the site is being burned. The area is then bandaged or in other ways protected from accidental or factitial damage. After a predetermined interval, the site is clinically examined for presence of a blister. In a few cases, microscopic examination of the tissue is done. In general, the blisters have appeared to resemble blisters which would form following real burns.

The fact that many investigators (including the present author)

* It would be redundant to review the scattered reports of hypnotic effects on other metabolites and on blood picture. Observations have been recorded on arterial oxygen, leucocyte count, phosphorus, acid-base balance, etc. Dunbar (33) may be consulted for summaries and bibliographic notations.

have been unable to produce blisters in deeply hypnotized persons suggests the necessity for a careful analysis of the possible sources of variation. Subject variation appears to be very important. Most, if not all, of the subjects who responded with dermatological change were hysterical patients. Careful anamnesis might have provided evidence that the patients were characterized by extreme lability of the vasomotor system. This would direct experiment and theory to a notion of *organic readiness* or *prior pathological experience,* a notion congruent with the general postulates of the role-taking theory of hypnosis (Sarbin, 76).

Schindler's case report tells of a woman with frequent and severe ecchymoses, refractory to other types of treatment, who responded successfully to hypnotic treatment. It was possible to produce the ecchymoses by hypnotic suggestion and to predict the time of appearance. On one occasion, the suggestion was given that the hemorrhage would burn. The ecchymosis appeared, also a blister. A few days later blisters developed without hemorrhage. The treatment, instituted after analytic therapy had failed, began with a 24-hour hypnosis. After this session, the patient was symptom-free for 8 days. Another treatment period produced permanent freedom from symptoms, according to a 6-year follow-up (Dunbar, 33).

The mechanism of the successful treatment is, of course, obscure. The present author would hypothesize that induced relaxation, with associated reduction in autonomic behavior, is one of the significant variables. Learning to use relaxation in life-stress situations may occur as a generalization from the prolonged hypnotic session. The cogency of this hypothesis is strengthened by my experience with two cases of urticarial wheals treated by hypnosis. Neither patient was somnambulistic, but both were markedly improved after a few months. Both acquired techniques of relaxation which could be practiced whenever the patient experienced stress.

The use of suggestion and hypnosis in the therapy of skin disorders has not been systematically studied. The fact that dermatological conditions may be produced, sustained, and controlled by social-psychological events is no longer doubted (Wittkower and Russell, 100). A host of psychological, physiological, and biochemical problems emerge from the recognition of the psychosomatic etiology. Such studies, for example, as those of Obermayer and Greenson (68), where warts were treated by suggestion, raise many questions. Some pertinent variables emerging from such studies are: the kind of wart, the length of time the patient had had the wart, age, sex, and other characteristics of the patient.

The preceding review demonstrates that under specified conditions certain persons respond to hypnotic induction and to hypnotic suggestions in multiple ways. Nearly every organ and every physiological variable can, in appropriately predisposed subjects, be influenced. The precipitating stimuli are social-psychological in nature. Observation of the responses to these stimuli are seen in increased involvement of the organism. The variety and complexity of observed and measured organismic responses makes necessary a general theory of the psychophysiology of hypnosis. We now turn to a preliminary sketch of such a theory.

A theoretical account of the psychophysiology of hypnosis

In the foregoing pages a number of observations, experiments, and clinical reports have been reviewed. The obvious conclusion is that the responses to cues introduced into the subject's psychological field through hypnosis (as in other social-psychological stimulus settings) may have far-reaching physiological effects. Because the magnitude of these effects appears to be disjunctive with the quality and intensity of the precipitating stimuli, it is incumbent on anyone trying to formulate a sound theory of hypnosis to attempt a description of the mechanisms by which such apparently dramatic organismic changes occur. It would be jejune to content ourselves only with a restatement of the ideomotor hypothesis: that verbal stimuli exert a *direct* influence on vegetative organs. A description of cardiovascular changes following verbal stimuli, for example, requires a consideration of what kinds of integration are allowed by the neural and circulatory networks.

Remaining within our naturalistic framework, which asserts that hypnosis is not some transcendental phenomenon but rather a specialized kind of social situation, our point of departure for theory building must be a careful, objective observation of the events in question, interpreted against a background of available knowledge drawn from psychology and physiology. What follows is in the nature of a preface to a general theory of psychosomatics, against which physiological changes in hypnosis may be evaluated.

Classification of organ systems. In order to provide a psychophysiological setting for this discussion a classification of organ systems is required. For this purpose, I am suggesting a threefold system.* As heuristic for the study of psychosomatic problems, organ systems may be classfied as:

Class I. Those which implement commerce of the organism with the external environment
Class II. Those which facilitate the exchange of chemical substances with the external environment
Class III. Those which maintain internal homeostasis

In Class I are those organs which are directly involved in transactions with the external environment, the exteroceptors and the striate musculature with its proprioceptive connections. These organ systems, of course, are involved in movement, motor skills, speech and language, in sign and symbol function, in thought and

* This is an adaptation of a fourfold system introduced by Kubie. His class of body-image manifestations is subsumed under my Class I.

imagery, in concept formation, etc. Disorders of these organ systems are of two kinds: those which result from trauma to or disease of the central nervous system and the sensorimotor apparatus and those dysfunctions of the perceptual and motor apparatus usually called *conversion hysteria.* The primary function of these organs is innervated by the somatosensory and somatomuscular networks, the autonomic nervous system performing a synergic role.

Class II organ systems have as their primary function the periodic exchange of chemical substances with the external environment. The oral cavity, the nasal passages, the anorectal segment, the urethra, etc., are the distal organs of these systems. The intake of water, nutriment, and oxygen and the output of gaseous and solid wastes and various external secretions are carried on by these organs. In considering the alimentary system, for example, we can observe a sequence of connected organs whose major innervations change along a gradient from the apertural organ to the internal organ. The apertures are innervated primarily by the central nervous system, but the functionally connected internal organs are innervated by the autonomic nervous system; the more proximal the organ, the more it is under the control of the autonomic system. In the organs of this group, the behaviors are initiated as somatomuscular activity, mediated by the central nervous system, but they terminate as autonomic action. As the complex act proceeds, "There is a gradual increase in the participation of autonomic function until finally, at the critical point, the autonomic nervous system takes off on an independent jet-propelled flight of its own. One sees this most clearly in swallowing, urinating, defecating, and of course, in sex . . ." *

Class III organs, the heart, the liver, the pancreas, the adrenals, the endocrines, etc., primarily maintain the internal economy of the organism. The function of these organs is internal homeo-

* KUBIE, L. S.: "The Central Representation of Symbolic Processes in Psychosomatic Disorders," *Psychosomat. Med.* 15:1–7 (1953).

stasis.* Their innervations are predominantly through the autonomic nervous system, the central nervous system performing a secondary role. The actions of these organs are, of course, not divorced from peripheral stimulation. Impulses originating in exteroceptors (and probably proprioceptors) reach the hypothalamus via the thalamus and trigger off the emergency reactions of the viscera. (See below for discussion of visceral brain concept.)

With this synoptic classification as a background, we can take a fresh look at the performances of a human being who is acting in the role of the hypnotic subject. If we take the position that the hypnotized person is actively *striving* to perform according to the instructions given him (wittingly and unwittingly by the hypnotist) within the limitations imposed by the subject's role-expectations, current perceptions, abilities, and prior organic-pathological experiences, it becomes apparent at once that any approach to mechanism must feature in a prominent way the striate musculature.

Effects on organ systems in hypnosis. CLASS I ORGANS. Let us look first at physiological effects which concern the organs of Class I. The catalepsies, the rigidities, contractures, observed increases in strength, etc., call for no special theory of behavior. Under appropriate instruction, the subject responds directly to cues presented by the hypnotist. The reduced sensory influx may facilitate concentration so that, for example, some hypermnesia may occur.

Such an observation implies no transcendance of voluntary capacities. The available research shows that levels of performance in hypnosis are closely tied to levels of performance in the waking state. The small increments in muscular strength, for example,

* The skin is somewhat more difficult to classify. While it serves the exchange of chemical materials with the environment, it does not have apertual organs which have striate muscle connections. The components of the skin which are intimately related to internal homeostasis, the capillary walls and the sweat glands, are, of course, innervated by the autonomic nervous system. For our purposes, then, the skin can be classified as a Class III organ system.

can be explained by decreased distractions, increased motivation, and perhaps by visceral side effects.

The actions of organ systems of Class I are for the most part accessible to self-observation and report. Words and images (symbolic structures) are available for communication to self and others. Continued self-stimulation through language cues instigates and sustains the motoric response.

The direct observation of hypnotic performances from the point of view that the subject is part of a social-psychological situation reveals most clearly the validity of the conative hypothesis. The subject is striving to behave in certain ways—striving to enact a role. One can "strive" only through the mediation of the somatomuscular system. The term *effort* is appropriately applied only to actions of striate muscles against resistance.

It is apparent from this discussion that no special theory of behavior is required in order to understand the effects of hypnotic stimulation upon responses of organs and organ systems of Class I. The hypnotic subject or patient performs actions consistent with his perception of his current role. The wide variety of responses is made possible by the efficient use of symbols, including images, in communicating and maintaining role-instructions.

CLASS II ORGANS. The physiological effects of hypnotic instructions on Class II organ systems would appear to demand other explanatory principles. Let us examine one of the experiments reviewed before. Lewis and Sarbin (59) demonstrated how gastric hunger contractions could be modified or eliminated as a result of hypnotic suggestions. The site of measurement was the stomach (by means of the Carlson balloon-manometer apparatus). The stomach is innervated primarily by the autonomic nervous system. Its functions are not directly mediated by the central nervous system, by efferent processes from the neocortex. We must answer the question: What is the mechanism by which social-psychological stimuli, i.e., the hypnotic instructions to eat a fictitious meal, can effect changes in one of the basic vegetative processes, the activities of the stomach in hunger?

The stomach is one of the proximal organs the aperture of which is the oral cavity. Oral activity, which is primarily movement of the striate muscles of the lips, the jaw, the tongue, and the epiglottis, initiates a chain of effector events which may continue after the termination of the initial voluntary act. Salivation and swallowing, for example, initiate peristalsis of the esophagus which, in turn, transmits movement to the gastric wall which, along with secretion of hydrochloric acid, gastric juices, etc., alters the contractile state of the stomach so that it is ready to receive and digest nutriment. The persons in the experiment who showed the largest and most consistent effects were persons who were judged to possess the role-taking aptitude. That is, subjects who were considered the best role-takers were able to accept the psychosomatic role of "eater," to behave *as if* they were ingesting food. These same subjects showed more active preparatory set and more organized oral activity during the period of fictitious feeding. In this context, role-enactment means motoric activity at the aperture (along with a general postural adjustment) sufficient in kind and intensity to activate in sequential manner the anatomically connected smooth muscle and glandular tissues.

The point I am trying to make is that physiological changes under hypnotic stimulation, with regard to organ systems of Class II, follow from stimulation initially produced by striate muscle activity at the distal aperture. The physiological changes occur *sequentially* through autonomic and humoral stimulation released by the initial apertural motor responses. The fact of a one- to two-minute refractory period between the verbal stimulus and the gastric response lends support to this hypothesis.

Class III organs. Now we consider the organs of Class III, the internal organs that have no direct anatomical linkages with the apertures. These organs are more truly autonomic. The cardiovascular system, the endocrines, the liver, and other viscera maintain the internal chemical equilibrium through neural, hormonal, and humoral homeostatic mechanisms. How these organs are influenced by stimuli of a social-psychological nature is the central question in psychosomatic theory.

Two lines of thought, probably supplemental one to the other, may be narrated as at least partial answers to the question. The first has to do with the well-known fact that measurable visceral responses are a result of motoric behavior. The second line of thought would place the skeletal response and the autonomic response as organismic parallels.

We shall first discuss the point of view that the autonomic response is a consequent of the somatic response. Whether the association between visceral and skeletal responses is the product of experience or is part of the organism's innate neural equipment (or both) is a question not completely answered. In a recent article, Kendon Smith (88) has argued that conditioned autonomic responses are an artifact of reinforced somatomuscular responses. What is *conditioned* or acquired to the unconditioned stimulus is not the psychogalvanic response (Freeman, 38), vasodilation (Beier, 8), or salivation (Razran, 74), but rather diffuse somatomuscular responses. According to Smith, the autonomic response is only an innately associated response. The measurement of the visceral response, both in hypnotic and in acquisition experiments, may easily distract the observer from the diffuse and often minimal skeletal responses which trigger off the visceral reactions. In short, experiments which have been interpreted as autonomic learning or conditioning, upon closer examination seem to justify the inference that it is skeletal response that is acquired and that attention to the monitoring of the autonomic responses has obscured the recognition of the motoric components. The same hypothesis may be stated for hypnotic behavior.

Nowhere is this seen more forcefully than in attempts at conditioning the electrodermal response to a noxious unconditioned stimulus. Careful observation reveals the typical subject straining the skeletal musculature, preparing himself, as it were, for the expected electric shock or other noxious agent. This preparation, or bracing reaction, sets off a chain of intraorganismic events one of which, at least, can be monitored by galvanometric methods.

The parallel in hypnotic research is seen in experiments designed to elicit autonomic responses, such as variation in cardiac performance, in blood sugar levels, in bladder pressure, in gastric secretory reactions, etc. Intent on the measurement of changes in the visceral organs following hypnotic stimuli, experimenters have for the most part neglected the intermediate effects. What does the subject *do* when he accepts a command? Careful observation of subjects' performances, i.e., motoric activity, either directly or monitored by muscle potentials, is a necessary step in order fully to understand the mechanism of what appears to be direct hypnotic control of autonomic processes.

Further to develop this point, I shall present a summary of a recent study reported by Lovett Doust (32). Levels of arterial oxygen saturation were found to be related to the depth of hypnosis. The two variables showed a linear relationship—the deeper the hypnosis the greater the anoxemia. Further, suggested emotions of grief, rage, anxiety, joy, and ecstasy showed changes in arterial oxygen which were related to the hedonic quality of the emotion. Both these findings would have been more clear-cut if the experimenter had systematically observed and reported on the molar performance of the subjects. The first finding presumably could be related to respiratory changes associated with relaxation of the skeletal musculature—such relaxation being among the first role-instructions ordinarily given the hypnotic subject. A description of the subject's observable responses when told to dream of an emotional experience would probably have shown for the "negative" affects (rage, grief, and anxiety) more motoric activity, including increased respiration; for the "positive" affects (joy and ecstasy) less motoric activity, more of a passive acceptance of imagined pleasurable stimulation.

In fact, Lovett Doust does include some notes which bear on this point. When under the "anxiety" instruction, the subject's "fingers clenched, sweat appeared on her brow and on her palms, and she began trembling . . ." For the experimentally induced depression, "both subjects wept profusely." For the "rage" instructions, the subject "appeared flushed, her brows were knit, and she frequently clenched her teeth." The suggestion is apposite that the variation in oxygen saturation was a function of the amount of muscular and respiratory activity performed by the subject in initiating the enactment of the prescribed role.

In this experiment, as in many others, the subjects were patients; three of the four were labeled hysterics. The role-enactment facility of hysterical patients is well known, their performances often being such that *as-if* behavior is a common differential diagnosis.

My point here again underscores the importance of the motoric aspect of role-enactment. The process of imagining, thinking about, dreaming, or "feeling into" an emotional state apparently does not occur in the absence of motoric activity. Jacobson (49), Max (66), Schultz (83), and others have shown how thought and imagination are associated (if not identical) with muscle potentials.

For many subjects it is necessary vividly to present visual and auditory stimuli by verbal devices in order to induce the emotional response in the subject, i.e., to involve more and more of the organism. Hypnotic instructions aimed at eliciting visual and auditory imagery are in the service of actuating the skeletal responses characteristically evoked by the object or situation which the instructions vividly symbolize. In a very real sense, the instructions assist the appropriately predisposed subject in distal focusing. Such focusing is carried on by the subject via the somatosensory apparatus; the organized response is (on this theory) somatomuscular, the visceral responses being concomitants of such somatic initiatory responses. As stated in the introductory paragraphs, the careful observer of hypnotic phenomena must assay an objective description of the many sources of variation—including the motoric and visceral concomitants of such focusing on auditory and visual symbols. The report of Schwarz and Loewy (cited in Dunbar, 33) illustrates this point. They found that suggestions delivered in vivid sensory language resulted in increases in bladder pressure. Examples of such instructions are: "It is very hot and you jump into a cold bath," or "you gulp a glass of beer on a hot summer day" (p. 489). Instructions which contained no aids to distal focusing, such as "you are undergoing a bladder operation," had no effect (84).

At least two forms of stimuli which induce imaginal focusing may be mentioned in this connection. The first is the obvious form of direct suggestion. The subject is told to imagine (i.e., to behave *as if*) an emotionally provoking stimulus is present. Subjects adept in *as-if* behavior respond as if the perception were object-focused rather than sign-focused. For example, a subject who is afraid of snakes will exhibit marked somatic and visceral responses when told that a rattlesnake is crawling up his arm.

The second form is indirect suggestion. The subject may, as the result of some incidental stimulus, focus on a threatening stimulus situation. Visceral behavior will be noted without the experimenter's being able to identify the cues or trace the stimulus-response chains.

In addition to imaginal focusing, at least two other response syndromes may produce autonomic shifts. The first is frustration. When the subject is motivated, let us say, to help the experimenter or to please the therapist by symptom relief, and fails in his efforts, he may show the skeletal and concurrent autonomic responses to frustration. Such apparently spontaneous visceral responses, if they are being monitored, may be spuriously interpreted as a characteristic of hypnosis. A similar skeletal response-produced syndrome may be noted in subjects who are striving to perform actions not under the control of the central nervous system. A case in point is that of an experimental subject who was told to develop a blister by "willing" it, by concentrating on it. Close observation revealed what would be expected under instructions to concentrate—straining of the skeletal muscles, pressure on the diaphragm, irregular respiration, etc. No blister appeared, but urticarial wheals developed over forehead, neck, and arms. One should add that lability of the subject's vasomotor system had been noted before, wheal formation following undischarged tension. On the view being reported here, the responses of organs of Class III are regarded as automatically fired when certain somatic responses occur. The visceral responses are seen as feedback * effects of skeletal responses to verbal and imaginal stimuli.

The feedback explanation just presented is a limited one. It leaves no room for the contribution of the central excitatory state to behavior. However, it has certain explanatory power, and, further, testable hypotheses may be deduced from it.

The second viewpoint on the mediation of responses of Class III organs (which may be a supplement rather than an alternative to the hypothesis already described) regards the autonomic response as parallel to the somatic response, the parallel functioning being mediated through neural and humoral networks. The question to be answered is: What conditions allow the inference of common innervation of somatic and visceral responses?

An answer to the question must be prepared by referring to refined observation of the hypnotic act. The subject is enacting a role as he perceives it on the basis of his concurrent and prior experiences. One of the major components of the hypnotic role, as contained in the expectations of the subject and reinforced by

* I am using the term *feedback* in a wider context than that used by the exponents of cybernetics. I am regarding the organism *in toto* as the energy system. *Feedback* here refers to changes in one part of the system as a result of changes in other parts of the system.

the instructions of the hypnotist, is muscular relaxation. Careful scrutiny of the subject accepting the "relaxation" instruction shows a loss in tonicity. This is easily tested by tendon reflexes, for example. In many subjects the relaxation observed in hypnosis, while not identical with, is remarkably similar to the cultivated relaxation described by Jacobson (49). In subjects who are able to relax most of the somatic muscles the decrease in tonicity reduces proprioception and produces a partial deafferentation. There is a decreased sensory influx in deeply hypnotized subjects which is not unlike that observed in normal sleep (see review of Barker and Burgwin, 4, above).

In addition to the reduced afferent influx, under certain specifiable conditions, concurrent metabolic effects of these initial relaxing performances of the skeletal musculature may modify the central excitatory state. Some evidence suggests anoxic anoxia (Lovett Doust, 32). The postulated anoxia which follows from peripheral anoxemia is not likely to be great. However, the kinds of quickly reversible behavior observed in hypnosis would not demand profound alterations in cerebral metabolism.

A speculative word is proffered as to how mild anoxia might result in the kinds of behavior cited on pages 6–7, i.e., changes in motility, shifts in orientation from distal to proximal stimuli, disinhibition of affective processes, and changes in covert behavior such as thought and imagery.

The present status of research suggests that under physiological conditions the over-all cerebral oxygen consumption is relatively constant (Kety, 51). Two other bits of information must be introduced: First, there is differential vascularity in the cerebrum. The most vascular parts of the brain are the supraoptic and the ventricular nuclei (Finley, 36). These ganglia are concerned with autonomic functions. Second, it is generally assumed that the vascularity is proportional to the oxygen consumption.

In this connection Cobb points out, "The lower centers . . . need an even continuous flow. The cerebral hemispheres, however, being more specialized and less continually active, have a less steady blood flow, and those parts of the cerebral cortex most actively functioning at any given time have temporary and local changes in blood flow." (21, p. 736)

Given these premises, if there is a mild anoxia, then the effect on the neocortex would be greater than the effect on subcortical centers. The *net* effect would be a *relative increase* in subcortical metabolism. This series of neural and metabolic events alters the central excitatory state so that afferent impulses are coordinated by a mildly (and not irreversibly) decorticated brain. As Cobb notes, ". . . there is evidence that the local supply to special areas of gray matter may vary according to the regional needs as determined by changes in neuronal activity." (21, p. 749) The classical phenomena of hypnosis, mentioned above, have many of the qualities of behavior performed without the pacemaking control of the neocortex, such as is seen also in alcoholic toxicosis, frontal lobe injuries, etc.*

Under such conditions, organ systems of Class III are more readily activated. The work of MacLean (65) following from implications of Papez's theory of emotion (69) is pertinent. Using the more apt term *visceral brain* to denote the structures formerly subsumed under the term *rhinencephalon,* he has described its close connections with the autonomic nervous system and its direct expression through the hypothalamic effector system. He has presented evidence and argument to show that the visceral brain is capable of a primitive kind of coding. That is, it could participate in sign functioning, but not in complex symbol functioning.

> *. . . the phylogenetically old brain (classically known as the rhinencephalon and arbitrarily referred to in this paper*

* That alterations in cerebral blood constituents can produce behavior changes is nowhere more dramatically demonstrated than in pernicious anemia. Bowman (12) has reviewed the literature and has listed many psychopathological correlates of pernicious anemia—abnormal mood reactions, intellectual changes, and conative alterations.

> *as the "visceral brain") is largely concerned with visceral emotional functions. This region of the brain appears to be so strategically situated as to be able to correlate every form of internal and external perception. In other words, the possibility exists in this region for bringing into association not only oral (smell, taste, mouth) and visceral sensation, but also impressions from the sex organs, body wall, eye, and ear. And in contrast to the neopallium, the rhinencephalon has many and strong connections with the hypothalamus for discharging its impressions. (65, p. 351)*

The application of this formulation to hypnotic stimulation of Class III organs is patent: If the central excitatory state is such that the visceral brain is regnant and signals are introduced via the exteroceptors, the firing is likely to be mediated by the hypothalamus. The particular disinhibition of affective response, so characteristic of somnambulistic subjects, would seem to follow from this formulation. The archaic form of thought and the focus on bodily functions would likewise be accounted for by the reduction of cortical control in favor of a relative increase in visceral brain functioning.

The shift in responsiveness from cortical to subcortical levels may be regarded as intracerebral preparation which makes possible greater degrees of organismic involvement in the role. The sometime spontaneous myoclonic contractions, cardiovascular changes, dermatoses, etc., can be seen as a result of temporary shift of dominance from the new brain to the phylogenetically older visceral brain.

The data to support such an hypothesis are meager. Among predisposed persons (apt hypnotic role-takers) we have some evidence of peripheral arterial anoxemia (Lovett Doust, 32). It is only a reasonable inference that mild cerebral anoxia follows. If this link is established, the differential cerebral effect of anoxia already established by Himwich (47) for the phyletic layers can be interpolated to support the hypothesis.

A few more statements are in order to round out this discussion. The effect of reviewing the psychosomatic literature is one of amazement in that nearly every form of physiological response can be produced or ablated by hypnosis. Most of the studies, however, are characterized by small numbers of subjects, absence of criteria for depth of hypnosis, lack of controls, and, most important, *the use of patients as subjects.* Whether the feedback hypothesis or the central-excitatory-state hypothesis is being analyzed we must note the use of patients with psychosomatic diseases (i.e., disorders of Class III organ systems) in hypnotic research.

In the light of current knowledge about psychosomatic illness, the production of physiological changes ranging from hypoglycemia in diabetics to wheal formation in urticarial patients is neither surprising nor does it make clearer the mechanism of hypnosis. Today we know that most psychosomatic symptoms are exceptionally labile. The following two quotations from Wolff (102) illustrate the lability of symptom formation among persons with psychosomatic illness. In these illustrations, stress was introduced directly by the experimenter. As pointed out before (p. 41), equivalent response-produced stimulation (indirect suggestion, frustration, and effort) may have the same effects.

> *Events either consciously or unconsciously interpreted as threats to security have been shown to produce in diabetic and nondiabetic humans a rise in the ketone bodies in the venous blood and fluctuations in the blood sugar level.* The magnitude of these reactions was greater in diabetic persons, *and when large enough and of sufficient duration led to ketosis and hyperglycemia in some, and to hypoglycemia in others, without the intervention of other factors such as intercurrent infections, changes in physical activity, or alterations of insulin and of food intake. During periods of stress a diuresis was produced in both diabetic and nondiabetic persons. In a diabetic such diuresis was associated with a massive loss of*

> *glucose and electrolytes, important in the development of dehydration and coma. (102, p. 103; emphasis added)*

In this connection, the findings of Nielson and Geert-Jorgensen (67) support my argument that the variance attributable to the hypnotic subject must not be discounted. These investigators were unable to produce through hypnotic instructions any blood sugar changes in *nondiabetics.*

The second quotation should be read with Pattie's review of hypnotic blister formation (71) in mind. Among various experiments reviewed by Pattie, there was a lack of agreement as to the genuineness of hypnotic blister formation. Such lack of agreement could be resolved if, among other things, more attention were directed to the characteristics of the subject. If a subject's prior organic experiences render the skin more reaction-sensitive, then it follows as a matter of course that the skin will quickly reflect induced organismic changes. Schilder and Kauders (82) had earlier suggested that a labile vasomotor apparatus was an essential prerequisite for blister formation. Although the description, from Wolff, which follows is concerned with acne vulgaris, the application to blister-formation experiments is obvious.

> *After initial washing the reaccumulation of sebum occurred gradually reaching approximately the pre-wash level within 60 minutes. During periods of tranquility an approximately constant facial sebum output was maintained. Observations on patients with acne vulgaris showed that during induced anger-evoking stress, sebum output was increased two- to five-fold. When emotional reactions of remorse and depression followed upon the anger, a relative decrease in sebum output occurred . . . The outstanding pattern of emotional response in a series of patients with acne vulgaris was intense anger followed by depression and remorse. A close correlation was found between these phasic emotional*

> *reactions, alterations in seborrhea, and exacerbations in the number of acne lesions. (102, pp. 101–102)*

In the light of such observations it is appropriate to say that the earlier work on physiological effects of hypnosis told us more about the particular disease syndrome than about hypnosis.

The two viewpoints sketched above as to the mediation of visceral responses have their historical roots in the James-Lange theory and in the thalamic theory of Cannon, respectively. That proprioceptive feedback is a factor in behavior cannot be denied; that intracerebral conditions (metabolic, electrical, temperature) can contribute to consummatory behavior is also indubitable (Hebb, 44). A fruitful theory of psychosomatics will have to incorporate both sets of observations (and probably others) in order further to explore how social-psychological stimuli can effect changes of Class III organ systems. Such a unified theory will help clarify the mediation not only of temporary visceral alterations observed in hypnotic experiments, but the long-time alterations which make up the psychosomatic disease syndromes.

Some implications for therapy *

The preceding discussion was based upon a threefold classification of organ systems. If the classification is more than a literary convenience, it should provide some footing for differential application of hypnotic therapy. From the theory as sketched, then, some concrete and necessarily oversimplified suggestions are given for the treatment of specific disorders insofar as they can be assigned to one of the three classes.

Disorders of Class I organ systems. These are the organ systems primarily innervated by the somatosensory and somatomuscular nervous system. The most frequent disorder, if not attributable to

* Space limitations prevent my going into one of the most important aspects of hypnotic therapy—differential responsiveness to hypnosis (see Sarbin, 76).

lesions of the central nervous system, is conversion hysteria. Here the patient is operating on a symbolic (cortical) basis. The rapid and almost sure-fire removal of symptoms by direct suggestion in hypnosis, or by other suggestion procedures, illustrates the high degree of participation of the voluntary musculature. However, as Freud and many others have discovered, symptom removal is ephemeral without concurrent alteration of the social-psychological conditions which produce stress, or modification of the patient's cognitive habits for neutralizing anxiety-producing cues.

An interesting demonstration of the symbolic use of the voluntary musculature by serial suppression of hysterical symptoms is provided by Seitz (86). The patient, a forty-nine-year-old woman, developed choreiform spasms and jerking of certain muscles following the death of her son. The psychodynamic inference was that the symptoms expressed symbolically her guilt feelings over the son's death—the symptoms being identified as masochistic and exhibitionistic. In a series of hypnotic experiments, attempts were made to replace these symptoms with others. When, for example, anesthesia of the scalp and itching of the ankles were suggested, the patient accepted and acted upon these suggestions, but the choreiform symptoms persisted. However, when a blush reaction and pruritis of the ankles with scratching (and resultant excoriation) were hypnotically induced, the chorea disappeared. Seitz explains the displacement of symptoms on the basis of their psychodynamic equivalence—the new symptoms, like the old, being identified as masochistic and exhibitionistic.

The hysterical disorders, then, must be treated at a complex symbolic level—with hypnotic or other therapy being aimed at identifying the excitants to anxiety and at developing cognitive habits for embedding the anxiety-producing cues in a neutral (nonsomatic) framework.

Disorders of Class II organ systems. Little substantial evidence has been offered to support the frequently advanced notion that *organ neuroses* are symbolic. In the first place, symbolic behavior is mediated by the central nervous system and involves the exteroceptors and the voluntary musculature. A parallel cortical network has not been isolated for such organs as, for example, the intestines or the stomach.

The criterion for classifying organ systems as Class II is that they mediate the exchange of substances with the external environment. The distal apertures of these organ systems have central-nervous-system connections; the proximal organs have autonomic connections. The aperture (for example, the mouth) being made up of striate muscle groups, can serve symbolic functions. Responses of the apertural organ, either through reflexes or through humoral mechanisms, trigger off the functioning of the proximal organs. In an *indirect* way, then, symbolic behavior can play a role in the development of an organ neurosis, e.g., a duodenal ulcer. This formulation has not had any experimental assay. However, on a priori grounds it is tenable.

One of the problems to be solved is the translation of anxiety-arousing social-psychological stimuli into symbolic responses via the apertural organs. A paradigm for this translation is based on the fixation of early-acquired interpersonal attitudes associated with responses of the apertural musculature. For example, attitudes of dependence are learned in infancy simultaneously with learning organized lingual, labial, glottal, and other oral habits. Certain predisposed persons, who have not acquired cognitive habits adequate for neutralizing anxiety-producing cues, may fall back upon oral behavior as a symbolic equivalent for dependency attitudes. Thus, in the man who is trying to be a successful assertive businessman, but whose early-acquired self-characteristics are incongruent with such a role, the conflict is handled by oral behavior—a symbol for dependency. (The oral responses may not be easily accessible to direct observation.) The minimal but frequent discharge of impulses and/or secretions * from the aper-

* Cf. Szasz (89, 90), also Winsor (99), whose research allows the inference that parotid secretion is a function of muscle activity and tonus.

ture prepares the stomach and intestines for the ingestion of food by hypermotility, hyperemia, and hyperacidity. This condition serves as the organic background for the development of an ulcer.

Granting that the paradigm just outlined is untested but plausible, we now move to the question: What are the implications for therapy? In the first place, necessity for medical and/or surgical treatment for the lesion must be assessed. Any hypnotic therapy or psychotherapy must be planned around the physician's survival program for the patient.

On the ideas briefed here, persons whose symptoms lead to lesions of internal organs are deficient in symbolic techniques with which they can cognitively focus on distal (outside-the-organism) stimuli. Symbolic focusing appears to be directed to somatic surrogates for tension reduction. Therefore, therapy should be directed (*a*) toward the development of cognitive techniques (such as fantasy) for distal focusing of anxiety reduction and (*b*) toward the learning of relaxation techniques for the control of *specific* apertural tensions.

Disorders of Class III organ systems. The form and content of hypnotic therapy or other psychotherapy in disorders involving organ systems of Class III must now be considered. If we subscribe to the feedback notion, that the visceral response is automatically tripped off by somatomuscular responses, then therapy must be aimed at breaking up the chain of somatomuscular responses to anxiety-producing cues. Since the response is diffuse rather than focalized (as posited for Class II organ systems) the aim of therapy must be the entire soma. Here, the relaxation produced in hypnosis—or in Jacobson's (49) or Schultz's (83) cultivated relaxation—would be the treatment of choice. Any direct suggestion should be aimed at learning techniques of relaxing the skeletal muscles when tensions begin. Analytic depth-probing would be contraindicated because of the arousal of anxiety which would militate against learning the hypnotic or other relaxation procedures.

If we subscribe to the second notion,* that the central excitatory state provides the background for a common innervation of both skeletal and visceral responses, the therapeutic rationale is somewhat different. Here we would be concerned with providing the patient with means of modifying the central excitatory state. This may be accomplished in at least two ways: (1) by reducing the afferent influx through the relaxation component of hypnosis and (2) by directing attention to learning cognitive techniques for the reduction of anxiety, i.e., defense mechanisms. The first step, which brings symptomatic relief, has the virtue of partially eliminating the perception of currently threatening stimuli; the second step is designed to modify the central state by providing cognitive mechanisms.

It is too early to assess the correctness of these formulations. It is quite possible that the feedback hypothesis could be incorporated into the central-excitatory-state hypothesis. At least in hypnotic therapy based on the feedback notion it is possible that the patient may acquire cognitive techniques for handling anxiety excitants incidental to the hypnotically induced relaxation.

To summarize, I have tried to show first, that hypnosis is a matter of role-taking; second, that one of the dimensions of roles is intensity, or organismic involvement; third, that such involvement may be monitored by nearly all physiological observations and indices; fourth, that physiological changes can best be evaluated against a general psychosomatic theory. Such a theory based upon psychological and physiological data has been sketched; and finally, I have pointed out briefly the rationale for hypnotic therapeusis which flows from the theoretical formulations.

* As stated before, it is probable that both formulations are necessary for a complete theory.

REFERENCES

1. Abramson, M.: "Hypnosis in Obstetrics and Its Relation to Personality," *Personality* 1:355–361 (1951).
2. Allen, A. H. B.: *The Self in Psychology*, London, Kegan Paul, Trench, Trubner & Co., 1935.
3. Astruck, P.: "Uber psychische Beeinflussung des vegetativen Nervensystems in der Hypnose. I. Hypnotische Beeinflussung der Herztatigkeit und der Atmung," Arch. Ges. Psychol. 95:266–280 (1923).
4. Barker, W., and S. Burgwin: "Brain Wave Patterns during Hypnosis, Hypnotic Sleep and Normal Sleep," *Arch. Neurol. & Psychiat.* 62:412–420 (1949).
5. Barry, H. Jr., D. W. Mackinnon, and H. A. Murray, Jr.: Hypnotizability as a personality trait and its typological relations. *Hum. Biol.* 3:1–36 (1931).
6. Bass, M.: Differentiation of hypnotic trance from normal sleep. *J. Exp. Psychol.* 14:382–399 (1931).
7. Beecher, H. K.: "Pain and Some Factors That Modify It," *Anesthesiology* 12:633–641 (1951).
8. Beier, D. C.: "Conditioned Cardiovascular Responses and Suggestions for the Treatment of Cardiac Neuroses," *J. Exp. Psychol.* 26:311–321 (1940).
9. Benedict, R.: "Anthropology and the Abnormal," *J. Gen. Psychol.* 10:59–82 (1934).
10. Bennett, T. I., and J. F. Venables: "The effect of emotions on the gastric secretion and motility of the human being," *Brit. Med. J.* 2:662–663 (1920).
11. Blake, H., and R. W. Gerard: "Brain potentials during sleep," *Am. J. Physiol.* 119:692–703 (1937).
12. Bowman, K. M.: "Psychoses with Pernicious Anemia," *Am. J. Psychiat.* 92:379–396 (1935).
13. Braid, J.: *Neurypnology, or the Rationale of Nervous Sleep in Relation to Animal Magnetism*, London, John Churchill, 1843.
14. Brauns, W.: "Zur Behandlung der Allergischen Erkrankungen, insbesonder des Heufiebers," *Med. Welt* 7:559–562 (1933).
15. Brenman, Margaret: "The Phenomena of Hypnosis," in *Trans. of the First Conference on problems of consciousness.* Ed by H. A. Abramson. New York, Josiah Macy, Jr. Foundation, 1951.
16. Brown, W.: "Sleep, Hypnosis, and Mediumistic Trance," *Character and Pers.* 3:112–126 (1935).
17. Brunswik, Egon: *Systematic and Representative Design of Psychological Experiments*, Berkeley, University of California Press, 1947.
18. Cannon, W. B.: *Bodily Changes in Pain, Hunger, Fear and Rage*, 2d ed. New York, D. Appleton-Century Company, Inc., 1929.
19. ———: " 'Voodoo' Death," *Am. Anthrop.* 44:169–181 (1942).
20. Carlson, A. J.: *The Control of Hunger in Health and Disease*, Chicago, University of Chicago Press, 1916.
21. Cobb, S.: "Cerebral Circulation: A Critical Discussion of the Symposium," in *The Circulation of the Brain and Spinal Cord*

(Assn. Res. Nerv. and Ment. Dis. Monogr. XVIII) Baltimore, 1938.

22. ———: *Emotions and clinical medicine*, New York, W. W. Norton & Company, Inc., 1950.
23. Crawley, E.: *The Mystic Rose.* Rev. by T. Besterman. London, Methuen & Co., 1902.
24. Darrow, C. W., E. C. Henry, M. Gill, and M. Brenman: "Interarea Electroencephalographic Relationships Affected by Hypnosis: Preliminary Report," *EEG. Clin. Neurophysiol.* 2:231 (1950).
25. ——— and M. Converse: "Frontal-motor Parallelism and Motor-occipital In-phase Activity in Hypnosis, Drowsiness, and Sleep," *EEG. Clin. Neurophysiol.* 2:355 (1950).
26. Davis, L. W., and R. W. Husband: "A Study of Hypnotic Susceptibility in Relation to Personality Traits," *J. Abnormal & Soc. Psychology* 26:175–188 (1931).
27. Davis, R. C., and J. R. Kantor: "Skin Resistance During Hypnotic States," *J. Gen. Psychol.* 13:62–81 (1935).
28. Delhougne, F., and K. Hansen: "Die suggestive Beeinflussbarkeit der Magen und Pankreassekretion in der Hypnose," *Deut. Arch. Klin. Med.* 157:20–35 (1927).
29. Dorcus, R. M.: "Modification by Suggestion of Some Vestibular Visual Responses," *Am. J. Psychol.* 49:82–87 (1937).
30. Dorcus, R., A. K. Brintnall and H. W. Case: "Control Experiments and Their Relation to Theories of Hypnosis," *J. Gen. Psychol.* 24:217–221 (1941).
31. Dorcus, R. M., and F. J. Kirkner: "The Use of Hypnosis in the Suppression of Intractable Pain," *J. Abnormal & Soc. Psychology* 43:237–239 (1948).
32. Doust, J. W.: "Studies on the Physiology of Awareness. Oximetric Analysis of Emotion and the Differential Planes of Consciousness Seen in Hypnosis," *J. Clin. Exp. Psychopath.* 14:113–126 (1953).
33. Dunbar, F.: *Emotions and bodily changes*, 4th ed. New York, Columbia University Press, 1954.
34. Dynes, J. B.: "An Experimental Study in Hypnotic Anesthesia," *J. Abnormal & Soc. Psychology* 27:79–88 (1932).
35. Feleky, A.: "The Expression of the Emotions," *Psychol. Rev.* 21:33–41 (1914).
36. Finley, K.: "The Capillary Bed of the Paraventricular and Supraoptic Nuclei of the Hypothalamus," in *The Circulation of the Brain and Spinal Cord* (Assn. Res. Nerv. and Ment. Dis. Monogr. XVIII) Baltimore, 1938.
37. Ford, L. F., and C. L. Yeager: "Changes in Electroencephalogram in Subjects under Hypnosis," *Diseases of Nervous System* 9:190–192 (1948).
38. Freeman, G. L.: "The Galvanic Phenomenon and Conditioned Responses," *J. Gen. Psychol.* 3:529–539 (1930).
39. Frick, H. L., R. E. Scantlebury, and T. L. Patterson: "The Control of Gastric Hunger Contractions in Man by Hypnotic Suggestion," *Am. J. Physiol.* 113:47 (1935).
40. Friedlander, J. W., and T. R. Sarbin: "The Depth of Hypnosis," *J. Abnormal & Soc. Psychology* 33:453–475 (1939).
41. Gidro-Frank, L., and M. K. Bow-

ersbuch: "A Study of the Plantar Response in Hypnotic Age Regression," *J. Nervous Mental Disease* **107**:443–458 (1948).

42. Glaser, F.: "Psychische Beeinflussung des Blutserumkalkspiegels," *Klin. Wochschr.* **3**:1492–1493 (1924).
43. Hansen, K.: "Zur Theorie der Symptombildung in der Neurose: Nach Versuchen in Hypnose," *In. Ber. üb. d. K. Allg. ärztl. Kongr. F. Psychotherapie*, Leipzig, S. Hirzel Verlag, 1927, pp. 86–93. (Cited in Dunbar, 33)
44. Hebb, D. O.: *Organization of Behavior*, New York, John Wiley & Sons, Inc., 1949.
45. Heilig, R., and H. Hoff: "Beiträge zur Hypnotischen Beeinflussung der Magenfunktion," *Med. Klin.* **21**:162–163 (1925).
46. Heyer, G. R.: "Psychogene Funktionsstörungen des Verdauungstraktes," in O. Schwarz, *Psychogenese und Psychotherapie körperlicher Symptome*, Wien, J. Springer, 1925. (Cited in Dunbar, 1954)
47. Himwich, H. E.: *Brain Metabolism and Cerebral Disorders*, Baltimore, The Williams & Wilkins Company, 1951.
48. Hull, C. L.: *Hypnosis and Suggestibility—an Experimental Approach*, New York, D. Appleton-Century Company, Inc., 1933.
49. Jacobson, E.: *Progressive Relaxation*, rev. ed. Chicago, University of Chicago Press, 1938.
50. Jenness, A., and C. L. Wible: "Respiration and Heart Action in Sleep and in Hypnosis," *J. Gen. Psychol.* **16**:197–222 (1937).
51. Kety, S. S.: "Consciousness and the Metabolism of the Brain," in *Trans. Third Conference on Problems of Consciousness.* Ed. by H. A. Abramson. New York, Josiah Macy, Jr. Foundation, 1952.
52. Kleitman, N.: *Sleep and Wakefulness as Alternating Phases in the Cycle of Existence*, Chicago, University of Chicago Press, 1939.
53. Koster, S.: "Experimental Investigation of the Character of Hypnosis," *J. Clin. Exp. Hypnosis* **2**:42–51 (1954).
54. Kretschmer, M., and R. Krüger: "Uber die Beeinflussung des Serumkalkgehaltes in der Hypnose," *Klin. Wochschr.* **6**:695–697 (1927).
55. Kroger, W. S.: "Hypnotherapy in Obstetrics and Gynecology," *J. Clin. Exp. Hypnosis* **1**:61–70 (1953).
56. ——— and S. C. Freed: "The Psychosomatic Treatment of Functional Dysmenorrhea by Hypnosis," *Am. J. Obstet. and Gynecol.* **46**:817–822 (1943).
57. Laudenheimer, R.: "Hypnotische Übungstherapie des Bronchialasthma," *Therap. Gegenwart* **67**:339–344 (1926). (Cited in Dunbar, 33)
58. Levine, M.: "Psychogalvanic Reaction to Painful Stimuli in Hypnotic and Hysterical Anesthesia," *Bull. Johns Hopkins Hospital*, **46**:331–339 (1930).
59. Lewis, J. H., and T. R. Sarbin: "Studies in Psychosomatics: The Influence of Hypnotic Stimulation on Gastric Hunger Contractions," *Psychosomat. Med.* **5**:125–131 (1943).
60. Lindsley, D. B.: "Emotion," in *Handbook of Experimental Psychology.* Ed. by S. S. Stevens.

New York, John Wiley & Sons, Inc., 1951.

61. Lipkin, M., E. McDevitt, M. S. Schwartz, and A. W. Duryee: On the Effects of Suggestion in the Treatment of Vaso-spastic Disorders of the Extremities," *Psychosomat. Med.* 7:152 (1945).
62. Loomis, A. L., E. N. Harvey, and G. A. Hobart: "Brain Potentials During Hypnosis," *Science* **83**: 239–241 (1936).
63. Luckhardt, A. B., and R. L. Johnston: "Studies in Gastric Secretion: I. The Psychic Secretion of Gastric Juice under Hypnosis, *Am. J. Physiol.* **70**:174–182 (1924).
64. Lundholm, H.: "An Experimental Study of Functional Anesthesias as Induced by Suggestion in Hypnosis," *J. Abnormal & Soc. Psychology* **23**:337–355 (1928).
65. MacLean, P. D.: "Psychosomatic Disease and the 'Visceral Brain': Recent Developments Bearing on the Papez Theory of Emotion," *Psychosomat. Med.* **11**:338–353 (1949).
66. Max, L. W.: "An Experimental Study of the Motor Theory of Consciousness: IV. Action-current Responses in the Deaf During Awakening, Kinaesthetic Imagery, and Abstract Thinking," *J. Comp. Psychol.* **24**:301–344 (1937).
67. Nielson, O. J., and E. Geert-Jorgenson: "Untersuchungen über die Einwirkung der Hypnotischen Suggestion auf den Blutzucker bei Nichtdiabetikern," *Klin. Wochschr.* 7 (part 2): 1467–1468 (1928).
68. Obermeyer, M. E., and R. R. Greenson: "Treatment by Suggestion of Verrucae Planae of the Face," *Psychosomat. Med.* **11**:163–164 (1949).
69. Papez, J. W.: "A Proposed Mechanism of Emotion," *Arch. Neurol. & Psychiat.* **38**:725–738 (1937).
70. Pattie, F. A.: "The Genuineness of Hypnotically Produced Anesthesia of the Skin," *Am. J. Psychol.* **49**:435–443 (1937).
71. ———: "The Production of Blisters by Hypnotic Suggestions: A Review," *J. Abnormal & Soc. Psychology* **36**:62–72 (1941).
72. Ravitz, L. J.: "Electrometric Correlates of the Hypnotic State," *Science* **112**:341 (1950).
73. ———: "Standing Potential Correlates of Hypnosis and Narcosis," *Arch. Neurol. & Psychiat.* **65**:413–436 (1951).
74. Razran, G. H. S.: *Conditioned Responses: An Experimental Study and a Theoretical Analysis* (Arch. Psych. No. 191), 1935.
75. Rosenow, C.: "Meaningful Behavior in Hypnosis," *Am. J. Psychol.* **40**:205–235 (1928).
76. Sarbin, T. R.: "Contributions to Role-taking Theory: I. Hypnotic Behavior," *Psychol. Rev.* **57**:255–270 (1950).
77. ———: "Role Theory," in *Handbook of Social Psychology.* Ed. by G. Lindzey. Cambridge, Mass., Addison-Wesley Press, 1954.
78. ———: "The Concept of Role-taking," *Sociometry* **6**:273–285 (1943).
79. ——— and J. H. Lewis: *Control of dysmenorrhea by hypnosis.* (Unpublished ms.)
80. Scantlebury, R. E.: *The Effect of Psychic Phenomena on the Movements of the Empty Stomach of Man.* (Wayne Univ. Grad.

Stud. Monogr. in Science No. 1.) Detroit, 1940.
81. ——— and T. L. Patterson: "Hunger Motility in a Hypnotized Subject," *Quart. J. Exptl. Physiol.* 30:347–358 (1940).
82. Schilder, P., and O. Kauders: *Hypnosis* (*Nerv. Ment. Dis. Monogr. Ser., No. 46*) New York, 1927.
83. Schultz, J.: *Das Autogene Training* (Konzentrierte Selbstentspannung) Leipzig, Georg Thieme Verlag, 1932.
84. Schwarz, O., and Loewy: (No title). Cited in Dunbar, 33)
85. Sears, R. R.: "An Experimental Study of Hypnotic Anaesthesia," *J. Exp. Psychol.* 15:1–22 (1932).
86. Seitz, P. F. D.: "Symbolism and Organ Choice in Conversion Reactions," *Psychosomat. Med.* 13: 254–259 (1951).
87. Selye, H.: *Stress,* Montreal, Acta, Inc., 1950.
88. Smith, K.: "Conditioning as an Artifact," *Psychol. Rev.* 61:217–225 (1954).
89. Szasz, T. S.: "Psychosomatic Aspects of Salivary Activity, II," *Psychosomat. Med.* 12:320–331 (1950).
90. ———: "Physiologic and Psychodynamic Mechanisms in Constipation and Diarrhea," *Psychosomat. Med.* 13:112–116 (1951).
91. True, R. M., and C. W. Stephenson: "Controlled Experiments Correlating Electroencephalogram, Pulse, and Plantar Reflexes with Hypnotic Age Regression and Induced Emotional States," *Personality* 1:252–263 (1951).
92. Weiss, E. J.: "Psychogenic Peripheral Spasm," *Psychosomat. Med.* 8:274 (1946).
93. Weitzenhoffer, A. M.: *Hypnotism—An Objective Study in Suggestibility,* New York, John Wiley & Sons, Inc., 1953.
94. West, L. J., K. C. Niell and J. D. Hardy: "Effects of Hypnotic Suggestion on Pain Perception and Galvanic Skin Response," *Arch. Neurol. & Psychiat.* 68: 549–560 (1952).
95. White, M. M.: "Blood Pressure and Palmar Galvanic Changes in Normal and Hypnotic States," *Psychol. Bull.* 37:577 (1940).
96. White, R. W.: "A Preface to a Theory of Hypnotism," *J. Abnormal & Soc. Psychology* 36: 477–505 (1941).
97. Whitehorn, J. C.: "Physiological Changes in Emotional States," in *The Interrelationship of Mind and Body.* (Ass. Res. Nerv. Ment. Dis. Monogr. XIX) Baltimore, 1939.
98. ———, H. Lundholm, and G. E. Gardner: "The Metabolic Rate in Emotional Moods Induced by Suggestion in Hypnosis," *Am. J. Psychiat.* 9:661–666 (1929).
99. Winsor, A. L.: "The Effect of Mental Effort on Parotid Secretion," *Am. J. Psychol.* 43:434–446 (1931).
100. Wittkower, E., and B. Russell: *Emotional Factors in Skin Disease,* New York, Paul B. Hoeber, Inc., 1953.
101. Wolberg, L. R.: "Hypnotic Phenomena," *Trans. Third Conference on Problems of Consciousness.* Ed. by H. A. Abramson. New York, Josiah Macy, Jr. Foundation, 1952.
102. Wolff, H. G.: *Stress and Disease,* Springfield, Ill., Charles C Thomas, Publisher, 1953.

Roy M. Dorcus, Ph.D. | 5

THE INFLUENCE OF HYPNOSIS ON LEARNING AND HABIT MODIFYING

THE TOPICS TO BE DISCUSSED in this section are habit forming, or learning, and habit breaking, or unlearning. Interwoven with these topics are a number of subtopics or psychological functions that will need consideration if an understanding of the main topic is to be adequate. The influence of hypnosis upon learning cannot be interpreted satisfactorily unless it is shown how memory is influenced by hypnosis. This may not be the case for all forms of learning, since there is reasonable doubt as to whether memory plays a part in some forms of conditioning. Forgetting may be only a negative aspect of memory, but there are special facts in this area which should be presented in any discussion of this subject.

One is forced somewhat farther afield when the problem of forgetting is related to the problem of retention in the unconscious. There is also the positive aspect of memory which is related to the length of time that hypnotic suggestions are retained and operate in the life of the individual.

The influence of hypnosis upon memory

It will simplify matters if we proceed first to a discussion of memory and leave the more complex problem of learning and unlearning to a somewhat later period. We can raise, therefore, the question: What influence does hypnosis have upon memory? In order that memory be tested, one must invoke one of three techniques, namely, recall, recognition, or relearning. More precise formulation of the question would then be: How does hypnosis affect recall, recognition, and relearning?

There are two kinds of evidence on this point. The first is derived from clinical situations in which attempts have been made to have patients recall materials or events which transpired in their earlier life and cannot be recalled under normal circumstances. The second type of evidence is obtained in controlled experimental situations in which subjects are required to learn standardized materials in the hypnotized state and in the normal state; after the lapse of a specified period of time, recall of the learned material is tested. These types of situations yield equivocal results and it becomes necessary for us to specify more precisely the differences involved in the recall and learning situations, if any analysis or synthesis of the results is to be made.

Clinical findings

Clinicians have demonstrated repeatedly that events dating back to childhood which ordinarily cannot be recalled, may be recalled under hypnosis. These events or incidents are usually assumed to have involved traumatic experiences. These situations are so well known that they scarcely need illustration. Nevertheless, one illustration will be set forth: Several years ago, an ex-soldier was referred to the author because of a speech difficulty which at times resulted in complete mutism. This young man had been in a series of hospitals, but had received very little help from the various therapies attempted. The speech problem arose during his service in the African campaign. A shell exploded near a group of soldiers, but aside from being partially covered by sand, the patient received no apparent physical injury. He was sent to a field hospital for examination, however, and subsequently returned to his unit. He then complained of fatigue and exhaustion, whereupon he was returned to a base hospital. He was injudiciously handled, and was accused of "gold-bricking," and it was at this time that his speech problem arose. Although several years had elapsed, he was unable to relate the circumstances until placed in a hypnotic state. He volunteered under hypnosis that, if that was the way people treated his complaints, there was no use in talking. The foregoing case is only one of the thousands which could be cited.

I should like to present another case which offers a contrast to the previous one: A middle-aged woman came into the author's office to see whether hypnosis would enable her to recall where some jewelry had been placed for safekeeping at an earlier date. She proved to be a good hypnotic subject and could be made to recall the events up to and subsequent to the actual hiding of the jewelry, but not the hiding place itself. This particular memory could not be reinstated.

The question that arises is: Is the difference in result due to the differing susceptibility of the subjects in these two cases? I believe that this is not the answer. The explanation, I feel, is to be found in the nature of the events. In the case of the ex-soldier, we presume that the events are retained in memory, but are blocked off by emotional factors associated with the event. In the case of the jewels, while it might be assumed that a similar situation exists and that the hypnotic procedure was inadequate for removing the emotional block, a simpler explanation seems more plausible: that is, that the hiding place was completely forgotten—therefore the event could not be recalled.

Experimental findings

Both these cases are related to the recall of relatively recent events and no actual proof of the antecedent events is possible. It is desirable, therefore, to present well-controlled experiments which contain such proof. True (18) had college students guess the day of the week on which certain events in their childhood, such as holidays and birthdays, took place. He then hypnotized these subjects and asked them to specify the day of the week for these events. He found that the days were correctly identified more frequently under hypnosis than in the normal state. This gives evidence that can be verified. Explanation for the differences in recall cannot satisfactorily be found in emotional blocking. It is my belief that the answer will have to be found in differential motivation.

Rosenthal (14) has approached the problem of whether emotional conflict related to learned material inhibits or facilitates the recall of the material in the hypnotic state. He found that affective factors associated with meaningful material tended to increase the hypnotic recall of the material, whereas hypnosis did not enhance the recall of meaningless material.

The experimental approach to the problem must of necessity deal with relatively short time spans. A number of experiments of this character have been conducted. They have usually been designed to answer some segment of a theoretical problem. Huse's experiment (6) is one of the best of this type; it was designed to determine whether hypnosis in some way lowers the threshold so that subliminal excitatory tendencies are able to evoke a recall. This is in contrast to the theory that emotional blocking inhibits recall. Huse had subjects learn materials (paired associates) to the point where they could just be recalled. These associations were allowed to deteriorate to the point where a fairly large number were barely accessible to the threshold level. The subjects were then hypnotized to determine whether the recall was improved. The experimental design was so arranged that extraneous factors could not account for the results. It was found that the hypnotic state did not enhance the recall.

Eysenck (5) studied the learning of nonsense syllables and the memory span for digits and patterns on playing cards. He found no significant difference between the trance and waking performances.

Young's experiment (21) on the recall of recently learned paired associates showed that there was no significant difference between the normal and hypnotic state. Stalnaker and Riddles (16) have confirmed in part the observations of clinicians. They found that poetry memorized in childhood could be recalled better in the hypnotic state than in the normal state. White, Fox, and Harris (20) found that meaningful material, such as poetry and motion-picture scenes which were recently learned, was recalled better in the hypnotic state. Here again, such material is more readily available under hypnosis.

If we attempt to sum up the situation at this point, the evidence tends to show that early experiences are more readily available under hypnosis; that events associated with traumatic experiences are made, by hypnosis, more readily accessible to recall; and that recently learned events of a nontraumatic nature are no more accessible to recall under hypnosis than under normal conditions. Just why early events of either a traumatic or nontraumatic nature, and traumatic events of recent time, can be recalled more easily under hypnosis than under normal conditions is not explicable on the basis of present theories.

We have discussed thus far the recall of materials learned in the normal state and recalled in either the hypnotic or the normal state. We have not dealt with the problem of whether materials learned in the hypnotic state can be recalled more efficiently in the normal or the hypnotic state. Studies of this problem are almost nonexistent. There is, however, one study which should be mentioned. Strickler (17) had subjects learn nonsense material and compared the rate of learning under hypnosis with the rate of learning in the normal state. He found that the rate of learning was accelerated in the trance state as compared with the normal state in the first few trials, but that the later trials were almost identical. With regard to total performance, there was not a significant difference.

Posthypnotic suggestion and memory

An indirect approach to the problem of learning and memory is to be found in the duration of posthypnotic suggestions or in the duration of suggestions which are not intended to become fixed in the mind of the subject. Popularly, this problem is often phrased in the following manner: Will hypnotized subjects come out of the hypnotic state of their own volition? While the question cannot be answered categorically "yes" or "no," there is some evidence that bears upon the point. We must discriminate between normal subjects and mentally disordered subjects who have obsessions and delusions; the latter group often give rise to the popular notion that individuals may be permanently hypnotized, for, in one sense, they may be permanently self-hypnotized. An experiment by Dorcus, Brintnall, and Case (3) showed clearly that hypnotized subjects, in the absence of a positive suggestion, did awaken and terminate the trance. In this experiment, subjects, one at a time, were hypnotized and told that they would be given further instructions. At this point, the experimenter was deliberately called from the room. Unhypnotized subjects were also asked to lie down and relax, and were told that in a few moments they would be given additional instructions. The experimenter was again called from the room. Observations showed that both groups of subjects behaved in a similar manner, with regard to time period and reasons, in leaving the experimental room.

Their interpretation of the situation and the urgency of other matters seemed to be the controlling factors in their departure.

Reports exist in the literature of the performance of acts at least a year after the original suggestion was made. These reports need verification by controlled experimental evidence. Patten (12) and Wells (19) have verified the fact that posthypnotic suggestions may be operative for even longer time periods. How long statements devoid of direct suggestion will influence subjects is not known. It is obvious that the effects of such statements may persist for very long periods of time, but it is the belief of the author that the attitudes of the subject will in a large measure determine this.

Hypnosis and amnesia

Increase in memory, as measured by recall, recognition, or relearning, is a positive aspect of learning phenomena which may take place under hypnosis. Decrease or loss of memory is another aspect of hypnotic phenomena. It is a well-known fact that some hypnotic subjects, after being placed in an hypnotic state, aver that no event which occurred during the hypnotic state can be remembered. It is also a fact that if the subject is rehypnotized the memory loss can be immediately restored. In other words, posthypnotic amnesia may arise in the absence of direct suggestions of amnesia. In contrast with this situation, amnesia for the trance state may result from direct suggestion. Can it be said that the two situations are similar? It is probable that both amnesic conditions arise essentially from similar causes. Attitudes, belief, and role-taking probably control spontaneous amnesia. Role-taking with direct suggestion probably accounts for the suggested amnesia. There seems to be little value in separating the two types of phenomena from the point of view of discussing amnesia. Is the amnesia real, or is the subject actively repressing material? This question is not easily answered. Before we attempt to answer it, it is desirable to present some of the experiments dealing with posthypnotic amnesia.

Strickler (17) had trance subjects learn nonsense material until it could be correctly recalled twice in succession. The subjects were given suggestions designed to provoke complete amnesia for the learned material in the waking state. Upon awakening, the subjects were tested for recognition of the nonsense material. There was almost 100 per cent amnesia, as measured by this method. However, when the subjects in the waking state relearned the nonsense syllables, they required only 50 per cent as many trials as were initially required to learn the material in the hypnotic state. In the absence of direct posthypnotic amnesia, subjects show a loss in recognition of about 20 per cent. The question that arises may be stated: Does the 20 per cent represent a spontaneous amnesia or is it the normal forgetting decrement?

Strickler attempted to answer this question by having control subjects learn similar nonsense material in the waking state. Hypnosis was then induced in these subjects to determine whether this experience would produce any effect on the recall in the normal state. No suggestions concerning the recall were given during this period. There was a decrement of about 16 per cent in the reinstatement situation, while the relearning situation showed no loss. In other words, the loss in recognition found in the absence of posthypnotic suggestion follows normal forgetting and should not be construed as spontaneous amnesia brought about by hypnosis.

A different type of learning process was investigated by Coors (2) who attempted to show how stylus-maze habits are influenced by hypnosis. A comparison of control and hypnotic subjects indicates that there is some amnesia for the hypnotic trials as measured by relearning. The differential between the two groups is about 45 per cent greater amnesia, or forgetting, in the hypnotic group than in the control group, where the number of trials required to relearn was the measure of amnesia. A similar loss was shown when errors were used as the criterion.

Another type of learning was studied by Patten (12) in his experiment on addition. In this situation, the subject has the essential skills, which are quite well fixed in memory, but practice develops an increase in facility for the use of the skills. If practice is pursued, a curve having a particular slope can be plotted which indicates the rate of learning. Any interference with the learning rate will cause an abrupt change in the slope of the curve. Patten was determining whether a practice curve established in the hypnotic state continues to rise at the same rate when the practice is shifted to the normal state. It was found that the curve continued to rise at about the same rate throughout both the normal and hypnotic states. Thus it was demonstrated that there was little or no spontaneous amnesia of the hypnotic condition. Life (8) tried a similar experiment for memorizing nonsense syllables. Her results were comparable to those of Patten.

A still different method of measuring the effect of the hypnotic state upon the normal state and vice versa is to be found in the amount of retroactive inhibition exerted in the learning of equated material. Mitchell (9) had subjects learn a list of three-digit numbers while hypnotized and in the normal state. She found that an interpolated learning series did not produce any significant effect upon relearning of the original material, whether the interpolated material was learned in the same state or a different state. Nagge (11) repeated Mitchell's experiment, with more subjects, and came to the opposite conclusion.

Amnesia may be either spontaneous or suggested. If amnesia occurs without direct suggestion, as it often does, the explanation will likely be found in the ideas of hypnosis that the subject holds. However, when the experimental situation is such that active inhibition of memory cannot be controlled by the subject, there is no real evidence that the hypnotic process produces spontaneous amnesia.

Hypnosis and physiological conditioning

How the trance state influences physiological conditioning or learning will have to be discussed. We might anticipate from the theories of hypnosis, particularly the theory of role-taking, that no effect would be produced. Since conditioning is presumably an elementary form of learning, it is necessary to see how conditioned reflexes are affected by the trance state. Bitterman and Marcuse (1) attempted to use autonomic responses in place of recall, recognition, or relearning as indices of posthypnotic amnesia. A subject in whom complete amnesia for certain words was established, was tested after the trance period. Despite the subject's inability to recognize or recall these words in the posthypnotic period, reactions of a physiological nature were such as to indicate an influence of the words. The physiological measures included changes in heart rate, pulse pressure, and respiration.

Scott (15) conditioned hypnotic subjects to the sound of a buzzer presented with electric shock. All the subjects conditioned rapidly. His reaction measures were hand movement, breathing, heart action, and the galvanic skin reflex. The subjects uniformly responded with these reactions while in the hypnotic state and upon the initial tests in the normal state. Here again, there is no evidence for amnesia produced by the trance state. LeCron (7) has shown that the control of the complex muscles of accommodation and conversion can be established through hypnosis and training. This in itself is not surprising because myopia has been corrected at least partially by training techniques not involving hypnotic suggestion. The critical point is whether correction takes place more readily or whether it can be accomplished in cases not amenable to ordinary corrective measures.

Erickson (4) produced anacusia in six subjects as measured by the absence of startle reflexes. In another experiment he established a conditioned response to an auditory stimulus in an hypnotic subject. The induction of anacusia under hypnosis caused a loss of the conditioned response. He also showed that the conditioned response could not be established in one subject in whom hypnotic deafness had been induced. The conditioned response did reappear when the hypnotic deafness was removed. These experiments need verification by other investigators.

Almost all the experiments have dealt with the effects of hypnosis on the posthypnotic normal state. Undoubtedly, if suggestions had been given concerning memory in the normal state, adverse results would have been obtained. Just how adverse the results would be we cannot at present say, although cases have been reported in which there was total lack of recognition.

Learning and habit control

From a therapeutic point of view, learning is involved in a number of different situations. Perhaps the most direct method of application is that employed in cases of addiction to alcohol and drugs. The method is a simple conditioning one similar to the aversion technique employed in medical therapy. Suggestions are given that the substance will be ill-tasting and even nauseating. These suggestions are repeated and reinforced over a period of time. While this form of learning is effective in isolated cases, the number of cases in which it will achieve lasting results is too small to expect that any widespread use of hypnosis for treating these cases will be employed. Drug addiction and alcoholism are complicated forms of activities involving both motor and ideational components. We should consider the use of hypnosis as a method of breaking other types of habits. Torticollus (Storment), tics of a simple or complicated nature, reflex actions such as hiccoughs and vomiting (Kirkner and Dorcus) have been successfully inhibited by the use of hypnosis. Conditioning or negative learning influences some cases of dysmenorrhea, in which a habit of expectancy seems to play a part. Similarly, in certain kinds of speech disorders, such as stammering or stuttering, re-learning may be successfully instituted under repeated hypnosis.

While phobias do not yield as readily to hypnosis as do compulsions, reports of breaking these habitual fears have been made in the literature. The writer has successfully treated a patient with temporary high blood pressure brought about by anticipatory fears of physical examinations. In such cases the phobia results in a somatic manifestation which may become the habitual response. With repeated conditioning the response is either diverted or held in abeyance. Moody (10) has shown that repeated relaxation under hypnosis will result in as much improvement in ulcer cases as results from other forms of therapy. In the ulcer patients, the habitual response to environmental stress has resulted in somatic difficulties. When the individuals are taught to relax under hypnosis there seems to take place a reorganization of the response processes.

The foregoing examples indicate rather clearly that hypnosis can modify the learning processes and can break long-established modes of action.

In some instances pain may even be initiated by the learning process. Many patients present complaints of pain long after any physical basis which may have existed has disappeared. The suppression of pain of this kind is reported from many sources in the literature. We may consider that conditioning has taken place and other vague physiological changes are perceived as pain. Under hypnosis this conditioned process can be broken.

Both negative conditioning, or unlearning at the physiological level, and habit modifying involving complex ideational components may occur under hypnosis. The precise manner in which they take place depends upon one's orientation with regard to the learning theories. There is at present no single theory that encompasses all the problems in the field of learning, and it would carry our discussion too far afield to attempt to relate hypnotic learning to the various theories of learning. This aspect of the problem is partly covered in an earlier chapter.

We may summarize from the evidence as follows:

1. Active learning is not appreciably affected by hypnosis, although direction of attention may give slight beneficial results in the initial trials.
2. Recall of materials learned in early life is influenced in a favorable way.
3. Recall of recently learned material is not improved by hypnosis.
4. Recall of material having emotional associations may be aided by hypnosis.
5. Spontaneous amnesia produced by hypnotic trance seems to be a function of attitude and role-taking.
6. Physiological measures indicate that supposedly amnesic material continues to influence the organism.
7. Much of the hypnotic amnesia has characteristics of active suppression.
8. Conditioning at the physiological level takes place under hypnosis.
9. Habit breaking, or unlearning, is possible for practically all levels of learned material.

Hypnotic motivation as an aspect of learning

There is one aspect of the learning process which has not been investigated to any extent. This is the use of hypnotic suggestion as a motivating device. While the technique is inherent in many of the early experiments on sensory capacity, because of the nature of the instructions given, no particular attempt has been made to isolate the factor of motivation. Motivation is an important consideration in many of the clinical cases which arise in the practice of psychology. Some patients have no interest in learning anything new; they are unwilling to use a limb that has been immobilized for a long period of time; they are unwilling or afraid to leave their beds after long confinement; they may not attempt speech following cerebral damage; or they may be unwilling to eat certain kinds of food following a stomach or bowel resection.

These aversions may be considered as phobias, but in many instances the unwillingness does not have the characteristics of full-blown phobias. The author has found that hypnotic suggestion will often start the desired activity, which then proceeds in the normal way. We have in these situations the beginning of the learning process, which has been instigated by hypnotic suggestion. How far this technique can be extended to various types of learning situations is uncertain. From the experimental evidence available it would appear that ordinary learning is not favorably influenced. We can assume that the motivational level attained by customary means is already so high that it cannot be raised further by hypnotic reinforcement.

REFERENCES

1. Bitterman, M. E., and F. L. Marcuse: "Autonomic Response in Post-hypnotic Amnesia," *J. Exp. Psychol.* 35:248–252 (1945).
2. Coors, D.: *A Determination of the Density of Post-hypnotic Amnesia for the Stylus Maze,* Madison, University of Wisconsin Press, 1928.
3. Dorcus, R. M., A. K. Brintnall, and H. W. Case: "Control Experiments and Their Relation to Theories of Hypnotism," *J. Gen. Psychol.* 24:217–221 (1941).
4. Erickson, M. H.: "A Study of Clinical and Experimental Findings on Hypnotic Deafness. II. Experimental Findings with a Conditioned Reflex Technique," *J. Gen Psychol.* 19:151–167 (1938).
5. Eysenck, H. S.: "An Experimental Study of the Improvement of Mental and Physical Functions in the Hypnotic State," *Brit. J. Med. Psychol.* 18:304–316 (1941).
6. Huse, B.: "Does the Hypnotic Trance Favor the Recall of Faint Memories?" *J. Exp. Psychol.* 13:519–529 (1930).
7. LeCron, L. M.: "Relief of Myopia by Hypnosis and Eye Training," *Disorders of the Nerv. Syst.* 12:1–4 (1951).

8. Life, C.: *The Effects of Practice in the Trance upon Learning in the Normal Waking State,* Madison, University of Wisconsin Press, 1929.
9. Mitchell, M. B.: "Retroactive Inhibition and Hypnosis," *J. Gen. Psychol.* 7:343–458 (1932).
10. Moody, M. M.: *An evaluation of hypnotically induced relaxation for the reduction of peptic ulcer symptoms.* (Doctoral thesis on file, University of California Library, Los Angeles, 1950)
11. Nagge, J. W.: "An Experimental Test of the Theory of Associative Interference," *J. Exp. Psychol.* **18**:663–681 (1935).
12. Patten, E. F.: "Does Post-hypnotic Amnesia Apply to Practice Effects?" *J. Gen. Psychol.* **7**:196–201 (1932).
13. ———: "The Duration of Post-hypnotic Suggestion," *J. Abnormal & Soc. Psychology* **25**:319–334 (1930).
14. Rosenthal, B. G.: "Hypnotic Recall of Material Learned under Anxiety and Non-anxiety Producing Situations," *J. Exp. Psychol.* **34**:369–389 (1944).
15. Scott, H. D.: "Hypnosis and the Conditioned Reflex," *J. Gen. Psychol.* **4**:113–130 (1930).
16. Stalnaker, J. M., and E. F. Riddles: "The Effect of Hypnosis on Long Delayed Recall," *J. Gen. Psychol.* **6**:429–440 (1932).
17. Strickler, C. B.: "A Quantitative Study of Post-Hypnotic Amnesia," *J. Abnormal & Soc. Psychology* **24**:108–119 (1929).
18. True, R. M.: "Experimental Control in Hypnotic Age Regression States," *Science* **110**:583–584 (1949).
19. Wells, W. R.: "The Extent and Duration of Post-hypnotic Amnesia," *J. Psychol.* **2**:137–151 (1940).
20. White, R. W., G. F. Fox, and W. W. Harris: "Hypnotic Hypermnesia for Recently Learned Material," *J. Abnormal & Soc. Psychology* **35**:88–103 (1940).
21. Young, P. C.: "An Experimental Study of Mental and Physical Functions in the Normal and Hypnotic State," *Am. J. Psychol.* **36**:212–214; **37**:245–256 (1925; 1926).

Frank A. Pattie, Ph.D.

6

THE GENUINENESS OF SOME HYPNOTIC PHENOMENA

When students see a demonstration of hypnosis, many of them believe that the performance is faked, not "genuine," not "on the level," or is due to collusion between the hypnotist and the subject. The present writer has, partly because of his efforts to convince students that the phenomena are produced in good faith, given thought to the question of what is genuine and what is spurious among hypnotic phenomena. Since the word *genuine* may have a variety of meanings and seems to give trouble to some critics, it should be defined at the outset.

The definition adopted for the purpose of this chapter has two divisions. First, those phenomena must be admitted to be genuine which the subject cannot deliberately produce or simulate either because (*a*) simulation would require knowledge which he does not possess or (*b*) the production of the phenomenon would require more ability than he normally possesses. An example under (*a*) of a genuine phenomenon is the production of the Babinski reflex in subjects who have no knowledge about this reflex and who are regressed to an age of a few months in the trance. An example of a spurious phenomenon would be the production of an anesthesia of one hand, ear, or eye under conditions in which the subject cannot distinguish the excitations of the right-hand organ from those of the left-hand organ; under testing, the unilateral anesthesia proves to be nonexistent, since the subject reports experiences which originate in the supposedly anesthetic organ or part. Under (*b*) an example of a genuine phenomenon is the hypnotically produced anesthesia which permits surgical operations to be performed.

The second use of *genuine* is in connection with the regression of subjects in the trance to an earlier age. We will call genuine the behavior of a regressed person if (*a*) it conforms to the norms of behavior for that age and (*b*) it shows no admixture of knowledge acquired after that age. If a person is regressed to the age of three years and he uses polysyllables in his conversation, the behavior is not "genuine."

The Genuineness of Anesthesias

In 1932 Dynes (3) published a report of experiments in which he produced deafness by hypnotic suggestion. No bodily changes in the subject were recorded instrumentally or by ordinary observation when a pistol was fired near the subject. This paper by Dynes is seldom referred to, as Hull omitted any reference to it in his book. In 1938 Erickson (5) reported that he had produced deafness which was "not distinguishable from neurological deafness by any of the ordinarily competent tests used." Both of these experiments seem to have been so carefully performed that there is no ground for criticism.

Hypnotic deafness of the kind produced by Dynes and by Erickson might be explained by two theories, the dissociation theory and the motivational theory. According to the dissociation theory, the neurological system belonging to the auditory nerve and its central connections is dissociated from the rest of the nervous system. According to the role-taking or motivational theory, the subject appears to be deaf because he is playing very successfully the role of a deaf person by ignoring all sounds.

If the dissociation theory is true, then it seems that one ear could be dissociated as easily as both ears, and a real or genuine deafness of one ear should be obtainable by hypnotic suggestion.

If the other theory is true, then when the ears are stimulated differently and the person cannot identify the stimuli being received by each ear (that is, cannot tell which of two different sounds he should ignore) the apparent anesthesia of one ear should disappear.

An experiment was devised. Two different steady tones, one of 500 cycles and the other of 502 cycles, were conducted separately to the two ears, one of which the subject had previously declared was deaf. The subject was told to report whether the tone he heard was steady or intermittent. If both ears were working, the report should be "intermittent," since in that case a binaural beat would be produced. If only one ear were hearing, the report should be "steady." The answer received from the subject was "intermittent." The subject indicated by hand movements that the frequency of the beat was two per second. (19)

Similar experiments were performed in an attempt to produce a blindness of one eye. (17) It was easy to show that both eyes of four of the five subjects were functioning, but the fifth subject was more clever than the rest, and she deceived me for a long time. When tested in a variety of ways she gave the appearance of blindness in one eye. Finally a complicated test was devised in which the subject had to read a line of letters while the "good" eye was covered with a red filter and the "blind" one with a green filter. The letters were made in several different colors, each letter being made of lines of different colors, and additional colored lines were added to the letters. If the "blind" eye was not functioning, the "good" eye, viewing the letters through the red filter (which would make the red, yellow, and orange lines invisible) should be able to see a group of letters (BFGHLM, etc.) which could be speedily read. If both eyes were functioning, all of the colored lines would be visible, forming a confused complex of lines not readable as letters. The test showed that the subject was seeing with both eyes. After the subject had failed this final test, I hypnotized her some days later and obtained from her a final statement, with great show of conflict, weeping, and general distress, as to how she had faked the tests. After the dehypnotization, she complained of headache, vertigo, faintness, and swimming movements of objects around her.

One part of the experiment was especially interesting. I tried at one time to plot the blind spot of the subject's "good" eye while both eyes were open. If one eye was blind, I reasoned, then having both eyes open should make no difference in plotting the spot. My results were negative; I obtained a blind spot but it was too large and very changeable, its projection moving all over the black screen I was using. A week later the experiment was repeated on a white projection screen with excellent results. The screen was used at three distances from the eye, and the areas of the projected spot conformed very closely to the geometrical relationships which govern the size of the projection at different distances.

During the last trance in the series, when I asked her how she had faked the experiment with the blind spot, she said she could not remember. She began to toss around in her chair with fists clenched, to show much emotion, and finally to weep. I then thought it best to change the topic of conversation, but before I could do so she said, "I've got it. It seems I did that in the laboratory as an experiment." I assured her that she had not done any experimenting of that sort. Then she remembered that she had called in a girl to her room at her home and asked her to hold a black coat on the wall and to move a small object about on it so that she could find out the location and area of the blind spot's projection. "I thought I must be getting very interested in psychology, and afterwards I forgot all about it." Here apparently there was a spontaneous, self-terminating trance with amnesia which came into being for the purpose of obtaining knowledge which would enable the subject to fake the test.

In another experiment (18) anesthesia of the hand of the subject was produced. The subject was then instructed to clasp his hands in the position of the "Japanese illusion," * and he was blindfolded. With the hands in this position it is very hard to tell, when one hand is touched, which one has been touched. When the experimenter and an assistant touched the fingers of the right and left hands, respectively, at a rate of one or two stimuli a second, the subject was no more able than a normal person with his hands in this position to count the number of times he was touched on the normal hand.

The difficulty of localization, due to the abnormal position, should not trouble the subject if one hand is completely anesthetic, and he should correctly and easily count the number of times the "good" hand is touched when two experimenters touch the fingers of the two hands at the rate of one or two a second. The subjects of this experiment were not able to do so; they showed no more ability to count the touches on one hand than normal persons do when their hands are put in this position. Thus it was shown that, when the sensations from the two hands were not clearly localizable as coming from the right or the left, the suggested anesthesia disappeared.†

* To put the hands in this position, extend the arms with the backs of the hands together and the thumbs pointing downward. Now cross the wrists, still keeping thumbs down, interlace the fingers, and clasp the hands. Now bring the hands toward the chin by flexing the elbows, then bring the elbows down until they touch the sides of the body, at the same time rotating the clasped hands through about 270 degrees until the thumbs point upward.

† Rosen (21, p. 209) reports a criticism of this experiment by Erickson—"maintenance of the hand position negates the test, and the same results probably would have been obtained if local anesthesia were used instead of hypnosis." The meaning of the first part of this statement is not clear to me. The second part states an irrelevant fact; the experiment showed

These results, like all negative results, are vulnerable. A universal negative proposition—"There are no genuine unilateral anesthesias in conditions which prevent localization of sensations from the two sides"—cannot be proved. All that one can say is that such anesthesias were not found in the experiments reported.

These results do not necessarily contradict the conclusions of other experimenters that total deafness, blindness, or analgesia can be produced. Certainly the fact of the genuineness of hypnotic analgesia which allows major surgical operations to be performed must be admitted. To ignore in the trance all sights, sounds, or pains may be possible, but it may not be possible for a subject to ignore the sensations from one lateral organ when he is stimulated bilaterally and the sensations, under the conditions of the experiment, cannot be localized as coming from the right or the left side.

The most recent work on total hypnotic deafness is an experiment by Kline, Guze, and Haggerty (11). Their results do not entirely agree with those of Erickson and Dynes. They used a new test in which they recorded the disturbances of their subject's speech when his speech was fed back to him through earphones with a delay of one-quarter second. The subject, who showed no startle reflexes or habitual responses to sound after deafness had been suggested, nevertheless continued to show a definite impairment of speech with delayed feedback. He was tested with and without the suggestion of deafness. The amount of speech impairment was greatly reduced when hypnotic deafness was produced. The authors conclude that hypnotic deafness "would appear to represent a valid alteration of hearing function but not a state akin to organic deafness."

---

that the suggestion of anesthesia did not annihilate the sensory functioning of the hand in this peculiar position, and this conclusion would not be affected by the same failure on the part of a chemical anesthetic. The experiment would have been as meaningful if it had been performed before the discovery of chemical anesthesia.

Dorcus' Experiments

Dorcus (2) became interested in the problem of the genuineness of reactions produced in hypnosis at about the same time that I did. It was he who suggested to me the necessity of devising some more adequate tests in my experiment on hypnotic blindness of one eye at a time when I was inclined to think that my results were genuine. Dorcus suggested to his subjects that they were being rotated and produced in them an illusion of rotation. A record of the eye movements made after the illusory rotation had ceased showed only voluntary movements; nystagmus was completely absent, although every subject in the experiment had previously been rotated in the Dunlap chair. In another test an illusion of rotation was produced while the subject was sitting in the chair with the head lowered to the level of the knees; there was no reaction of falling when the illusory rotation was stopped and the subject was told to raise his head. (In this case it was of course necessary to use subjects who had never been subjected to rotation and the subsequent falling reaction.) Also Dorcus found that no change in the size of the pupil was produced following a suggestion that the electric light at which the subject was looking was being dimmed. He failed to produce negative afterimages of the genuine color when he suggested an hallucinatory experience of color except in subjects who knew beforehand what the color should be.

There is a controversy on the last topic between the Ericksons (4, 6) and Hibler (8). The former workers declare that they have produced, in naive subjects, afterimages of the correct color after producing visual hallucinations of colored areas. Hibler denies this finding, and states that the correct color appears in the afterimage only when the subject "knows the answer." There is a full account of these experiments in the chapter in this book on the control of sensory functions.

Regression to an earlier age

One of the major fields of conflict over genuineness is the problem of age-regression. There are two theories: One may be called the ablation theory, and the other the role-taking theory. According to the latter theory, the behavior of the subject who is regressed in hypnosis to an earlier age, say six years, is simply an enactment of the role of a child of that age, which may be better than the subject can do in the normal state because of the hypermnesia of hypnosis and the freer expression of emotion, made possible by the subject's relative isolation from the environment and his preoccupation with the reliving of his memories.

According to the ablation theory, when the subject is regressed to age six, all knowledge acquired after that age is absent, and his functioning on tests of all kinds is that of a person of that age. The tests used in studies of regression have been tests of intelligence, the Rorschach, and drawing.

Studies of intelligence. The first studies on the mental ages of subjects regressed to childhood were made by Russian psychologists. Only one of three articles was published in English: Platonow (20) claimed that the mental age conformed accurately with the chronological age to which his three subjects had been taken. Young (26) criticized the Russian work and did an experiment of his own. Nine subjects were regressed to age three and tested with the Binet test. The IQ's obtained in the trance ranged from 153 to 225 and averaged 198, but when the subjects were tested in the normal state the average IQ was only 102. A control group of seven unhypnotizable persons were asked to imagine that they were three years old and to respond to the test accordingly. Their average IQ's were: in simulated regression, 179; under normal conditions, 105. The non-hypnotizable subjects were more accurate in taking the role of a child than the trance subjects were.

Some very peculiar results were reported in 1950 by M. V.

Kline (10). He regressed ten college students to ages fifteen, ten, and eight and tested them with equivalent forms of the Otis self-administering test. There were three regressed IQ's for each subject and one normal IQ. The IQ's under waking conditions averaged 117; they averaged 118 at each of the regressed ages. If we take the lowest IQ achieved by each subject and subtract from it the highest IQ he obtained under these four conditions, in none of the ten cases does the difference amount to more than 4 points. The average difference for the ten subjects was 2.9. The author notes that the changes in IQ showed less variation than one would find when testing and retesting the same person under normal conditions. He does not refer to any previous literature on this topic, hence he makes no effort to explain why other experiments have resulted in findings very divergent from his. His brief description of the experiment affords no basis for criticism.

Sarbin (22) worked with nine hypnotizable and three nonhypnotizable subjects who had taken the Binet tests at the age of eight or nine years, the records of which were still available. The hypnotized subjects were regressed to the age at which they had taken the Binet and were then tested. A week later they were given the test again under normal conditions with instructions to simulate the behavior of a child of that age. The results confirmed Young's finding that the subjects did not go back far enough in time, so that in every case the mental age in regression was higher than that achieved years before when the original test was administered. But the regression in the trance was a closer approximation than the simulated regression; the average overestimation of the nine subjects in regression was 3 years and 6 months; for simulated regression, 5 years and 3 months. The correlation between depth of hypnosis and an index of regression was found to be .76, which becomes .91 if the three nonhypnotizable subjects are included. Sarbin believes that this finding supports the theory of hypnosis as role-taking; those who are most deeply hypnotizable also enact the role of a child more accurately.

Studies involving projective techniques. Four case studies (1, 14, 15, 24) show the results of the Rorschach test when administered to regressed patients and also the drawings made by these persons at different regressed age levels. These papers, each describing only one case, do not lend themselves to condensation. Undoubtedly some readers of these cases will be convinced of the ablation theory and others of the role-taking theory. In my opinion the case that makes the best argument for the ablation theory is the one presented by Mercer and Gibson (14), in which the Rorschach protocols are given. The absence of control experiments, in which a subject is asked to *enact the role* of a child taking projective tests, without regression to an earlier age, makes a decision on this matter difficult.

The most thorough experimental investigation of age-regression appeared in 1951. In this study by Orne (16), ten somnambulistic subjects were regressed to the age of six. Rorschach records and drawings were made in the regressed condition and also in the normal state with instructions to simulate regression. In this experiment all the control tests in the waking state were made after the tests in the regressed state; since Orne points out some peculiar cases in which memories were carried over from the hypnotic to the waking state, a much better procedure would have been to have half the waking control tests precede, and half follow, those made in the regressed state. In a number of cases the pictures done under instructions to imagine the behavior of a child of six were almost identical with those drawn under regression.

The drawings were submitted to Karen Machover for her expert opinion. She stated: "The drawings . . . do not resemble those of six-year-olds. Mature and immature features are intermingled, and in certain respects the drawings in regression are more mature than those done in the waking state. The term 'sophisticated oversimplification' seems appropriate for these drawings." In the case of one subject, some drawings which had actually been made at the age of six were available. They were not at all similar to those made in the regressed state. The lettering under the drawings was very different in the two cases, being much more sophisticated and adult in the regressed state.

In the Rorschach study Orne thought it reasonable to predict that the regression records would differ from the controls in certain ways. He believed that the regression Rorschachs would show fewer M responses, a lower ratio of M to FM, a smaller number of FC, a larger ratio of CF to FC, a decrease in shading responses, a small number of responses, and a higher A per cent.

When the protocols were read, there was no difficulty in determining which were the regression records—"There are marked childish verbalization, confabulations, occasional color naming, poor F responses, even poor FM, and, occasionally, poor FC responses. Nevertheless, every single record of 'regressed' subjects shows some features which could never be expected in the record of a six-year-old child, and when we consider the formal characteristics alone, it becomes impossible to say which of the Rorschach tests were given in 'regression.' " Orne presents a table showing the various signs which are supposed to change with increasing age. The number of M decreases in three cases but increases in two. The A per cent increases in three and decreases in three. "Not one individual hypnotic record shows a shift toward several of the signs with any degree of consistency." There was, however, one uniform change—the form levels were considerably lower in the hypnotic records. There was "a trend toward less specification, occasional inaccuracy, and on the whole a marked decrease in combinatory responses." This consistent change reflected, not personality organization, but intellectual capacity and critical ability. The form level, Orne states, is "the one feature of the Rorschach record which is most subject to conscious control and which tends to be markedly affected by the mood of the moment."

Orne concludes that it is apparent that deep personality changes occur in regression and are reflected in the Rorschach, but to determine what these changes are in each subject would require a longitudinal study. In the present work all that can be established is the fact that the kinds of reaction to the suggested regression are by no means uniform. "The personality organization seems to change, but at all times we are dealing with the personality organization of the adult."

Orne next proceeds to show certain inconsistencies in the subject's reactions under regression. One subject wrote in childlike fashion without a mistake in spelling the following dictated sentence: "I am conducting an experiment which will assess my psychological capacities." He also defined correctly the word *hypochondriac.* Another subject, when asked whether he was good in arithmetic, answered "yes." Then he was asked, "Are you as good as you are now?" and he answered "no." Another subject, who at the age of six had lived in Germany and understood no English, continued to communicate with the experimenter in English; when asked to hallucinate his mother and to tell what she said to him, he gave her remarks in English. It was then suggested that the mother must have spoken in German. This comment caused momentary confusion and from then on all the subject's responses were in German.

Confabulations occurred frequently and could have been very deceptive if they had not been sometimes detected. A subject who was regressed could not recall the name of his first-grade teacher. When a visual hallucination of her was induced he described her in detail and suddenly called her "Miss Curtiss." This name, however, was actually the name of his teacher in the seventh grade. A subject, when it was suggested that he was in school on the day after his birthday, said, "No, there is no school; it is Saturday," but the calendar proved that the day was Monday.

If Orne's results are taken at their face value, they are very damaging to the ablation theory.

Erickson's criticism, made in discussion at the California Symposium on Hypnosis, of the study by Orne is that the trances were not deep enough and the regression was too rapidly induced. Time must be given for the occurrence of the physiological and psychological changes underlying deep hypnosis and regression. Orne's statement on this point is brief: He used only subjects "who showed a genuine somnambulistic state," and "extreme care was taken in establishing beyond any doubt the somnambulistic condition of each subject in every single hypnotic session by the use of all accepted criteria for this state." Progress toward agreement in this field would be made most rapidly by collaborative research, one person furnishing the subjects who have met Erickson's requirements and another doing the experimenting. All the proceedings should be recorded verbatim.

Erickson points out the obvious fact that in regression experiments the hypnotist must be transformed into some person, say a teacher, known to the subject at the earlier age. Orne's paper makes no mention of this point. Even if such a precaution was taken, such a question as "Are you as good in arithmetic *as you are now?*" would be likely to shatter a real regression and turn it into role-taking.

Data from the Rorschach, the draw-a-person test, and clinical observation were used by Sarbin and Farberow (23) to illustrate "the use of the concepts of role and self in interaction in explaining apparently equivocal results in age-regression experiments." The data are used to illustrate the application of the authors' theory, and interpretations and data are intermingled; the authors do not address themselves specifically to the problem of the genuineness of regression, since that is precluded by their theory of role-taking. Their data show that the drawings correspond to more mature ages than those to which the subjects were regressed, and the Rorschach responses were not consistent with the statistical norms for these ages.

Other studies. Gidro-Frank and Buch (7) regressed three subjects to an age of less than six months. When the sole of the foot was properly stimulated, the Babinski reflex (extension and fanning of the toes) occurred. This reflex is characteristic of infancy and changes to, or is overlaid by, the adult response (flexion of the toes) at an age of about seven months. The subjects had no knowledge of this reflex or the intention of the investigators. This finding has been confirmed by True and Stephenson (25), but they were unable to produce changes in their subjects' electroencephalograms, which retained their adult form. The discovery of the Babinski reflex in regressed subjects must be accepted as genuine. While the response to plantar stimulation in adults may revert to its infantile form as a result of several conditions, some of which are pathological and some physiological, these conditions certainly did not occur in these experiments.

Kupper (12) reports the case of a twenty-four-year-old man who had convulsive seizures, the first of which had occurred at age eighteen. Regressed to ages below eighteen the electroencephalogram became normal until age eighteen was reached, when it resumed its abnormal adult form.

LeCron's chapter (13) on regression presents a number of cases, many of which give the impression that they represent genuine regression yet somehow fail to furnish proof of the point. He tells of two experiments of his own, in which he set up conditioned hand-withdrawal and eye-wink responses, then regressed the subjects to a time prior to the conditioning and found that the subjects no longer responded to the conditioned stimuli. The experiments are not conclusive, and he gives reasons why they are not. An additional criticism is that the responses used are too susceptible to voluntary control; an autonomic response, the galvanic skin reflex, would be better. Among his best cases is one in which regression to age three brought on an attack of the asthma from which the subject suffered in childhood. LeCron presents his data quite soberly, not claiming that they settle the question.

Kelsey (9) gives us the ultimate in regression, reporting the fantasies of birth and intrauterine experiences (fertilization of the ovum, parental intercourse, attempts to procure miscarriage) occurring in hypnoanalysis. One of his three patients reported being choked by the umbilical cord at birth and being a breech presentation, while another reported head presentation and hands pinned to his sides during birth, and these reports were confirmed. From the sensations reported by a patient regressed to prenatal life during parental intercourse the physician cleverly deduced that the intercourse must have been a posteriori with the mother standing; this was confirmed. Kelsey writes: "Eventually he reached his conception, in which he saw himself as the ovum being raped, rather than wooed, by the over-anxious sperm of his over-anxious father. Though I have phrased this rather jocularly, I am in fact in earnest about its significance . . ." All this is published in a conservative British journal.

Conclusions on regression

If the question of the genuineness of regression is ever settled, it will be settled by systematic research and not by an accumulation of impressions. The past history of hypnosis and animal magnetism is full of erroneous ideas which were held by the authorities of their time and were based on impressions. James Braid, the surgeon, believed in *phrenohypnotism*, combining the ideas of phrenology and hypnosis; he thought that a subject in hypnosis would kneel in prayer when the bump of veneration was touched. Mesmer believed in *magnetized water*, and Liébeault kept a supply of it in his clinic. The idea that persons could be magnetized at a distance died very slowly, as did the idea that magnetized subjects had clairvoyant powers. Ricard about 110 years ago had the impression that he might be able to exert a magnetic influence on the clouds and thus avert a shower of rain, and he proposed a modest hypothesis to that effect.

The reality of age-regression has been proved for the cases involving the appearance of the Babinski reflex and of preconvulsive brain waves. Role-taking and knowledge are certainly excluded in these instances. Why certain other changes, such as the brain waves characteristic of infancy, have not occurred is not known.

The ablation theory of age-regression must be regarded as not proved in other fields. It is difficult to reach a conclusion. First, there is the question of the comparability of the various experiments as to the depth of the trances, about which the experimenters often give little information. Second, authorities state that a given episode of age-regression may be a mixture of dramatization of the remembered past and an actual reliving with a temporary ablation of experiences acquired later than the age assumed. Third, authorities state that spontaneous changes occur in the depth of the trance which might, when it decreases in depth, affect the character of the performance.

It seems that if any kind of performance may be exempt from the second and third difficulties, it would more likely be the taking of a test than the reliving of one's sixth birthday. The preponderance of the evidence from tests of intelligence, drawing, and the Rorschach test favors, in my opinion, the role-taking theory. The main objections that can be urged against the best experiments in this field are based more on what the writers failed to tell us about their procedures than on other grounds. The ablation theory may in the future win over its rival theory; there is certainly no reason for keeping one's mind closed in the present ambiguous state of our knowledge. Much might be accomplished, as I have stated above, by collaborative research by exponents of the two theories.

REFERENCES

1. Bergmann, M. S., H. Graham, and H. C. Leavitt: "Rorschach Exploration of Consecutive Hypnotic Chronological Age Level Regressions," *Psychosomat. Med.* 9:20–28 (1947).
2. Dorcus, R. M.: "Modification by Suggestion of Some Vestibular and Visual Responses," *Am. J. Psychol.* 49:82–87 (1937).
3. Dynes, J. B.: "An Experimental Study in Hypnotic Anesthesia," *J. Abnormal & Soc. Psychology* 27:79–88 (1932–1933).

4. Erickson, E. M.: "Critical Comments on Hibler's Presentation of His Work on Negative After-images of Hypnotically Induced Hallucinated Colors," *J. Exp. Psychol.* **29**:164–170 (1941).
5. Erickson, M. H.: "A Study of Clinical and Experimental Findings of Hypnotic Deafness," *J. Gen. Psychol.* **19**:127–167 (1938).
6. ——— and E. M. Erickson: "The Hypnotic Induction of Hallucinatory Color Vision Followed by Pseudo Negative After-images," *J. Exp. Psychol.* **22**:581–588 (1938).
7. Gidro-Frank, L., and M. K. B. Buch: "A Study of the Plantar Response in Hypnotic Age Regression," *J. Nervous Mental Disease* **107**:443–458 (1948).
8. Hibler, F. W.: "An Experimental Investigation of Negative After-images of Hallucinated Colors in Hypnosis," *J. Exp. Psychol.* **27**:45–57 (1940).
9. Kelsey, D. E. R.: "Phantasies of Birth and Prenatal Experiences Recovered from Patients Undergoing Hypnoanalysis," *J. Mental Sci.* **99**:216–223 (1953).
10. Kline, M. V.: "Hypnotic Age Regression and Intelligence," *J. Genet. Psychol.* **77**:129–132 (1950).
11. ———, H. Guze, and A. D. Haggerty: "An Experimental Study of the Nature of Hypnotic Deafness: Effects of Delayed Speech Feed-back," *J. Clin. Exp. Hypnosis* **2**:145–156 (1954).
12. Kupper, H. I.: "Psychic Concomitants in Wartime Injuries," *Psychosomat. Med.* **7**:15–21 (1945).
13. LeCron, L.: "A Study of Age Regression under Hypnosis," in *Experimental Hypnosis*. Ed. by L. LeCron. New York, The Macmillan Company, 1952, pp. 152–174.
14. Mercer, M., and R. W. Gibson: "Rorschach Content in Hypnosis: Chronological Age Level Regression," *J. Clin. Psychol.* **6**: 352–358 (1950).
15. Norgarb, B. A.: "Rorschach Psychodiagnosis in Hypnotic Age Regression," in *Experimental Hypnosis*. Ed. by L. LeCron. New York, The Macmillan Company, 1952, pp. 178–214.
16. Orne, M. T.: "The Mechanisms of Hypnotic Age Regression: An Experimental Study," *J. Abnormal & Soc. Psychology* **46**:213–225 (1951).
17. Pattie, F. A.: "A Report of Attempts to Produce Uniocular Blindness by Hypnotic Suggestion," *Brit. J. Med. Psychol.* **15**: 230–241 (1935).
18. ———: "The Genuineness of Hypnotically Produced Anesthesia of the Skin," *Am. J. Psychol.* **49**:435–443 (1937).
19. ———: "The Genuineness of Unilateral Deafness Produced by Hypnosis," *Am. J. Psychol.* **63**:84–86 (1950).
20. Platonow, K. I.: "On the Objective Proof of the Experimental Personality Age Regression," *J. Gen. Psychol.* **9**:190–209 (1933).
21. Rosen, H.: *Hypnotherapy in Clinical Psychiatry*, New York, Julian Press, Inc., 1953.
22. Sarbin, T. R.: "Mental Age Changes in Experimental Regression," *J. Personal.* **19**:220–228 (1950–1951).
23. ——— and N. L. Farberow: "Contributions to Role-taking Theory: A Clinical Study of Self and Role," *J. Abnormal & Soc.*

Psychology 47:117–125 (1952).

24. Spiegel, H., J. Shor, and S. Fishman: "A Hypnotic Ablation Technique for the Study of Personality Development," *Psychosomat. Med.* 7:273–278 (1945).
25. True, R. M., and C. W. Stephenson: "Controlled Experiments Correlating Electroencephalogram, Pulse, and Plantar Reflexes with Hypnotic Age Regression and Induced Emotional States," *Personality* 1:252–263 (1951).
26. Young, P. C.: "Hypnotic Regression—Fact or Artifact?" *J. Abnormal & Soc. Psychology* 35: 273–278 (1940).

Roy M. Dorcus, Ph.D.

7

THE USE OF HYPNOSIS AS A DIAGNOSTIC TOOL

THERE ARE MANY TYPES of illness that may be either organic or psychogenic in origin; there are other types in which there may be a psychogenic component superimposed upon a basic or borderline organic factor; and finally, there are instances in which malingering is involved. In these types of illness consideration should be given to the various components which need to be known if proper therapy is to be instituted.

Therapy may be of an organic nature primarily or of a psychological nature, depending upon whether the disease syndrome arises from an organic or a psychological condition. It may be argued that adequate diagnostic procedures are available for detecting organic causes of disease. This is true in those areas where the situation is unambiguous, but is certainly not true in many borderline diseases.

In the cases to be presented in the following part of the discussion, the reader will become aware of the fact that in many instances diagnosis becomes interwoven with therapy. The diagnosis may actually depend in part upon the outcome of therapy. If it is demonstrated that suggestive therapy eliminates or ameliorates the symptoms, one is on reasonably safe ground in assigning their origin to psychogenic causes.

Hypnosis and the diagnosis of conversion hysteria

Perhaps the simplest way to approach this problem is through the use of illustrative case material. One large area in which hypnosis may serve a useful purpose is in detecting cases of conversion hysteria. I should like to cite a number of cases in which the technique proved useful.

A young woman was swimming with a male friend at the beach one afternoon. A heavy wave rolled in and upset her, and in falling she struck the right side of her face on a rock. While en route home she became dizzy and nauseated, and her hearing was badly impaired on the side which struck the rock. Otological examination left the situation in doubt. Since there were certain unusual circumstances in the social situation existing between the young woman and her escort, the possibility of a conversion symptom entered the picture. The young patient was tested with an audiometer and her hearing on the right side showed a loss of about 85 decibels. She was placed under hypnosis and was informed that she would be able to hear normally with both ears. Audiometer testing under these circumstances revealed that her hearing was quite adequate. The fact that she could hear normally under hypnosis demonstrated quite clearly that her symptomatology was of a conversion type and that the blow on the side of the face was only the precipitating factor. There is no need to discuss the psychological background of this case since the only problem involved at the time was establishing whether the condition was a conversion symptom.

Another case history will lend additional evidence in the same general area. A young woman was confined to a hospital bed for a period of about six months with a paraplegic condition following a fall from a stool on which she was standing. Neurological examination, including skiagrams and spinal fluid examination, did not reveal any specific cause for the paraplegia, but the physicians were uncertain whether some injury might not be responsible. The patient was hypnotized and told that she wanted to move her legs, that she would make attempts to move them, and that she would be able to walk with some assistance. Following this suggestion, she was able to swing her legs voluntarily when sitting on the edge of the bed and could take steps when partially supported by the nurses and doctors.

A third case of a conversion type did not represent a real diagnostic problem since the physicians were relatively certain as to the nature of the difficulty. It is presented because hypnosis could be used to convey to the patient certain information that he was unwilling to accept previously. The patient was an ex-soldier who had entered the hospital for the removal of a piece of cartilage from his knee. Following the operation, the lower leg and knee were immobilized by a plaster cast. When the cast was removed the knee joint was stiff and the patient was unable or unwilling to attempt bending the knee. He complained of excruciating pain when he tried to support himself on that leg or bend his knee. Under hypnosis the patient was shown that he could bend the knee without pain and was induced to try supporting himself on the operated leg. After a relatively short period of psychotherapy the patient became ambulatory and left the hospital. The conditions were established without question as being of a functional type.

Hypnosis and diagnosis of neurotic symptoms with organic components

All the above cases were rather clear-cut with regard to the diagnostic problem; either they were functional or organic in origin. The next case that is presented is more complicated in that the diagnostic problem is not as clear-cut.

The case was that of an ex-WAC whose chief complaint was black-out attacks. Physical examination revealed that the patient had a borderline diabetic condition. The question that arose in this case was whether her black-outs should be attributed to her diabetic condition or whether there was superimposed upon this condition a psychogenic reaction. There was some suspicion of the latter, since the black-outs seemed to occur when she became excited in traffic. This could, of course, be a result of her diabetic condition. When she was hypnotized her black-out attacks could be readily induced, and when she was regressed it was established that the black-outs had first occurred prior to the onset of the diabetic condition. As a result, the patient was placed in psychotherapy.

The case to be presented at this point is similar to the one just discussed but has a different background. A sailor was discharged from the Navy because of convulsive phenomena. The patient's difficulties arose following a blow on the head by a crane on the deck of a ship. The individual became unconscious for a period of time but gradually seemed to recover completely. Following a furlough at home, he complained of seizures which seemed to be petit mal in character. Electroencephalograms and skiagrams of his skull did not demonstrate any organic pathology, but because of the original head injury organic pathology could not be entirely ruled out. It was decided that hypnosis would be tried for two purposes: (*a*) to see whether the convulsions could be induced, and if so, (*b*) to uncover the underlying conflict. The first question was answered in the affirmative. The convulsions could be initiated and could be terminated while the patient was under hypnosis, which indicated a probable psychogenic basis for the difficulty. The patient was given suggestions that he would experience the events leading up to the first seizure and that he would have all the feelings and actions that occurred at that time. It was discovered that the first seizures arose when he attempted to break off an engagement with a girl, who did not want the engagement terminated. In this case, as well as in the previous cases, the etiology was fairly easily established.

Perhaps a few comments relative to the use of hypnosis as a diagnostic tool in convulsive states would be useful. The author has found in hysteroepileptics, as well as in some cases of idiopathic epilepsy, that seizures can be easily induced. There seems, however, to be a difference as to what happens in the two conditions when an attempt is made to terminate the induced seizure. The idiopathic epileptic seizure seems to run its course and cannot be terminated, while the hysteroepileptic seizure can be terminated. The use of hypnosis for diagnostic purposes in convulsive states is by no means foolproof but it may be used successfully in some situations.

Use of hypnosis for motivational purposes in organic brain damage

A case reported by Kirkner, Dorcus, and Seacat (2) illustrates an entirely different kind of situation in which hypnosis served at least a dual purpose: i.e., as a motivational tool as well as a method of determining that the underlying pathology was not sufficiently severe to prevent speech retraining. This material is presented at some length, since the pathology was well established, but how far the pathology interfered with the speech processes was not as readily ascertained.

> *The patient was a 41 year old, white, married male. He had suffered a crushing injury to his left wrist on February 1, 1951. On February 2, 1951, a cerebral vascular accident occurred which, at the time, was attributed to an embolism. He arrived at the Aphasic Clinic of the Veterans Administra-*

tion Hospital, Long Beach, California, in August 1952. The condition of the patient at the time of his arrival is described in the following neurological reports:

8–16–52: *This man comes in walking in no apparent distress but he is mute. He makes no effort even to vocalize. He answers . . . positive or negative in nodding or shaking of the head. The deep reflexes on the right side of the body are greater than on the left, and there is a very good Babinski sign on the right, but a weak one on the left. There is also some loss of sensory perception in the right hand, and in addition an astereognosis. He can tell the difference so far as size is concerned between a fountain pen and a flashlight . . . but he cannot tell that the metallic flashlight is colder than the celluloid fountain pen. He has a complete ideokinetic apraxia of speech which is equivalent to motor aphasia. In addition to this, he has a lesion of the left optic nerve which does not respond to direct light but does consensually, while the right responds to direct light but does not consensually. The lesion of the left optic nerve is incomplete, although it is quite advanced. This lesion came a year after the other, and we therefore have to explain the two lesions separately. I believe the first one was a cerebral thrombosis, and probably the second was also a cerebral thrombosis. The candidate should be good for aphasia retraining, except for his general ineptness in language and his apparent lack of interest in recovery.*

8–27–52: *This patient has been seen in the Neurological Section and we have found that he has had a diabetic thrombosis in two areas, one of which gives him ideokinetic apraxia. He has very good understanding in spoken language . . . He is barely able to write and the little that he wrote for us today was in mirror writing. He also reads very poorly. We therefore have difficulty in our approach to the problem unless we attempt to educate him beyond his pre-*

> *morbid level. The diagnosis is cerebral thrombosis with ideokinetic apraxia in speech.*
>
> *Although the patient had the feeling that he could verbalize following the accident, when he attempted to talk he found that he was unable to and adjusted to the new situation. Since previous attempts of retraining were unsuccessful, and we believed in part because of lack of motivation, it was thought that hypnosis might be used as a motivating technique. Hypnosis was applied, using the visual object method.*
>
> *The order in which the hypnotic phase of the treatment progressed was that the patient was able to vocalize* (a) *in the trance for the hypnotist,* (b) *in the trance for the speech therapist, and* (c) *without the aid of the hypnotist for the speech therapist and others.**

Since the outcome of the hypnotic suggestions and speech retraining was in a favorable direction, it is possible to state that hypnosis served a useful purpose that was at least partially diagnostic in nature.

Hypnosis as a diagnostic aid in determining glandular functioning

In a number of anxiety situations conversion symptoms are not manifested, but symptomatology reflecting overactivity of functions controlled by the autonomic nervous system are predominant. Such activity may be caused by either organic glandular pathology or by glandular dysfunction brought about by anxiety. While tests of glandular dysfunction are reasonably reliable, there are numerous borderline patients about whom decisions should be reached. In some of these patients, hypnosis may be utilized to reduce temporarily the anxiety so that more adequate determinations of glandular function may be made. Perhaps cases involving

* Reprinted by permission of *The Journal of Clinical and Experimental Hypnosis* and the Woodrow Press.

dysmenorrhea will illustrate the complicated relationship. A number of these patients in whom no organic pathology could be found have been seen by the author. These patients had been treated with conventional therapeutic hormones; nevertheless the dysmenorrhea symptoms continued. When treated by hypnosis for several months, and in some instances only once, the symptoms were held in abeyance. This demonstrated clearly that the symptoms were linked with psychological problems which in turn brought about the glandular difficulty and symptoms.

Mrs. C. J., aged 38 years, requested a panhysterectomy (1). All previous treatment had given no relief. She had had no preconceived complexes in regard to menstruation. However, her first menstruation was marked by pre-menstrual tension. After eight hours of suffering and bleeding, she revealed her embarrassing condition to her mother. With each succeeding period the girl's suffering grew worse until chills, syncope, and uncontrollable nausea and vomiting accompanied all periods. The usual home remedies and surgical dilatations of the cervix were tried with indifferent success. Marriage and pregnancy gave no relief. Presacral neurectomy was performed without relief. However, a succeeding pregnancy was accompanied by several episodes of painless contractions with bleeding, and was terminated in a precipitate delivery free of pain, demonstrating the interruption of the sympathetic nerves. This was in marked contrast to her previous deliveries. With return of menstruation, the original intense dysmenorrhea symptoms reappeared, preceded each time by a week of nervous tension and anticipation, chills, syncope, nausea and vomiting, and bed for three days.

Through partial hypnosis her symptoms were greatly relieved for two periods, and the patient was able to carry on her household duties for the first time. Estrogen was then given to suppress ovulation, and the next period was so relieved that she came to the office to report her appreciation.

The next period was preceded by a painless diagnostic curettage, and secretory endometrium was found. This period was more painful. Restriction of sodium and the administration of chloride was tried and gave some relief at the following period. At present, the patient feels greatly relieved and will seek no further help if this status can be maintained. Result: *Partial relief by hypnosis; definite relief by suppression of ovulation.**

The preceding patient's case history gives evidence of a functional disorder. The difficulty of interpretation as psychogenic or organic in origin is obvious from the different therapeutic approaches—i.e., surgical and glandular therapy. Even after both of these methods were tried, symptoms were presented. However, after hypnotherapy, the symptoms were mitigated, which established clearly the psychogenic origin of the difficulties. Hypnosis served in an indirect manner as a diagnostic aid.

Hypnosis as an aid in determining importance of psychological factors

It has been shown that hypnosis can be of assistance in arriving at a differential diagnosis in a variety of situations. The case presented by Madison (3) that follows demonstrates that hypnosis may also be of service in ascertaining which of two apparent psychological conditions may be basic in a functional disorder.

Harry R. was referred by his classroom teacher who considered him to be a stutterer. "His speech is all mixed up," she said, "but I think it's mostly due to his stuttering. He probably substitutes words because of this difficulty." At the time of his referral, Harry was 8.5 years old. His health and physical condition were definitely superior. His motor development, coordination, and strength were about equal to those

* Reprinted by permission of *The American Journal of Obstetrics and Gynecology* and the C. V. Mosby Company.

of the average ten year old. A neurological examination revealed no traces of dysfunctioning.

Developmental History: *After a nine months pregnancy, labor was relatively brief and easy. This was the first pregnancy and there has been none since. The mother was 23 years old at the time of Harry's birth and the father was 31. Both parents were in good health. The mother worked during the first six months of pregnancy and returned to work when Harry was about five months old. For the first 15 months Harry's health and development were above average. By that time he had begun toddling around the house and, according to his parents, had a vocabulary of 20 to 25 words which were understandable.*

At 15 months Harry had a rather severe case of measles followed by a long convalescent period complicated by several colds. During this six months illness, his speech regressed. He stopped speech and vocal play altogether, except for an occasional word or sound. There was no record of any other serious illness. After this illness, he very rapidly regained his physical strength and was soon equal or superior to his peer group in motor development. His health since his recovery has continued to be very good. His speech, however, was badly retarded and progress was very slow.

The home environment was not favorable for speech training. The mother worked and had little time to devote to the child. But, becoming worried about his speech, she took him during his pre-school years to two different physicians for physical examinations. She said they assured her that there were no physical or neural causes for his speech disorder and that "he would probably outgrow it when he went to school." The mother's aunt, who kept house for the family, also felt he would outgrow it, so did little or nothing to train him. Because of his work, the father was home for only a few days at long intervals.

Psychological Examination: *On the Stanford-Binet, Harry had an I.Q. score of 106, but his speech handicap made the validity doubtful. His score on the Draw-A-Man test was 112. At the time of his referral, Harry was in the third grade. His classroom teacher considered him to be average or above in all of his work except spelling and reading. With a little special tutoring and added homework, he was overcoming these deficiencies. His social adjustment was excellent. He had a cheerful, outgoing personality which made him a favorite both with adults and his peer group.*

Speech and Hearing Examination: *Harry was given a pure-tone audiometer test and the results showed normal hearing in both ears. Articulation tests with pictures, words, and simple sentences revealed scores of substitutions and omissions, together with faulty voicing and unvoicing of consonants. There was no apparent pattern or consistency in his substitutions. For example, he almost indiscriminately interchanged (m, b, p, f, and v) and often substituted (w)* for *any one of them. However, with care he could produce all of the speech sounds in isolation or with a single vowel, with the exception of initial (s).*

The testing was made difficult by his frequent blocking. The blocks were characterized by a deep inhalation followed by a tonic spasm of the speech and breathing musculatures. Some of the blocks would last as long as 10 to 15 seconds, during which time he was rigidly immobile. Harry also complained of pain in the region of the lower ribs. The mother reported she had noticed some blocking starting about his fourth year. During his attendance in the first grade, the blocking or stuttering almost entirely disappeared and he showed considerable improvement in his articulation. Soon after he began the second grade (about a year and a half before his referral) the blocking returned and rapidly became much worse. His articulation problem also became worse and he soon began to have difficulty even with the words which he had previously been pronouncing correctly.

The Problem: *To organize a plan of treatment and to decide on a point of departure for therapy, it was necessary to make a preliminary diagnosis as early as possible. The problem for the therapist was to decide whether Harry's speech defect was primarily stuttering or an articulation disorder. That is, he must answer the question: Was the blocking true secondary stuttering?*

Indications of secondary stuttering included:The severity and frequency of the blocks; a slight torticollic movement at the beginning of the spasm; the complete immobility and apparent mental blocking during the spasm; the possibility that the substitutions and omissions of sounds were, in part, release mechanisms.

There were also several contra-indications for a diagnosis of stuttering. For example, Harry had no Jonah words; he made no attempt to avoid or substitute words; he made no use of starting mechanisms. One of the most important contra-indications from the author's viewpoint was Harry's reaction to the frustrations of his speech disorder. He was primarily frustrated by his inability to communicate, rather than by the speech block itself. Secondly, contrary to what might be expected in stutterers, the resulting aggression was very high in an extropunitive and very low in an intropunitive direction.

Hypnodiagnosis: *At the first meeting Harry was given practice in progressive relaxation, using the rag-doll and scarecrow games. The results of suggestibility tests were almost entirely negative. Induction was attempted by the postural-sway technique and proved unsuccessful. At the second session, several other methods were tried. A brief, very light trance was induced by eye fixation, but could not be repeated.*

During the third meeting, Harry related that he had attended the movies the night before and as usual had gone to sleep and missed most of the show. He said that he could never keep awake at a motion-picture show. Using Salter's "feedback" technique, the room was darkened, a flashlight spot was turned on the wall, Harry was seated in an armchair and told to imagine he was in a motion-picture show. Using sleep suggestions, a medium trance was induced in about ten minutes. This was deepened by fractionation. A post-hypnotic suggestion was given that in the future the trance could be induced by counting.

At the next session, after a period of relaxation, a deep trance was induced in four minutes by eye fixation and counting. Articulation tests were given by aural stimulation. Under hypnosis the blocking was entirely absent, but there were no significant changes in the articulation test results. Before Harry was awakened, suggestions were given to relieve the tension and pain in the lower rib area.

As a check, at the next session another group of articulation tests was given by aural stimulation during the wakened state and the same and equivalent tests administered under hypnosis. Because of Harry's almost random substitutions and omissions, the results of the tests differed qualitatively, but quantitatively they were almost identical.

Therapy: *It is not the purpose of this paper to discuss the therapy used in Harry's case, except to indicate how the diagnosis influenced the plan of treatment. From the above tests and others given as the speech block lessened, it was evident that Harry's problem was primarily an articulation disorder. It was discovered that he was almost completely unable to hear his own errors at the time of production. Although he did not know how to correct his errors, he almost never failed to detect them when they were reproduced by the therapist or his speech was played back to him on the tape recorder.*

His family, teachers, and others had been "helping" him by interrupting his speech and forcing him to correct his errors —errors which he could not hear and did not know how to correct! The cooperation of the parents and teacher was secured to relieve this environmental stress.

Hypnosis was induced at every session for the first four weeks, and about once a week afterward. In the first period, only an indirect attack was made on the blocking by suggestions which would relieve the muscular tension. Because Harry did not consider himself a stutterer, no direct mention of the blocks was made either in the wakened state or under hypnosis. During the latter period of therapy, the trances were induced for two purposes: (*1*) *to aid relaxation when necessary, and* (*2*) *for added concentration to speed up the learning process.*

The spasms diminished rapidly, both in frequency and severity, from the start of the hypnotherapy. Within a period of three weeks (*nine sessions*)*, they had entirely disappeared. For a few weeks there were infrequent and brief non-tension hesitancies. These differed entirely from the former spasms in the absence of muscular rigidity. Secondly, they seldom lasted more than a second or two while Harry was experimenting with the speech mechanism preparatory to producing a sound. These, too, disappeared as the articulation defect was reduced.**

The next patient demonstrates what was pointed out earlier in our discussion, namely, that the outcome of the therapy itself may finally establish a clear-cut diagnosis. The case history and outcome is one from the files of Dr. Charlyne Storment-Seymour (4).

* Reprinted by permission of *The Journal of Clinical and Experimental Hypnosis* and the Woodrow Press.

This former pilot was a captain in the U. S. Air Force during World War II. He was shot down in combat, sustaining a spinal injury which paralyzed him for over a year. During this time he was a wheelchair patient, lost control of bowels and bladder and sexual ability. He was married and had 2 children, a boy and a girl who are now 7 and 9 years of age. After an operation on his spine it was found that there had been no complete lesion but rather a pressure on the nerves, and he gradually regained ability to walk and control of bowels and bladder. He was, however, unable to regain his sexual abilities.

During the period of his paralysis and gradual return of functions, he had become a dependent, frustrated individual, who stayed at home and took care of the children while his wife worked and took over the authoritative controls of the family. She began staying out at night with other men and finally left the patient and remarried. He went to live with his grandmother, and after finding the children being cared for by a Negro family and the mother in financial difficulties, he was able to take the children's care over with the mother's consent.

Recently he fell in love with a divorcee who works in the same office as he does. He found that he was able to have erections when he was in the presence of this girl and could have an orgasm when he masturbated alone but was unable to have sexual relations with the girl. His physician felt that in all probability he should be able to have normal sexual relations but could not be positive that such was the case. It was felt that his impotence with women was now functional, due partly to the severe emotional trauma of the past four years.

After thorough explorations of his psychological problems, it was decided to attempt to overcome his recent attitudes on sex through hypnotherapy. The first session took place on

September 11th with post-hypnotic suggestions as to his fears, hopes, and general attitudes toward sex. It was suggested that his attitudes and feelings toward women would revert to what they were previous to his injury, that he would have complete confidence in his sexual ability and generally feel extremely masculine and independent as he did before his injury.

*On his next visit, September 13th, he reported his first heterosexual success since before he was injured. Stated that he felt "like he used to feel, confident and happy." Post-hypnotic suggestion was reinforced along the same lines as before and the patient is due in on September 20, 1951, for a check-up and further reinforcement in post-hypnotic suggestions. He wishes to marry the divorcee but has stated that this has depended on his ability to recover his sex functions.**

Hypnosis as a tool for determining nature of pain

In some cases following severe physical trauma when the effects of the trauma have disappeared, complaints of severe pain are a dominant part of the picture. In many of these cases it is difficult to determine whether the pain can be considered a conditioned type of feeling or whether organic factors are still in operation. The case of patient C.A.B. illustrates the fact that some of these conditions can be brought under control and the cause can be attributed to a conditioned type of feeling.

This 23 year old service connected veteran sustained a severe injury in Korea when a portion of his spine was blown away. He was addicted to narcotics which had been administered to him for pain, at the time of his arrival at the Hospital. He continued to complain of considerable pain at frequent intervals, and has been nearly continuously on a Stryker frame.

"On August 31st, the patient had been crying constantly

* Quoted by permission of Dr. Charlyne Storment-Seymour.

from about 6 a.m., and apparently was in severe pain. His physical condition was such that the physician in charge deemed it inadvisable to administer narcotics. At about 2:30 p.m., with the full cooperation of the patient, it was decided to attempt hypnotherapy for intractable pain. He was quite suggestible to the therapist's efforts almost at once. Post-hypnotic suggestions regarding his abilities to place himself under hypnosis and thus relieve himself of the pain when necessary were given. On awakening, the patient stated that he felt 'very much better.' He was hypnotized subsequently on September 4, 7, 10 and 14 with excellent results. He reported feeling practically no more pain since the first session on August 31. He is now able to give himself suggestions as to his pain relief under auto-hypnosis in order to reinforce the original suggestions on this topic. Patient checked September 24, 1951; still feels very much better; hypnotizes self.

This patient wants to obtain a high school diploma. He plans on living at home with his parents when he is physically able to do so. He would like to start work on the high school diploma here, and on vocational testing as soon as he is able to do so.

The patient is a rather intelligent, but quite dependent and emotionally immature individual who relies a great deal on his close attachment to his mother. He is essentially well-adjusted except for this dependence.

Occasional contacts will be maintained with him to check his progress.

*Status: Improved.**

Hypnosis as a means of detecting malingering

Another area in which hypnosis may be useful as a diagnostic tool is in detecting malingering. Two cases that have been detected

* Quoted by permission of Dr. Charlyne Storment-Seymour.

with this technique by the author will suffice to illustrate the point.

One case involved a steamship pilot who was claiming compensation for colorblindness resulting from a blow on the head while performing his duty as a ship's officer. He had been refused a renewal of his navigator's license because he could not pass the color tests. This deprived him of his job and he had instigated suit for a large sum of money. While there are appropriate means of detecting pretended colorblindness with visual tests, the individual was referred to the author to determine whether malingering was involved. Hypnosis was induced and the individual was able to read the conventional charts for colorblindness without difficulty. When this information was conveyed to him the suit was dropped.

The other case involved a feigned paraplegic condition. The patient had been in a number of hospitals for a period of about seven years. He confined himself to a wheel chair and was unable, according to the patient, to move his lower extremities. He was hypnotized, placed on his back on a table, and instructed that he would want to move his legs and that he would be able to do so. He proceeded to carry out these acts without difficulty. Subsequently the patient was placed under close observation and it was found that he was walking about his room when he did not know he was under observation.

While both of these cases might have been considered cases of conversion hysteria, circumstances were such in the case of the pseudo colorblind individual as to indicate that it was malingering. There was no doubt about the pseudo paraplegic, since he moved about when he thought he was not under observation.

The foregoing cases show that, while hypnosis is by no means an infallible diagnostic tool, it is useful as a supplemental diagnostic device in the hands of a capable technician.

REFERENCES

1. Hunter, W. E., and B. B. Rolf: "The Psychosomatic Aspect of Dysmenorrhea," *Am. J. Obstet. Gynecol.* 53:123–131 (1947).
2. Kirkner, F. J., R. M. Dorcus, and Gloria Seacat: "Hypnotic Motivation of Vocalization in an Organic Motor Aphasic Case," *J. Clin. Exp. Hypnosis* 1:47–49 (1953).
3. Madison, L.: "The Use of Hypnosis in the Differential Diagnosis of a Speech Disorder," *J. Clin. Exp. Hypnosis* 2:140–144 (1954).
4. Storment-Seymour, C.: Unpublished case history.

Milton V. Kline, Ph.D.

8

SYMPTOM CONTROL BY DIRECT SUGGESTION INCLUDING THE CONTROL OF PAIN

THE USE OF DIRECT suggestion techniques within hypnotherapy is an aspect of treatment management usually misinterpreted in the general literature of psychotherapy. In contemporary hypnotherapy direct suggestion has come to be viewed as a clinical technique within psychotherapy, and it becomes important to differentiate it from the earlier use of direct suggestion as a definitive therapy in itself. Unfortunately, the regressive and outmoded suggestion therapy of Freud's time and before is too often still associated with directive hypnotic techniques in modern psychotherapy. There is no role for direct suggestion as definitive therapy in contemporary hypnotherapy, any more than there is in non-hypnotic therapy consistent with modern psychological and psychodynamic concepts; there is, however, a realistic and significant place for it within the more fully comprehended clinical treatment setting. This ambiguity should be clarified if this method of therapeutic intervention is to be employed judiciously and with effective results.

There is a trend in current scientific terminology to use *directive hypnotherapy* as a term to replace *direct suggestion.* At this time both terms are in use, and they may be considered synonymous provided direct suggestion is viewed, not as a means of attempting symptom suppression or clinical cure, but as a technique designed to bring about conditions within the patient (or his treatment relationship) which will *lead to* more productive therapeutic activity and effectiveness. This chapter is concerned with directive hypnotherapy—or direct suggestion, in the current sense—with respect to its specialized use in symptom management and pain control.

Historically, direct suggestion in hypnosis has been used to produce two types of response in the patient: (1) direct responses to verbal suggestion while the subject is *in the hypnotic state,* and (2) behavioral responses *in a posthypnotic state.* The historical failure of direct suggestion as a definitive therapy was due to the inability to produce and maintain posthypnotic responses rather than to the hypnotic state per se, and this led to its eventual abandonment. The nature of posthypnotic behavior is dynamically different from hypnotic behavior with regard to the nature of the interpersonal relationship involved (8) and, consequently, with regard to the essential meaning of the behavior to the subject. Thus, we now recognize that within the framework of directive hypnotic techniques there are different types of behavior-organizing mechanisms involved; it is these mechanisms rather than the hypnotic suggestions or directions per se that materially determine the character of the behavior response.

The realization that direct suggestion is not a simple therapeutic device is perhaps the most important fact that we have learned from contemporary research in hypnosis. It is, despite its apparent simplicity, a rather dynamic aspect of the hypnotic relationship. When well understood it can be skillfully and effectively employed in the clinical management of psychotherapy and still be consistent with the more fundamental structure of total treatment. There need be no conflict between directive techniques in hypnotherapy and their integration within any type of therapeutic activity. This, however, presumes a full awareness of the dimensions of both therapeutic hypnosis and direct suggestion techniques.

The elucidation of response activity in hypnosis will generally be related to two aspects of the hypnotic suggestion or direction:

1. The level of hypnosis required for excitation. That is, for certain psychophysiological conditions, and related neuropsychological functions, a somnambulistic or deeper trance state will usually be required.
2. The purpose or meaning of the directed behavior activity.

Directions for either symptom activity or behavior which involves the resistances of the patient will be either inhibited or displaced. In either instance, particularly in psychotherapy, the subtle, almost spontaneous responses of the patient to direct hypnotic suggestion reveal meaningful aspects of his character organization and pattern of resistance. Careful evaluation of these responses can serve as a pertinent guide to the eventual handling of the patient (10, 28).

The nature of resistance as a phenomenon of the psychotherapy of neuroses plays a significant role in restricting or obliterating the effects of direct hypnotic suggestion (10). It was Freud's awareness of this factor, among others, which prompted his abandonment of hypnosis as a direct form of treatment (11). There appears to be a sharp contrast between the response to direct suggestion on the part of the experimental subject and that of the clinical patient. The difference becomes greater in proportion to the neurotic needs of the patient and his altered state of neuropsychological functioning as compared with a non-neurotic or less neurotic subject. For this reason certain patients, especially those suffering more from somatic response to emotional stress than from characterological pathology, display effective and therapeutically desirable reactions to directive hypnotherapy.

Indications for the use of direct suggestion

The decision to use directive techniques in hypnotherapy should be carefully arrived at. Direct suggestion in the hypnotic state has distinct contraindications in certain emotional disorders where symptom replacement, rather than symptom amelioration or elimination, results. To be able to predict a patient's dynamic reaction to hypnotherapeutic technique becomes a prime prerequisite for the hypnotherapist and analyst. Naturally such predictions will be limited by the realities of modern psychodynamics. The utilization of diagnostic projective techniques, especially within the hypnotic state, increases this predictability considerably (16).

In attempting to summarize the salient conditions which determine the extent to which direct suggestion can be utilized as a therapeutic technique, the following factors appear most important:

1. The level of hypnosis obtained.
2. The extent to which posthypnotic as well as hypnotic activity becomes necessary in the maintenance and/or reinforcement phase of treatment.
3. The characterological structure of the patient, and the dynamic equilibrium of the symptom being treated.
4. The extent to which the induced behavioral reaction relates to the functioning correlates of the symptom or group of symptoms.

In this connection the recognition of conversion mechanization becomes an important consideration in the planning of directive techniques. Conversion mechanization does not usually respond very well to direct suggestion therapy. Replacements, and related displacement phenomena, take place which invalidate the therapeutic approach and frequently produce a more complicated psychopathological picture. Seitz's work (29, 30) in this connection is most pertinent. In symptom formations and pain reactions which appear to involve mechanisms other than conversion directive hypnotic techniques become more desirable and more efficacious, within the framework of the particular patient's difficulty. The recognition of conversion mechanization as distinguished from other forms of symptom and pain formation becomes a critical factor in the indications and contraindications for directive hypnotherapy.

The distinction between directive hypnotherapy (direct suggestion) and other types of hypnotherapy and hypnoanalysis lies more in therapeutic orientation and goals than in procedure per se. Certainly within hypnoanalysis and certain forms of hypnotherapy, recourse to directive methods will be undertaken. In essence, directive hypnotherapy involves the application of hypnotic techniques for the immediate control of distress. It is distinctly a symptom-oriented therapy rather than an etiologically oriented therapy. The need for effective symptom-oriented therapeutic techniques requires no substantiation here. It is well recognized that in the treatment of neurotic symptomatology the very mechanisms of the neurosis may create a barrier to psychotherapeutic goals consistent with broader concepts of character structure and personality in a large number of patients. Unfortunately there are many patients who cannot enter into therapeutic relationships except within the limits of their own personalities and their dynamic characteristics. Psychotherapy must be structured to meet the needs of the patients, that is, the form of treatment must follow the function of the patient's own personality (14). The decision to employ directive hypnotherapy of necessity must rest upon a global understanding of the patient and his difficulties, with therapist insight into the meaning of the disorder under treatment. Although therapy may be associated with etiological recapitulations ad infinitum as in some forms of psychoanalysis, the therapeutic decision to employ directive hypnotherapy must be based upon a comprehensive and etiological understanding on the part of the therapist.

It is our purpose here to deal with the nature of directive therapy in hypnosis, not to elaborate the psychodynamic justification for such treatment, technique, or procedure, which relates more to the basic aspects of therapeutic management. In the light of contemporary hypnotherapy we see that the use of directive hypnotherapy as a technique of symptom control and pain alleviation assumes both distinctiveness and effectiveness not in its procedure, which is fundamental to hypnotic behavior, but in its selective application and skillful management.

Types of suggestion and response

In spite of the fact that we use the term *direct suggestion,* in general we employ directions rather than suggestions in the directive techniques of hypnotherapy. The psychological nature of suggestion and the concept of suggestibility currently play an important role in psychodynamic research and, to some extent, in psychological theory. The reports of Eysenck and Furneaux (5) and Benton (4) are pertinent in this regard, particularly because they are in apparent conflict. Eysenck and Furneaux have been able to isolate what they describe as *primary* and *secondary suggestibility* among a patient population. Benton in investigating these characteristics failed to find them in a nonpatient population. There would seem at this point to be some question as to whether or not suggestibility as an independent unitary trait of personality exists. From a hypothetical point of view, suggestibility would appear to be related to a means of handling and recognizing anxiety rather than to be a characteristic trait of personality per se.

As a mechanism of response to the communication process,

clinical experience both in psychology and medicine bears witness to the reality of suggestibility. We are not at this point concerned with the isolation or, in fact, even the nature of suggestibility, but rather with its implications in directive hypnotherapy. Whether we use suggestion or direction matters less than that we take cognizance of the central issue: *communication* is the instrument through which we attempt to induce behavioral activity. The response to either a direction or a suggestion cannot be limited to the symbols used by the therapist, but relates to the correlated spontaneous and somewhat autonomous activity associated with this communication. For emotional reasons, a seductive, soothing, gradual process of behavioral intimation (suggestion) may, at times, be effectively employed. At other times a more definitive, descriptive, illustrative process (direction, instruction, interpretation) may be utilized. What we have called *hypnotic suggestion* historically, in reality has been more often direction and instruction. Suggestion, when effective, usually lies in the more compliant aspect of the communication process. Thus two means of evoking hypnotic response can be defined: the *implicit* (suggestion), which is to be found as much in nonhypnotic as hypnotic therapy, and the *explicit* (direction), the most frequently employed directive hypnotherapeutic method.

The response of the patient to the suggestion or direction is also twofold, comprising primary and secondary reactions. Often the secondary spontaneous reactions are more pertinent in the treatment procedure. Secondary reactions of both somatic and ideational nature constitute the *indirect reaction* to directive procedure. Perhaps one of the differentiating factors between positive and negative patient response to direct suggestion is the existance, nature, and strength of the secondary or indirect activity stimulated. This of necessity involves us in a somewhat theoretical area of hypnotic behavior which impinges upon neuropsychological theory and cybernetic concept. It has been experimentally determined that hypnotic techniques of a directive nature are capable of inhibiting auditory feedback mechanization to a significant extent (19). It seems likely that other hypnotic techniques could stimulate feedback mechanization as well. This functional capacity of hypnosis and of hypnotherapy is pertinent to its effectiveness and clinical application in a large range of symptomatic disturbances.

A distinctive illustration of the relationship between direct suggestion and secondary, or indirect, reaction has been described in an experimental study of the effect of hypnosis on oral temperature (18). It was found that when a subject was told directly, "Your temperature will go up," or "Your temperature will go down," or "You will become very hot," or "You will become very cold," the subject evidenced *clinical signs* of these conditions but displayed *no change in measured oral temperature.* On the other hand when he was instructed to hallucinate himself in an airplane at an elevation of 100,000 feet, his oral temperature dropped in five minutes from 98.6 to 95.3 *without* any suggestion either of being cold or of a temperature drop.

Thus as we deal with the techniques of directive hypnotherapy we are of necessity dealing with a more involved instrument of treatment and of response than appears on the surface. There are several types of direct suggestion techniques and a differentiation of them is essential, both in our use of directive therapy and in our understanding of the psychodynamics and behavior organizations involved in their use.

Symptom-removal techniques. This method of hypnotherapy singles out the distinctive symptom of the patient, with directions that the symptoms will, within a general or specific time, either be better of disappear. In selected cases, within a framework of psychotherapy cognizant of the dynamics of the symptom formation and of the more fundamental characteristics of the patient's personality, such a method has a role. The decision to use such a technique must be based upon planning and therapist insight, and not upon the apparent simplicity of the procedure. This technique generally will be more effective with certain types of residual somatization processes and referred or associated pain responses, whereas it is generally contraindicated in dealing with pain or symptom formation based upon conversion mechanization.

Amelioration technique. At this point in the use of direct suggestion we become more aware of the secondary or indirect responses related to the initial direction. Although the approach is direct with respect to the treatment goal, the process involves indirect concomitant activity which assumes a significant role in the treatment activity and outcome. Within this approach we find the use of induced changes in sensation, preception, and stimulus reception playing a large role in treatment procedure. Postural and vasomotor relaxation constitutes the generally most applicable and effective means for dealing with anxiety and somatic symptoms on this level.

Symptom-replacement techniques. Essentially this is a symptom-substitution device. Though it has long been recognized that patients often replace one symptom with another, the effective use of directive hypnotherapy and symptom replacement has been brought about by further understanding of the symbolism and neuro-organizational characteristics of the original symptom. Symptom replacement is one of the most specialized of the directive hypnotherapeutic procedures.

Intervention techniques. Similar to replacement methods in that new responses and activity are stimulated in the patient, intervention techniques aim not at symptom substitution but at adding additional sensation or perceptual characteristics to the symptom pattern. In some instances new activity involving the symptom area appears to effect, through retroactive inhibition, symptom elimination without recourse to replacement (14). Included within this technique of therapy would be the use of such hypnotic phenomena as hallucinations, various sense-modality images, age regression, and time alterations (15, 17). Their use in treatment is designed, however, for the direct effect upon the patient's distress rather than for more fundamental changes in self-understanding and insight processes. To this extent they fall distinctly within the realm of directive hypnotherapy.

Experimental foundations

Experimental hypnosis has greatly influenced advancements in hypnotherapy, and to a considerable extent future refinements in therapeutic procedure will be based upon experimental research. With specific respect to the problem of symptom control and pain alleviation through direct hypnotherapy, certain problems must be critically examined. In general they fall into two major areas. First, with direct hypnosis it is possible to induce alterations in ideational, somatic, and affective functioning more effectively and frequently than to remove the existing patterns of behavioral activity. The experimental as well as the clinical literature consistently reflects this significant difference.

Second, generally a somewhat deeper hypnotic state is required for response to hypnotic direction on the part of clinical patients than on the part of experimental subjects. Resistance to the deeper levels of hypnosis appears to be more characteristic of patients than experimental subjects, and to relate to their impulse-handling defenses. With respect to certain types of symptom formation (again essentially nonconversion in origin) hypnotic control at times appears to be more efficaciously achieved in a setting which does not of necessity assume the usual characteristics of a psychotherapy setting with emphasis on and acceptance of the dealing with emotion and personality difficulties. Where the approach is more palliative or distinctly distress-oriented, both with experimental and clinical subjects, response to directive hypnotherapy appears increased. It therefore becomes important in the use of directive hypnotherapy to orient the total treatment relationship with the patient on a level consistent with this technique, and not to introduce this technique as a second order or lower form of psychotherapeutic activity.

The research literature in experimental hypnosis reflects the capacity of hypnosis to alter significantly the physiological functions of man. Gorton (7) in his excellent review cites evidence for the fact that emotional changes induced through hypnosis are capable of altering electroencephalographic recordings as well as a large variety of other neurophysiological and neuropsychological functions. Suggestions of cardiac dysfunctions have, in experimental investigations, resulted in definitive and pathological-like changes in the electrocardiograph (3). Fulde (6) reported that suggested excitement caused increased pulmonary ventilation, oxygen consumption, and CO^2 production. Changes in respiration, circulation, and vasomotor activity have also been reported. Likewise, hematological and muscular changes have been described (7). Weitzenhoffer (32) offers an excellent review of the experimental work dealing with alterations in physiological, neuropsychological, and perceptual functions.

Certain conflicting results do appear and bear pertinent relationship to clinical applications. Often the term *direct suggestion* is used to refer only to the direct effect upon the organ system involved in the very statements of the hypnotist. Thus, suggestion to increase the heartbeat is usually considered a direct suggestion. The direction to experience an emotion such as anger or sexual excitement either upon verbal direction or through associative activity is usually referred to as an indirect suggestion. In the therapeutic consideration of directive hypnotherapy, directions of both a direct and indirect nature must be included. Since the goal is still the production of specific organizational activity, the use of interpolated activity of an imagery, affective, or sensorimotor nature in no way alters the directiveness of the therapeutic procedure.

The subject or patient response is indirect, but this is true of all psychological activity in general. The basic S-O-R process of activity renders all human behavior organization except reflex functions indirect from a neuropsychological point of view. Directiveness as it relates to hypnotherapy refers to the therapeutic procedure and orientation alone, not to the process of response formation.

In the literature of experimental hypnosis there is a large body of factual evidence which points to the capacity of hypnosis to bring about alterations in physiological, neuropsychological, and emotional reactions. Some activity (temperature change, circulatory alteration, and hematological variation) demands a profound state of hypnosis. Other reactions (muscular, proprioceptive, sensory, and motor) can be brought about with light to medium states of hypnosis.

Interpolated procedures, utilizing emotional responses, image activity, and associative functions often greatly facilitate direct hypnotic responses. In general, directly induced hypnotic activity is more distinctive in the hypnotic state than in the posthypnotic state. Responses acquired during the hypnotic state can often be used, however, in the posthypnotic state to implement response activity.

Thus, from an experimental point of view, the use of directive hypnosis has proved to be effective in bringing about distinct alterations in many areas of behavior functioning. With specific respect to somatic functions, including pain, hypnosis appears to have potentialities of therapeutic value still unexplored. With increased understanding of the dynamics of human behavior, with skill and continued insight into the use of scientific hypnosis, direct hypnotherapy for symptom control and pain alleviation has an encouraging future.

The clinical-therapeutic literature

The application and techniques of directive hypnotherapy for symptom control and pain alleviation date back to the prescientific stages of both medicine and psychology. For an accurate historical perspective on the use of direct suggestion hypnotherapy, reference to more basic texts on hypnosis should be made (33). For a contemporary review of therapeutic concepts and techniques in this area, reference to the *Annual Review of Hypnosis Literature* (12), *Medical Hypnosis* (33), *Hypnosis in Modern Medicine* (27), *Hypnodynamic Psychology* (13), and *Hypnotherapy in Clinical Psychiatry* (26) should be made. The review of clinical material which follows represents a selection of illustrative reports, therapeutic problems, and techniques, which of necessity omits many references.

Ambrose (1, 2) has found both the induction of hypnosis and the use of directive hypnotherapy effective in dealing with a wide range of emotional disorders in young children. This type of hypnotherapy has been effective in the treatment of childhood asthma, enuresis, hysterical epilepsy, stammering, insomnia, and less well-defined psychosomatic reactions to emotional conflict. The collaborative involvement of the parents in the total therapeutic approach is undertaken in a manner consistent with present-day child-guidance concepts. With young children ranging from four or five to early adolescence there appear to be developmental or ego barriers in the general use of insight therapeutics. Relationship therapy, usually through activity structure, has proved thus far to be the most effective general approach to psychotherapy with children. Little work has been done in this country with hypnotherapy in the treatment of children's emotional disorders and Ambrose's work represents the most impressive and extensive use of this method. He has found that with directive hypnotherapy the length of treatment is generally significantly reduced and the results are somewhat better than those obtained with orthodox play or analytical therapy. He reports a tendency toward more frequent somnambulism among children than adults though he finds light hypnosis effective in the treatment of many disorders of childhood.

Kirkner and West (9) have reported on the use of hypnosis in the treatment of a severe case of hiccough of organic origin. In this case both carbon dioxide inhalation and a phrenic nerve block failed to provide more than momentary relief. Directive hypnotherapy involved three phases: (1) the control of the hiccough involving its immediate termination and subsequent reduction in the frequency of its reappearance; (2) the control of the hiccough and the control of hypnotic sleep; (3) the induction of sleep through self-hypnosis to overcome insomnia. In evaluating the effectiveness of hypnotherapy in this case, Kirkner and West came to the conclusion that through hypnosis a cerebral suppressor effect may be exerted on the center of the entire musculature. Although further experimental research is necessary to clarify this point, such a concept and the development of hypnotherapeutic techniques to produce such activity greatly extend the use of hypnosis in the control of many somatic responses both of organic and psychic origin.

LeCron (20), using hypnosis and directive techniques in conjunction with the Bates system of eye training, reports on the relief of a long-standing case of myopia. LeCron and others (21) report on the use of hypnosis in relieving postoperative prolonged hiccoughs through directive methods.

McDowell (23) reports a case of a thirty-two-year-old divorced woman who was afflicted with a moderately severe case of juvenile warts involving the backs of both hands, face, and neck. The patient was referred by a dermatologist, her condition having become progressively worse despite considerable medical and x-ray treatments. At the first interview the patient was found to be suffering from a chronic anxiety state, nail biting, insomnia, general tenseness, recurrent functional headaches, and gastrointestinal upsets. The warts had been first noted while her ex-husband was visiting her during a military leave. Hypnosis was induced at the first session and the patient proved to be a good hypnotic subject. A sensation of increasing warmth in the skin in areas involved by the warts was given and this was acknowledged by the patient who was then informed that the warts would disappear. During the second visit two days later, a slight clearing of the warts on one hand was observed. The patient was somewhat resistant to therapy during this session, but the hypnotic suggestions were reinforced. Eleven days after the beginning of treatment the patient returned for a third visit, and at that time the hands were found to be 90 per cent clear and the face about 50 per cent clear. The patient reported that occasionally the face became quite flushed and warm without apparent reason. No medication or cosmetics were used in that period. No attempt was made to deal therapeutically with the patient's other neurotic problems, but suggestions concerning the disappearance of the warts were repeated and some general reassurance was given. Two weeks later the patient reported that her skin had steadily cleared after the last treatment, eighteen days after the first visit. The author believed that there was sufficient evidence to suggest that the skin condition was playing a psychodynamically active symptomatic role in this neurotic woman.

Kline (14) discusses a case of neurodermatitis of more than twenty years' duration which had proved refractory to all types of medical therapy. Hypnosis and the development of interpolated sensations of warmth, cold, and alterations of size with posthypnotic imagery proved effective in eliminating the disorder within six weeks. No suggestions were given at any time with respect to symptomatic improvement or alleviation. A follow-up one year later revealed no relapse.

Obermeyer and Greenson (25) report on a case of verrucae planae of the face in a twenty-one-year-old unmarried white woman. The symptoms first appeared two years before her contact with the writers. She had undergone Röentgen treatment without success. Other treatment techniques included injections of bismuth subsalicylate in oil, peeling ointments, solid carbon dioxide, and a solution of podophyllum in acetone. All such treatment was ineffective. The psychotherapist made a preliminary examination which revealed no obvious neurotic symptoms, and he expressed the idea to the patient that, while there was no contraindication to suggestive therapy, the outcome of such treatment was in doubt. The patient was seen on only three occasions, at weekly intervals, and throughout the hypnotic sessions appeared to be capable of entering only a light trance. By the third and last visit the patient reported that her warts had become scaly. Two weeks later her skin was free of lesions and an inquiry six months later revealed that no recurrence had taken place.

Rosen (26) in discussing the hypnotic and hypnotherapeutic control of severe pain emphasizes that in the clinical application of hypnosis an awareness of pain as both an emotional and sensory experience must be taken into consideration. As previously pointed out, it is this aspect of the relationship of symptom and pain to emotions, as well as sense modalities, that determines the indications and contraindications for directive hypnotherapy. Rosen has developed five methods of hypnotherapeutic pain control which involve varying degrees of direct suggestion:

1. Deep sleep may be suggested.
2. Direct suggestion can be given that the patient feels nothing.
3. Hostility may be abreacted upon direct suggestion.
4. The psychological equivalent of a lobotomy may be suggested.
5. The fantasies back of the pain or symptom may be acted out.

Rosen has also reported upon the use of symptom substitution (26) which, while utilized within the framework of a dynamic understanding of symptom activity, represents the use of directive techniques in handling aspects of distress response.

Seitz (29, 30), in his clinical experiments on the substitution of symptoms by hypnosis, has dealt with both the unconscious psychological mechanisms involved in symptom substitution and the application and management of this hypnotherapeutic technique. He found that certain hypnotically induced substitute symptoms could successfully replace the original conversion reactions but that other hypnotically suggested symptoms could not be substituted in this way. In further studies Seitz (30) investigated the psychodynamic relationship between the original conversion reaction and the successful substitution symptom. This problem and its approach has theoretical relationship to the concepts of parallel neurosis (26) and stimulus equivalence (15) in hypnotherapy and perhaps relates more clearly to problems of hysterical disturbance in which there is a predominant use of conversion mechanization. Psychodynamic equivalence, which Seitz finds to be essentially basic for effective symptom substitution, relates on a neuropsychological basis to Kline's concept of stimulus equivalence (15) in the use of hypnotic techniques in general, and with specific reference to the direct management of responsive behavior in hypnotherapy and psychotherapy.

Moody (24) reports upon the use of hypnotically induced relaxation for the reduction of radiologically diagnosed peptic ulcers. Directive hypnotherapy included the use of self-hypnosis as well as direct suggestion in producing and maintaining relaxation. Comparison was made with a control group of patients treated pharmacologically. No medical therapy was employed in the experimental group utilizing hypnotically induced relaxation. The results showed clinical improvement in terms of symptom reduction to be better after treatment by hypnosis than by medication.

Stoltzenberg (31) reports on the successful use of directive hypnotherapy in the treatment of bruxism and hysterical trismus. Follow-up studies in both cases revealed effective therapeutic results with no evidence of secondary symptom formation. Levbarg reports on the use of directive hypnosis in the treatment of stammering in a patient with emotional difficulties (22).

Contemporary hypnotherapy displays an increasing use of directive methods, and their use in modern psychology and medicine reflects the increasingly integrated use of hypnotic techniques within a framework of insight into the meaning and the mechanization of the patient's disorder. Directive techniques in the control of somatic symptoms and pain offer an increasingly favorable area both for research and clinical application. Our current knowledge and skill in this area lead to two major conclusions:

1. Hypnosis as a method of psychological intervention in the control of somatic symptoms and pain can be utilized effectively in a large and varied number of clinical situations.
2. The effectiveness of directive hypnosis lies primarily in the insightful and skilled management of hypnotic techniques in relation to the etiological and dynamic aspects of the symptom and the patient. In marked contradiction to earlier thinking, effective hypnotherapy demands more skill, greater awareness of psychodynamics, and a firmer understanding of the neuropsychological basis of behavior functioning than any other type of therapy.

Techniques of directive hypnotherapy

In this section, specific techniques of directive hypnotherapy for symptom control and pain modification will be outlined. The choice of technique, as already indicated, will be determined by the level of hypnosis, the therapeutic goals, and the psychodynamic characteristics of the patient. In general, the following outline of hypnotherapeutic techniques parallels the degree of hypnosis which may be required.

Relaxation. Within a light hypnotic state, a considerable degree of physiological and emotional relaxation can be induced by direct suggestion. In a number of medical, dental, and psychological situations, effective relaxation in itself promotes symptom relief and alters pain thresholds. Conditioned or self-hypnotic procedures can be employed to maintain tension reduction over a prolonged period of time. In a number of psychosomatic disturbances, postural alterations, concomitant with hypnotically induced tension reduction, lead to spontaneous symptom improvement and pain alleviation. Situational anxiety as well as more chronic anxiety states may be modified at this level of treatment, thus preparing the way for more intensive treatment of the presenting or underlying difficulties.

Direct hypnotic control. Requiring a deeper level of hypnosis than techniques for relaxation alone, this approach may utilize hypnotically induced anesthesia or analgesia as a more definite means of symptom and pain control. In surgical and dental applications anesthesia or analgesia for specific areas of the body may be induced and maintained throughout treatment as well as on a post-treatment basis when necessary.

In many somatization responses, such as migraine, gastrointestinal distress, and muscular tension, hypnotically induced anesthesia for a brief period will often lead to symptom palliation without any use of additional direct suggestion. Certain dermatological disturbances have also responded well to brief treatments of hypnotically induced anesthesia.

Removal, Replacement, and Interpolated Techniques. The use of hypnotic techniques for the removal of symptoms directly may be approached in a number of ways. In a deep hypnotic state where posthypnotic reactions have been determined to be effective, specific reductions of pain and discomfort may be suggested. The direct elimination of certain symptoms may be attempted, though favorable response to such an approach has met only with indifferent success.

Direct removal through a *reduction process* often yields better results. Thus, over a period of several sessions suggestion can be given for the gradual reduction of discomfort both hypnotically and posthypnotically.

In selected cases it is possible to substitute or replace one symptom with another. Replacement or substitution, as pointed out by Seitz, will be effective only when the substituted response is equated symbolically with the original symptom. Such approaches are useful with certain compulsive symptoms where the symptom in itself creates anxiety. By replacing an anxiety-producing as well as perhaps a painful symptom with a less anxiety-producing or less painful symptom, the patient gains considerable relief and may be in a better position to make further therapeutic gains.

Interpolated techniques involve essentially the introduction of hypnotic activity relating to the symptom directly. With this technique no suggestions for symptom improvement or pain control are given verbally.

Induced imagery involving visualization of the symptom and of changes in the visualized characteristics of the symptom may bring about spontaneous improvement in the symptom itself. Induced sensations and alterations in the perception of symptoms can also be utilized to produce better levels of psychophysiological functioning. Sensations of temperature change and of alteration in size on an imagery level have been found to be effective in either significantly relieving symptomatic conditions or eliminating them. Similarly, alteration in time and age (15) can be used to control symptom formations. Direct suggestions for symptom improvement that are given at regressed ages or distorted times have proved to be more effective in the immediate reduction of distress than direct suggestion without age or time alteration. Regression in time or age to a period before the distress will often eliminate the symptom spontaneously, and posthypnotic suggestion can be utilized to create substitute or replacement symptoms which are more desirable.

In conclusion, direct suggestion techniques in hypnotherapy constitute a form of specialized procedures in contemporary psychotherapy. Directive therapy with hypnosis is not thought of as a definitive psychotherapeutic approach, but rather as a method of clinical management in certain types of symptomatic disturbances where pain and organ system functioning play the major role.

The decision to use directive hypnotherapy rests largely upon the nature of the presenting problem and the psychodynamics of the patient. The selection of specific techniques of direct hypnotherapy will largely be influenced by the level of hypnosis attained and the degree of symptom management that is required.

Although direct suggestion therapy has a significant place in psychotherapy, its use requires insightful and judicious awareness of the total treatment process and relationship. Therapist insight rather than patient insight becomes the major prerequisite in its use. As our knowledge of behavior organization and psychodynamics increases, the value of directive hypnotic techniques as a specialized form of psychotherapy takes on increased significance in medicine and psychology.

REFERENCES

1. Ambrose, C.: "The Technique and Value of Hypnosis in Child Psychotherapy," *Brit. J. Med. Hypnotism* 1:10 (1950).
2. ———: "The Value of Hypnotic Suggestion in Anxiety Reactions of Children," *Brit. J. Med. Hypnotism* 2:20 (1950).
3. Bennett, L. L., and N. E. Scott: "The Production of Electrocardiographic Abnormalities by Suggestion under Hypnosis: A Case Report," *Am. Practitioner* 4:189 (1949).
4. Benton, A. L., and A. Bandura: "Primary and Secondary Suggestibility," *J. Abnormal & Soc. Psychology* 3:336 (1953).
5. Eysenck, H. J., and W. D. Furneaux: "Primary and Secondary Suggestibility: An Experimental and Statistical Study," *J. Exp. Psychol.* 35:485 (1945).
6. Fulde, E.: "Uber den Einfluss Hypnotischer Errengunszuntande auf den Gasaustausch," *Z. Ges. Neurol. Psychiat.* 159:761 (1937).
7. Gorton, B. E.: "The Physiology of Hypnosis," *Psychiat. Quart.* 23:317, 457 (1949).
8. Guze, H.: "Hypnosis as Emotional Response: A Theoretical Approach," *J. Psychol.* 35:313 (1953).
9. Kirkner, J. F., and P. M. West: "Hypnotic Treatment of Persistent Hiccup: A Case Report," *Brit. J. Med. Hypnotism* 1:22 (1950).
10. Kline, M. V.: "Toward a Theoretical Understanding of the Nature of Resistance to the Induction of Hypnosis and Depth Hypnosis," *J. Clin. Exp. Hypnosis* 2:32 (1953).
11. ———: "Freud and Hypnosis: A Critical Evaluation," *Brit. J. Med. Hypnotism* 2:1 (1953).
12. ———, Ed.: *The Annual Review of Hypnosis Literature,* New York, Woodrow Press, 1953.
13. ———, Ed.: *Hypnodynamic Psychology,* New York, Julian Press, 1955.
14. ———: "Delimited Hypnotherapy: The Acceptance of Resistance in the Treatment of a Long

Standing Neurodermatitis with a Sensory-image Technique," *J. Clin. Exp. Hypnosis* 4:18 (1953).

15. ———: "Stimulus Transformation and Learning Theory in the Production and Treatment of an Acute Attack of Benign Paroxysmal Peritonitis," *J. Clin. Exp. Hypnosis* 1:93 (1954).
16. ———: "Hypnosis and Diagnostic Psychological Testing," *Personality* 1:243 (1951).
17. ———: "Visual Imagery and a Case of Experimental Hypnotherapy," *J. Gen. Psychol.* 46:159 (1952).
18. ———, and H. Guze: "The Alteration of Oral Temperature Through Hypnotic Techniques. I. Pilot Experiments," *J. Clin. Exp. Hypnosis* 3:233 (1954).
19. ———, H. Guze, and A. D. Haggerty: "An Experimental Study of the Nature of Hypnotic Deafness: Effects of Delayed Speech Feed-back," *J. Clin. Exp. Hypnosis* 2:145 (1954).
20. LeCron, L. M.: "Relief of Myopia by Hypnosis and Eye Training," *Diseases of Nervous System* 12:1 (1951).
21. ———, I. A. Fields, and E. B. Levine: "Postoperative Prolonged Hiccups Relieved Through the Uncovering Through Hypnosis of the Psychological Cause," *Ann. West. Med. Surgery* 5:937 (1951).
22. Levbarg, J. J.: "Treatment Used in a Stammerer with Marked Mental Disturbances," *Eye, Ear, Nose Throat Monthly* 3:38–42 (1941).
23. McDowell, M.: "Juvenile Warts Removed with the Use of Hypnotic Suggestion," *Bull. Menninger Clin.* 13:124 (1949).
24. Moody, H.: "An Evaluation of Hypnotically Induced Relaxation for the Reduction of Peptic Ulcer Symptoms," *Brit. J. Med. Hypnotism* 2:1 (1953).
25. Obermeyer, M. E., and R. R. Greenson: "Treatment by Suggestion of Verrucae Planae of the Face," *J. Psychosomat. Med.* 11:163 (1949).
26. Rosen, H.: *Hypnotherapy in Clinical Psychiatry,* New York, Julian Press, Inc., 1953.
27. Schneck, J. M., Ed.: *Hypnosis in Modern Medicine,* Springfield, Ill., Charles C Thomas, Publisher, 1953.
28. ———: "The Elucidation of Spontaneous Sensory and Motor Phenomena During Hypnoanalysis," *Psychoanal. Rev.* 39:79 (1952).
29. Seitz, P. F. D.: "Symbolism and Organ Choice in Conversion Reactions," *Psychosomat. Med.* 4:254 (1951).
30. ———: "Experiments in the Substitution of Symptoms by Hypnosis: II," *Psychosomat. Med.* 5:405 (1953).
31. Stoltzenberg, J.: *Psychosomatics and Suggestion Therapy in Dentistry,* New York, Philosophical Library, Inc., 1950.
32. Weitzenhoffer, A. M.: *Hypnotism,* New York, John Wiley & Sons, Inc., 1953.
33. Wolberg, L. R.: *Medical Hypnosis,* Vol. I, New York, Grune & Stratton, Inc., 1948.

G. Wilson Shaffer, Ph.D.

9

HYPNOSIS IN SUPPORTIVE THERAPY

THE CIRCUMSTANCES under which hypnosis may be used as a psychotherapeutic device deserve careful scrutiny. It is necessary first to consider the general objectives of psychotherapy. In addition it is important to know the methods available for the attainment of these objectives and the ability of the individual patient to participate satisfactorily in the treatment. The objective of treatment is to secure the soundest degree of mental or psychological health that is possible. The attainment of this general objective is dependent upon many different factors. Of utmost importance is the resourcefulness of the individual patient. The degree to which the environment has been or is likely to be favorable, as well as the possibilities for successful manipulation of the environment, will also condition the soundness of mental health that may be obtained. Finally, the relationship that is developed between the patient and the therapist, as well as the adroitness of the therapist, will be of great importance. It is necessary first to know what the patient is like.

The neurotic patient comes to the therapeutic situation with a series of complaints that are difficult to understand. The casual observer is likely to note that the patient does not make use of his own resources for solving his problems. The fact that the patient cannot take the steps necessary for satisfactory adjustment causes other people to see him as stupid. This conclusion is arrived at because he appears to be capable of acting, but does not do so. Although he seems to have the resources necessary for attaining mastery and a strong need for that attainment, he appears to be unable to put his resources to work. He is seen as desiring affection and capable of affection and yet he remains cold and unresponsive. He appears to be capable and interested in obtaining rewards in many areas of behavior and yet he never finds the satisfactory approach. However, the stupidity or naiveté is not descriptive of all of the patient's behavior. While showing average or superior adjustments in some areas, the neurotic may appear stupid or naive in others. Many of the areas of difficulty cannot readily be spotted and some of the manifest behavior difficulties may later be recognized as cover-ups for deeper unacceptable agonies.

The patient is unable to resolve his own difficulties because he is in serious conflict and the conflict is in part obscured from him. If he takes the ordinary risks he is miserable in fear of the consequences, but if he does not take them he is equally miserable because he does not attain the goals. He cannot approach love, marriage, social experience, or responsible work because of the dangers involved and yet the satisfactions in these areas are necessary to him. He is strongly driven to attack and to flee, is unable to act, and consequently remains in misery. Much of the conflicting material is not available to him because it is repressed. He then presents a variety of symptoms and complaints. He is unable to sleep, becomes rapidly fatigued, is irritable, fearful, and anxious, and suffers from headaches, nausea, and a variety of complaints. Many of the competing drives are not satisfactorily labeled and as a consequence the patient has no language to describe his conflicting emotions. Since he is in no position to describe his problems he is unable to use his intelligence to solve them.

The handling of the patient's dilemma must depend upon a thorough understanding of all the factors that contribute to the difficulty. The resources of the patient, the degree to which the patterns of the illness are modifiable, and the extent to which the environment is favorable or modifiable must all be evaluated before a plan can be developed for the treatment. The therapist cannot decide about the methods of the treatment without these basic understandings. Some of the necessary understandings may be obtained directly from the patient in the beginning diagnostic interviews. Others the therapist will obtain in interviews with those who have lived in close contact with the patient and by the examination of the patient's record of living and the conditions under which this record was made. Physical examinations and psychological diagnostic tests will provide other essential information. The combined information obtained in the case history, the physical and psychological tests, and the interviews with the patient provides the means for determining the ultimate goals of the therapy and the methods to be utilized in obtaining these goals.

The use of hypnosis in supportive therapy can be discussed and evaluated only when the meaning of *support* in relationship to other forms of therapy is clearly understood. In general two types of therapy have been distinguished by the terms *insight* and *support*. These terms have developed naturally out of recognition of the fact that the patient needs both insight and support. *Insight* or *uncovering therapy* refers to the treatments designed primarily to bring about a permanent change in the ego by the development of insight into the reasons for the difficulty. The increasing ability of the ego to achieve satisfactory life adjustments is seen as coming in part from the emotional growth that is developed through insight. When the therapeutic effort is aimed primarily at providing support to the ego rather than gaining a permanent ego change the method is called *supportive.*

A considerable degree of misunderstanding has developed out of the efforts to distinguish between these two positions and to label a therapy as being either *uncovering* or *supportive.* Actually, all patients require some insight and some support and all therapy provides some of each. If one refers back to the ultimate goal of therapy or even to plain principles of sound mental health, it is at once evident that one should strive for the greatest degree of insight that is possible and effective. The patient benefits by being enabled to manage his own ego-defense system satisfactorily. He has developed naive, rigid defensive habits of dealing with his dynamic needs, and this needs to be corrected. He will be benefited by the development of understanding of his repressions and anxieties. He needs to reduce his emotional stresses and become able to face new experiences objectively. He needs to deal with dynamic drives in ways that are socially acceptable and that will bring for him satisfactory interpersonal relationships. He will be benefited by acquiring an appreciation of his conscious and unconscious motivations. Through corrective emotional experience and continuous growth he is encouraged to develop a sense of security and feelings of personal worth and adequacy and thus to rid himself of his infantilism and be enabled to meet anxiety situations with emotional security. The accomplishment of these objectives will sometimes be dependent upon situational changes, relationships established in therapy, support, and insight.

The insistence that the treatment be labeled as *situational, relation, insight,* or *supportive therapy* is undoubtedly a mistake. In the course of any treatment the patient will need to develop some important insight, will require some support, and may be aided by some situational adjustments. It is a part of the strategy of therapy to determine the degree of insight that may be effective and possible. Wherever the resources of the patient and the circumstancs of the situation make good insight possible, this should be the fundamental objective of the therapy. Insight increases the integrative faculty of the ego and frees the patient from his fixed neurotic defenses and thereby makes possible more flexible adaptive behavior. Such insight, however, is not attained by simple intellectual discovery. The treatment may be long and painstaking since the patient must bring to the fore the emotional situations which he has been unable to face, those which he has repressed and around which he has developed his fixed neurotic defenses. The conflicting emotional material must be analyzed in the therapeutic situation, and the adaptive emotional behavior developed in the therapeutic relationship must be gradually expanded by trial and use in real-life situations. The therapist must decide at each stage of the treatment the extent to which insight and support are to be utilized.

Although recognizing that whenever possible one should attempt the development of insight, we see that in many instances success is most likely to be obtained when support is given a prominent place in the therapeutic situations. There are in particular two types of situations which call for a high degree of support in the therapeutic endeavor. Supportive therapy may be called for (1) in certain acute cases where it is clear that the ego's functions are only temporarily impaired and (2) in certain severe chronic cases where the illness is so long-standing, the resources for health are so poor, and the environmental blocks are so great that there is practically no hope of effecting a permanent change.

In the first of these situations we are dealing with persons who have been well adjusted most of their lives and who become maladjusted or develop acute neurotic disturbance as a result of extremely difficult environmental circumstances. The fact that they have functioned satisfactorily most of their lives suggests the probability that no permanent ego change is necessary and that with some situational adjustments and therapeutic support healthy personality attitudes may be reestablished. The support of the therapeutic relationship enables the patient to reduce the intensity of his anxieties and to regain the necessary self-confidence. In the course of the treatment the patient will undoubtedly develop some new insights and acquire some understanding of the development of his acute maladjustment. A complete analysis of the patient will, however, be unnecessary since he has a long history of satisfactory adjustive behavior.

The second of these situations which call primarily for supportive treatment involves those people whose illness is so longstanding that the effecting of a permanent change through insight is hopeless. The combination of circumstances, lack of resources, environmental blocks, and length and severity of the illness make it impossible to analyze all the difficulties. The guilt, anxiety, and inferiority feelings cannot be traced back to the source. They may, however, be lessened by the protection, permissivity, and reassurance of the therapeutic situation. Again some insight may be developed in the course of the treatment, but the major help will be support given to the patient which is not expected to bring about a synthesis of the personality but rather to strengthen the patient's spontaneous defenses and to provide at least temporary and relatively satisfactory adjustment.

In addition, support may be of great importance even when the major objective of the treatment is to obtain deep insight. At many points in the treatment of the individual patient it may be impossible to go further in the development of insight until the patient receives sufficient support. At such times the strategy of the therapy becomes extremely important. In each situation some things may need to be done immediately, or progress will be impossible, and some things must be avoided to prevent therapeutic disaster. Appropriate steps must be taken to meet these circumstances no matter what name the therapist gives to his treatment.

The dangers of supportive therapy are so well known that it is unnecessary to repeat them at length here. Everyone is familiar with the fact that the symptoms are only signposts and that their removal does not bring about recovery. Not only do substitute symptoms usually replace those removed, but the successful removal of the symptoms may provide sufficient relief to the patient to result in the destruction of his motivation for continued treatment.

It should be recognized, however, that this is not an invariable rule. In some instances the symptoms may be so distressing or incapacitating that it may be necessary to deal with them immediately if any success is to be obtained in the search for the real causes of the difficulty. In other words an effort to find the cause may make it necessary to eliminate the symptoms that interfere with progress. Unfortunately supportive therapy has too frequently been directly identified with symptom removal or simple reassurance and persuasion. This has resulted in the general opinion that support is superficial and worthless. That this is an unjustified conclusion can be attested to by practically every therapist regardless of the school of therapy with which he is identified.

It must be clearly recognized that ultimate objectives may occasionally have to wait upon more immediate ones. Patients who have been inhibited and surrounded with taboos and who need release of vicarious aggressive action may need the support of various diversions; among other things, experimental efforts to improve in social and occupational experiences may be necessary. The temporary attention and movements for support in these activities do not mean that the therapy can now be called situational.

In general the foregoing material is presented in an effort to make clear some of the common misconceptions about supportive therapy. Actually there do not exist two completely distinguishable treatments that can be properly designated as *insight* and *supportive therapy*. It is true that at any one moment in the treatment one may be aiming directly to develop insight or to provide support. It is also true that when insight is the primary objective the support that is utilized may be incidental. The two, however, go hand in hand in most therapy. Insight may itself provide support and support may provide insight. That either, at times, may be disadvantageous as well as advantageous should be clearly recognized. The proper use of each is an important part of the strategy of the treatment. The disadvantages of overuse of support have been presented at length by many theorists and clinicians, so much so that one hesitates to talk about support without being apologetic. The disadvantages of some of the long and unsuccessful efforts in pure insight have been rather generally ignored.

Hypnosis, like support, has through a great part of its history been in bad repute. More recently it has tended to gain favor primarily because of the recognition of its use in obtaining insight. Hypnosis, however, continues to be useful not only as an important device for helping the patient to secure insight, but also as a device for providing the support that the patient needs in the therapeutic situation. The patient in treatment may be aided by symptom removal, suggestion, persuasion, desensitization, reeducation, catharsis, emotional growth, and insight, and in selected cases hypnosis may be useful in promoting these activities.

Hypnosis in symptom removal

The earliest use of hypnosis as a therapeutic device was for the removal of symptoms. The symptoms were what the patient brought to the therapist's office, what he believed to be his difficulty, what he desired to be rid of. The removal of these symptoms by hypnotic command was a most dramatic event. In the prevailing number of instances, however, the patient was not really cured. In some people the same symptoms recurred and in others new symptoms even more devastating took their place. In only a small number of cases did the patient remain symptom-free and reasonably well.

The symptoms are surface manifestations of deep fundamental conflicts. They serve the important function of maintaining psychobiologic equilibrium and prevent the discharge of anxiety. Hence the sudden and indiscriminate removal of the symptoms may result in the appearance of new symptoms or the liberating of great quantities of anxiety sufficient to cause an acute excitement.

In other cases the indiscriminate use of hypnosis for symptom removal may result also in the elimination of the incentive to continue the therapy. In other words the patient may be made comfortable enough in his symptom-free condition to lose the incentive to analyze the source of the symptoms.

In spite of these contraindications there are a considerable number of persons who may be greatly benefited by symptom removal through hypnosis. Some patients refuse to explore the origin of their neurosis and will not or cannot participate in a thorough study that might provide for insight and understanding. In other patients the need for the symptom no longer exists, but the symptoms persist as a habit pattern. In certain instances, therefore, where careful study of the cases reveals that these circumstances prevail, symptom removal may be indicated. The results of symptom removal may be best when the patient has strong incentive to be relieved of his symptoms and the symptoms themselves serve a minimal defensive purpose, or when the patient has no other motivation than the removal of his symptoms and will not or cannot participate in therapeutic efforts to trace the source of his difficulties. Under such circumstances some psychosomatic symptoms and many habit patterns such as excessive drinking and smoking, stammering, nail biting, and insomnia may be eliminated by suggestion under hypnosis. This may be particularly true when the symptoms are so incapacitating as to have no great protective value.

The successful treatment of the stammerer, for example, usually requires the development of insight and emotional growth, but on occasions, where the original insecurity has been greatly diminished and the stammering persists as a habit pattern, hypnosis may be indicated. In some cases a combination of hypnotic suggestion and reeducation based on negative practice proves effective.

It should be noted that the removal of symptoms can have advantageous effects on the total functioning of an individual. People who have limiting symptoms frequently suffer further anxiety and insecurity around the disturbing symptoms. They are embarrassed in the company of others, lose their self-respect, and tend to withdraw from normal interpersonal relationships. The removal of the symptoms may give them sufficient confidence and self-respect to enable them to make some of the steps necessary for better personality adjustment. Thus the removal of a stammer or a functional tic may provide the support that is needed for further steps in personality organization.

Indeed in some instances the symptoms may be so disabling as to block all psychotherapeutic efforts, and it may be necessary to remove a symptom before any other therapy can be attempted. Such supportive procedures may be particularly indicated when the patient's ego strength is weak and when his motivations for deep understanding is minimal. The fact that the therapy begins with support and symptom removal need not mean that all effort for deeper understanding and therapy is blocked. The symptom removal may be used not only for support but as the beginning point for the explanation of the symptoms and the development of insight.

When it has been decided that hypnosis is to be used for symptom removal, a number of questions regarding method and technique must be met. One of the most important of these questions is the degree of participation to be allowed to the patient. In some instances a strong directive approach with minimal patient participation is indicated. While no general rule may be prescribed, the authoritarian prestige suggestion approach with minimal patient participation is utilized when the patient is of advanced chronological age, the ego strength is weak, the motivation for understanding is minimal, the symptoms are severe or incapacitating, and the patient appears ready to accept the authority.

With other patients who are not likely to accept the strong authoritarian approach, and particularly with those who have reasonable ego strength and some possibilities for better understanding, a much more active participation on the part of the patient is encouraged. The patient is given reasonable explanation for the suggestions that are presented and he may even be encouraged to accept or refuse the suggestions in terms of their usefulness to him. Hypnosis is admirably suited to the process of demonstrating to a patient that his situation is not hopeless, that he has not lost control over his functions, and that the mind has important influence over the body. The ability, under hypnosis, to bring about anesthetic areas and paralyses by suggestion and to remove them by command enables the patient to see how he can exercise control over body functions that are similar to his symptoms.

When the strong authoritarian method is being used for the removal of a symptom like excessive drinking, it may be necessary to proceed gradually. A posthypnotic suggestion may be given that will remain effective for a week, at which time the patient returns and is hypnotized again and is given a posthypnotic suggestion of longer duration. It may be necessary to reinstate the suggestion several times before it is completely effective.

When hypnosis is being utilized with greater patient participation, the patient is brought to understand the influence of the mind over the body by producing such symptoms as anesthesia and paralysis in the trance state. When the patient gains this understanding symptoms like his own may be produced in other parts of the body. It is then possible to begin the gradual reduction of the patient's own symptoms by suggestion. It may be necessary to leave the patient with some residue of his own symptoms. He is encouraged to believe that this residual symptom will have the same meaning for him as did his old symptoms. In this way the patient is provided with considerable relief and support, but retains some protective defensive symptom. It is then necessary to give the posthypnotic suggestion that the gains obtained here will remain effective in the waking state. Such procedures are most effective when it is possible under hypnosis to engage the patient in some activity in which it is evident that his symptoms have disappeared and to bring him out of the hypnosis in the midst of this activity.

The patient may now be given further understanding of the influence of the mind over the body. He is now in a better position to understand how his own symptoms may have resulted from certain suggestions that he gave himself unconsciously. Since he is now able to see that his condition can be altered, he may be in a better position to understand that a careful study of the reasons for his personality difficulties may enable him to make far more important gains. Thus the way may be opened for further treatment by different therapeutic means. It need not be assumed that because the patient has begun treatment by hypnosis other doors of treatment are closed for him. It is true that if further treatment is to be attempted a new kind of relationship will have to be carefully defined for the patient so as to enable him to see that the deeper kind of treatment must be accomplished by the analysis and synthesis of his problems. This, he must understand, cannot be accomplished by prestige suggestion.

Reassurance and persuasion

Some reassurance and persuasion as supportive devices appear in most patient-therapist relationships. These devices should not be considered as forms of therapy but as supportive aids to be used when indicated.

Reassurance is likely to be most useful in the treatment of patients who are not frankly neurotic, but whose maladjustments and fears are based on misunderstandings and misinterpretations. Also, in many mild neurotic conditions the patient worries so much about his symptoms that he exaggerates them and concentrates all of his attention upon them. Reassurance regarding his symptoms may be necessary in order to direct the patient's attention to the more basic problems of his neurosis. Even though such reassurance is quite superficial, it may serve the useful purpose of directing attention to the more important causes of the difficulty. Such reassurance, however, must not be given before the patient is ready to receive it. The therapist must listen to the complaints with sincerity and must be careful not to seem to disbelieve or ridicule the patient. Because the reassurance is so superficial, its successful use is dependent upon the patient's acceptance of the therapist as a sincere and omniscient authority. This kind of relationship is stronger when the patient is in the hypnotic state and, consequently, reassurance given under hypnosis is likely to be more effective. Care should be exercised in determining the patients who may safely be subjected to such reassurance. It must be recognized that self-devaluation serves a very useful purpose for many neurotic persons. The self-depreciation protects such persons from having to live up to their own expectations or the expectations of others. The rebuilding of self-esteem in some may plunge them into serious anxiety. Many, when assured that they are all right, may not be able to accept their mediocrity and may interrupt treatment or seek a therapist who will completely accept their symptoms.

When the patient has sufficient ego resources, reassurance should be held to a minimum and emphasis placed on the effort to dynamically work through the problems. Nevertheless, in many patients reassurance carefully given may provide needed and useful support, and it may be most effectively given under hypnosis because of the patient's acceptance of the therapist's omniscient authority.

In the time of DuBois and Déjérine there existed actual therapeutic systems that were dependent upon persuasion. Today there is no real therapeutic system of persuasion, but in a great many therapeutic situations persuasion is put to a useful purpose. Persuasion is used on the assumption that the patient has within himself the power to modify his situation by the use of reason and will, while the old authoritarian directive therapy depended to a considerable degree on persuading the patient to accept the authority and position of the therapist.

DuBois taught his patients a philosophy of life and enabled them to substitute thoughts of health for those of disease and suffering. His aim was to build up in the patient confidence in himself through the education of the will or the reason. The patient had to be shown that his symptoms were the result of emotional stresses which, though disturbing, were not in themselves serious. The patient had to believe that he was going to get well and every improvement was held up to him and exaggerated. The patient's views of life had to be criticized and corrected. Déjérine also emphasized the reeducation of the reason, but gave greater attention to emotion than to the weakened will. He stressed the need to liberate the personality from the harmful emotions. He put great emphasis on the necessity for the patient to talk about traumatic events and to develop an emotional relationship of great confidence with the therapist. Persuasive devices as they are utilized in therapy today stem mainly from these positions. Efforts are made to get the patient to accept the real difficulties and limitations that cannot be changed, to learn to face adversity, to overcome emotional stresses by reason and will, to magnify and build on his own resources, and to develop a philosophy of life which emphasizes moral and humanistic values. The persuasions, therefore, are concerned with facing adversity, overcoming and correcting worry, fear, and physical suffering, with redirection of goals and thought control and emotion control.

Persuasion like reassurance is superficial. As a major device it is useless and in some instances harmful since it attributes greatly exaggerated values to the reasoning powers for accomplishing recovery from emotional stresses. As an adjunct and supporting device when judiciously used, persuasion may be helpful. Even some obsessive-compulsive personalities may profit by carefully utilized persuasion. When it has been decided to make use of some persuasion, hypnosis may be most advantageous since suggestions will be more readily accepted and put to profitable use in the hypnotic state. Under hypnosis the patient is in a better position to receive and accept statements to the effect that all persons have within themselves great sources of strength and that these sources may be liberated to overcome the feelings of helplessness and inadequacy that have been dominating them. The extent to which thought and emotion control are at all possible is more easily attained under hypnosis. The posthypnotic suggestions that the new attitudes and beliefs will continue in force may on occasion provide considerable relief.

Desensitization and reeducation

The devices of desensitization and reeducation have occupied prominent places in the history of psychotherapy. Most maladjusted individuals react to certain situations and ideas with exaggerated sensitivity, and a part of the treatment involves desensitization to these areas. Desensitization consists of attempts to make the patient comfortable in the face of situations that have been highly charged, and reeducation implies a retraining of his habits of response; therefore, the two processes become inseparable.

Situations that are traumatic for one person may not be traumatic for others. These situations develop in the unique and individual life history of each person. The development of specific fear responses will serve to show some of the principles here involved.

> *A child who has had no experience with animals may be quietly playing when a noisy and menacing dog suddenly descends upon it. The child may become badly frightened and flee in tears and anxiety. Following this experience the child may show anxiety to the approach of animals as well as to various associated phenomena. Such fear and anxiety may become exaggerated or attenuated depending upon the child's other experiences. If the child is gradually introduced to animals in settings that are secure and peaceful, the fear response may disappear. If the dog and associated experiences are used to threaten the child, the fear reaction may be continued and may also become associated with neutral elements of the situation in which it occurs. The reaction may then spread by association processes and may eventually be called forth by stimuli only remotely and indirectly connected with the primary experience. These derived and indirectly developed fear reactions may persist in their own right, and in some instances they may remain traumatic even though the individual is desensitized to the originally feared object or situation.**

Many patients give evidence of having persistent habit patterns of fear and anxiety that function as adjustment devices to evade a memory of a primary traumatic experience or to avoid reliving a similar or associated one. Some of the elements of these situations are conscious and fully known to the person, others are so frightening or distasteful that they have been completely re-

* Shaffer and Lazarus, *Fundamental Concepts in Clinical Psychology*, p. 333. McGraw-Hill, 1952.

pressed. The individual overreacts to incidents that threaten to bring the hidden material into consciousness. The reactions may be called forth by situations that are reminiscent of a primary traumatic experience directly or by a variety of situations that are associated with the traumatic experience. Desensitization consists in having the patient, under special circumstances, face again and again the traumatic experience in such a way that the emotional response to it is gradually attenuated. Only by facing these experiences, by dissociating them from misinterpretations, and by reevaluating them is it possible to gain any degree of comfort.

The method by means of which desensitization is accomplished will depend upon the amount and degree of repression. The material which the patient is conscious of may be handled directly in discussion while the unconscious material will require the longer process of analysis and interpretation.

In any event hypnosis may prove to be most useful in the process of desensitization. The ventilation of the material occurs most readily when the relationship between the patient and the therapist is such that matters of great intimacy may be easily discussed. In the hypnotic situation the patient is frequently able to talk about material that he is unable to discuss in the waking state. Furthermore in the deep trance it is frequently possible to get direct recall of repressed memories. Perhaps the most advantageous opportunity is offered by the process of regression. Under hypnosis the patient may be regressed to a very early age and may be encouraged to live through the traumatic emotional experiences in a relatively short period of time. Under these circumstances the hypnotic situation may provide opportunity for the uncovering of the repression and for the gradual attenuation of the fear and the anxiety as the patient lives again the experiences, age by age. It should be recognized that, while the maximum benefits will be obtained by desensitization of the primary traumatic experiences, it may be necessary and useful to desensitize derived stimuli. Because of the tendency toward spread and diffusion to associated experiences, desensitization to these experiences may provide the patient with considerable comfort and support even in the absence of the discovery of the primary traumatic experience. This is particularly pertinent in view of the possibility that the primary experience may never be revealed.

Hypnosis then may be useful in a variety of ways in the desensitization of traumatic experiences. The simple induction of the trance is often beneficial to recall and serves to dissolve some of the resistances. The patient presents and discusses items which are blocked from discussion in the waking state. At this point it is important not to force the uncovering of the traumatic incidents, which might result in panic and the development of further resistances. The situation must be adroitly handled so as to allow the patient to feel his own way, but with sufficient encouragement he will usually proceed more easily than in the waking state. Care must be exercised with regard to the use of the material divulged in the hypnotic trance. This material should not be presented to the patient in the waking state until he is sufficiently comfortable with it to allow for such discussion. However, one frequently finds that the ventilation of material under hypnosis makes it easier for the patient to discuss the same material in the waking state.

One of the most useful aspects of hypnosis is the possibility of creating artificial situations which enable the patient to participate in extensive practice with emotion-producing stimuli and which provide the opportunity for insight into his habitual modes of response. The artificial situation may be recognized as bearing some similarity to the situations set up in play therapy and the psychodrama, but it has all the extra advantages provided by the hypnotic trance. Thus, with the patient hypnotized, an artificial situation may be set up which is calculated to bring about an open expression of emotion. In these artificial situations the therapist may have to play different roles as he does in play therapy. Under these circumstances it may be possible to show the patient how his emotions are aroused and why he feels he must repress the expression of them. Since in deep hypnosis the patient may be regressed to various ages, it may be possible not only to trace and develop a series of events providing insight, but also to allow for ventilation, desensitization, and relearning. The creation of artificial situations is much more frequently useful in dealing with traumatic experiences of which the patient is fully conscious since it may more easily be arranged to have the patient face again and again the traumatic events. The experiences are subjected to discussion and the discussions are continued until the patient no longer reacts emotionally to them or until he acquires the capacity to tolerate disturbing emotions. The patient continues to build self-respect and to rid himself of the damaging effects of anxiety and hostility as he learns to express his fearful experiences in the therapeutic atmosphere.

Reeducation like desensitization is one of the important devices of psychotherapy. The process is one involving the retraining of the individual in his habits of response to situations, ideas, and emotional expressions. Reeducation may be used to provide support to the patient, but it also involves an attempt to teach the patient the nature of his difficulties and to give him insight into the development of his neurosis. The patient's character structure has developed out of his early experiences and conditionings. Those whose early lives have been filled with insecurity, rejection, or overprotection may develop a character structure that makes a healthy adjustment impossible. Since the learning or education has been bad, they must proceed through a process of reeducation if they are to develop any degree of comfort within themselves and in interpersonal relations. This may involve the revising of situations and goals so as to bring them in line with social and biological needs. Reeducation is more difficult than education since it involves, in addition to new learning, the more difficult feat of destroying old unhealthy habits.

The success of the reeducation will, in part, be determined by the degree to which the therapist is able to diagnose the patient's character structure and to understand how it prevents his satisfactory adjustment to living. In part also it will be dependent upon the patient's ego strength along with his ability to develop insight and understanding.

When for any reason deep analytic insight is not the goal of the treatment, less emphasis will be placed upon the origin of the character drives and more emphasis upon the retraining of habit patterns that are necessary for present satisfactions. In the course of such treatment some insights will be developed. Insight by itself, however, may not be sufficient to bring about satisfactory adjustment. The patient may still be unable to prevent feeling the way he does. He may have to be taught a great deal about the reasons for his insecurity and the meaning and purpose of his symptoms. He may have to learn how to evaluate his assets and liabilities and what relationship they bear to his life goals. He will have to appreciate what satisfactions are possible for him and what dissatisfactions he may have to learn to endure. Minor gains in personality understanding and new possible satisfactions may provide him with the support to delve deeper and to participate in new retraining.

In reeducation therapy, as in desensitization, hypnosis may prove most useful. To a considerable degree success depends upon understanding the genesis of the difficulty as well as the function and consequences of the patient's strivings. Hypnosis may be most valuable in this process of diagnosis. In the trance state the patient may be urged to bring forward material that is not accessible in the waking state. The therapist may, therefore, in much quicker time be made aware of the patient's dynamic strivings, the circumstances under which his insecurities have developed, and the basis for his characteristic abnormal attitudes. The patient's tolerance for this material may be gradually built up to the point of enabling him to consider the material in the waking state, thereby setting the stage for the retraining that is necessary. Suggestions may be offered during hypnosis that will provide the support that the patient needs to go further into his problems. Reeducation may also be fostered under hypnosis by resort to regression studies. Since in deep hypnosis the patient may be regressed, it is possible to study the development of his unhealthy attitudes from very early beginnings. The material gathered from these studies may, in addition, be used as a basis for setting up experimental conflicts under hypnosis. Situations similar to the original sources of his anxiety may be presented under hypnosis to demonstrate to the patient how he reacts automatically to certain kinds of stresses.

For example, a young male graduate student complained of a series of painful and annoying physical symptoms which had caused his withdrawal from social contacts. He insisted that the symptoms prevented his casual social association with the other students and he resisted any implication that the situations might be responsible for the symptoms. He had become most demanding and was pleading for surgery for the removal of the symptoms.

Under hypnosis a fictitious situation was introduced involving his participation in a social expedition to take pictures with another student. It was suggested to him that upon awakening he would have all of the feelings that would regularly be associated with such a situation. When he came out of the hypnotic trance, he had a severe attack of his symptoms. This incident was repeated three times with the same results. The student was gradually able to recognize that the symptoms served the purpose of preventing the development of this kind of relationship. Shortly after this he was able for the first time to talk of his fears regarding homosexuality. His symptoms, however, protected him just as well from engaging in association with females. Similar experimental conflicts set up under hypnosis demonstrated this to be true. Regression studies under hypnosis then revealed considerable early trauma regarding his degree of masculinity. The patient was soon able to participate in analytic therapy sessions and in a short time was able to work satisfactorily through his problems, which centered primarily around his early inability to meet his father's standards of masculinity.

In many instances the experimental conflicts set up under hypnosis may be used to demonstrate to the patient the ways that his drives operate and the purpose of the symptoms and the anxieties. Hypnosis may be used to provide necessary support and can also show the patient the need for the development of more mature attitudes.

In conclusion it should be emphasized that hypnosis should not be used indiscriminately either to provide support or to obtain insight. It should not be considered as a complete system of psychotherapy, but rather as a device to be utilized when its need is indicated. Under special and ideal circumstances, however, it may be a most useful device. On rare occasions it may be indicated for symptom removal and quite frequently it may be most useful in providing needed support through reassurance, persuasion, and desensitization. In many instances, also, it may be quite useful in reeducating the patient and under these circumstances it may be used to develop important insights.

In most instances hypnosis will be an adjunct therapy used discriminately in a broadly conceived therapeutic program. Examples of the use of hypnosis may help clarify the meaning of this.

A young man asked for help regarding his long-standing stammering. In the course of the first thirty-minute interview he was able to produce only two sentences. The man was referred from a speech correctionist who had not been able to reduce the stammering. He had, however, obtained a history which the patient had written beautifully, but which was of little value, first, because of its superficiality and, secondly, because in the therapeutic session the patient was unable to talk further about it. The patient was hypnotized and told that he could talk if he kept in rhythm with the beats of a metronome which was set in action.

He was given some poetry in simple iambic tetrameter to read and did so without difficulty, keeping time with the metronome. In later hypnotic sessions he was told that he could read and then talk in different time sequences and found that he was able to do so. It was then suggested that he could talk fluently and easily without regard to rhythm and found this also possible. During the next several interviews he talked fluently under hypnosis and revealed many of the sources of inner conflicts.

The first advantage of the hypnosis in this situation was the production of a therapeutic situation which was not possible otherwise since, when not hypnotized, the patient could not talk. Later posthypnotic suggestions were given that he would be able to talk well in the therapeutic session when not hypnotized. While he stammered some in the posthypnotic sessions, his performance was reasonably satisfactory and made possible the discussion in the waking state of much of the material revealed originally under hypnosis. The rest of the therapy was carried on by analysis and synthesis of his problems in the waking state and required considerable time. While he never completely recovered from the stammer, the speech hesitancy that remained was not in any way incapacitating. The greater part of his recovery was due to his new insights. These, however, could not have been attained without the hypnosis. In addition the support that he obtained early by his demonstrated ability to speak fluently under hypnosis contributed markedly to his final recovery.

In another case a patient who had a mild speech hesitancy that had recently been exaggerated was found to have no other serious difficulties and considerable resources so that a simpler handling of his problem was possible. He was hypnotized and told that he could talk fluently and without hesitation and demonstrated his ability to do so. He was brought out of the hypnosis in the midst of a fluent recitation and the support and reassurance that was provided him proved sufficient to render unnoticeable the hesitations in his speech. Situations like the latter are most infrequently encountered, whereas those like the former, when support and insight are handled together, are constantly experienced.

As an adjunct supportive device the hypnotic technique, when judiciously used, will prove to be a most useful technique. In the course of its use some new insights will usually be obtained and in any case it need not interfere with later insight therapy.

REFERENCES

Appel, K. E.: "Psychiatric Therapy," in J. McV. Hunt, *Personality and the Behavior Disorders*, New York, The Ronald Press Company, 1944.

Diethelm, O.: *Treatment in Psychiatry*, 2d ed. Springfield, Ill., Charles C Thomas, Publisher, 1950.

Dorcus, R. M., and G. W. Shaffer: *Textbook of Abnormal Psychology*, 4th ed. Baltimore, The Williams & Wilkins Company, 1950.

Horney, K.: *The Neurotic Personality of Our Time*, New York, W. W. Norton & Company, Inc., 1937.

Schaffer, G. W., and R. S. Lazarus: *Fundamental Concepts in Clinical Psychology*, New York, McGraw-Hill Book Company, Inc., 1952.

Wolberg, L. R.: *Medical Hypnosis*, New York, Grune & Stratton, Inc., 1948.

———: "Goals and Objectives in Psychotherapy," *N. Y. State J. Med.* 14:1792–1796 (1944).

Harold Lindner, Ph.D.

10

HYPNOANALYSIS: METHODS AND TECHNIQUES

WITHIN THE PRESENT DECADE alone, the volume of literature on the subject of hypnosis has been staggering. At the time of the preparation of this manuscript, six textbooks and more than fifty reprints lie on the writer's desk. Each contribution provides the student with a comprehensive survey of the interest-area. Leafing through these works, one cannot help but conjecture on the fact that hypnosis has finally grown of age and is now quite a respectable avenue of research and practice. Even the youngest among our colleagues must remember that in his graduate school days the subject of hypnosis was met with faculty condescension and contemptuous innuendo. Today, however, it is generally recognized that hypnosis is a technique of vast clinical applicability and that it is a matter of important theoretical concern.

In this chapter the writer will restrict himself to a discussion of hypnoanalysis—that adjunct of hypnotic theory and practice which owes its origin and orientation to psychoanalysis. The usual historical introduction to the topic will be found elsewhere in this volume.

So that we may commence this discussion in proper perspective, the reader should recognize that were it not for psychoanalysis there would be no hypnoanalysis. This is so because hypnoanalysis is nothing more than a specific blend of hypnosis and psychoanalysis. Those techniques of hypnosis which are not based on psychoanalytic theory and practice do not, strictly speaking, fall within the orthodox definition of hypnoanalysis. When Freud, in his early studies before the turn of the century, utilized hypnotic techniques, he laid the foundations for what has since become a fairly organized body of theory and practice. Unfortunately for the future of hypnoanalysis, because of certain difficulties that Freud found in his uses of hypnotic techniques, he abandoned hypnosis as a principal technique of psychoanalytic practice. This abandonment had the effect, except in rather rare instances, of putting the technique in an area beyond the interest of psychoanalysts. It was relegated to the hinterlands and most reputable practitioners looked upon it as an "untouchable."

Within the past decade, spurred by the necessity to discover briefer psychotherapies during and after World War II, a number of noted therapists gave hypnosis another opportunity to exist among other respectable techniques. Workers such as Brenman and Gill, Erickson, R. Lindner, Schneck, Wolberg, and Rosen explored the possibilities of revitalizing hypnosis in conjunction with psychoanalytic knowledge. Their contributions were so substantial that today, with little more than a decade of work behind them, a complete listing of worthy contributors to hypnoanalytic theory and practice would require much more space than the writer has available here.

Definition

Hypnosis is a generic term and *hypnotherapy* is a loosely used term applicable to any and all forms of hypnotic treatment.

Hypnoanalysis, however, is a specific term and should be restricted to that treatment in which there is a commensurate reciprocation between psychoanalysis and hypnosis. Psychoanalysis contributes to this blend the great orientation of the treatment program, the theoretical foundation, and the interpretative justification. Hypnosis affords an instrument for a rapid application of the psychoanalytic treatment. The net affect of this harmony is a treatment tool which, without detracting from certain basic psychoanalytic theoretical concepts, offers the recipient a briefer therapy.* In a variety of conditions it proves to be a tool which can more effectively cut through those resistances and contraindications to a successful resolution of a treatment program than conventional psychoanalysis—because of its inherent character and time-consuming requirements—is capable of doing.

Methods

As Schneck (12) pointed out there are, basically, two major hypnoanalytic methods. The *first major method* is based on orthodox psychoanalytic concepts and offers a fairly standardized methodology; it is exemplified in the work of R. Lindner (5). The *second major method* is less structured and subjected to varying technical procedures, depending upon the patient and situational needs of the treatment program. Perhaps the leading exponent of this latter method is Erickson (2).

Both procedures commence with an extended period of indoctrination. The patient, for as long as proves necessary, is trained to be hypnotized. The training continues until the patient can immediately enter a satisfactory hypnotic trance without

* This statement may be held questionable in view of recent developments in psychoanalytic theory. Today, much greater emphasis is being placed on *ego psychology* and *ego analysis,* including the analysis of the defensive mechanisms. These, typically, preclude the cursory attention given them by the hypnoanalyst, whose concept of psychoanalysis remains relatively fixed to an earlier stage in the evolution of the field.

any wasteful expenditure of energy on the part of either the therapist or himself. This training time has been found necessary because it serves a double function. First, it permits the patient to verbalize his preconceived notions about hypnosis so that those resistances to hypnosis which one almost always finds in one's patients can be clarified and removed. Secondly, it teaches the patient how most expeditiously to reach the desired hypnotic depth-level so that, whenever hypnosis is required, it can be achieved without wasteful time.

Those who utilize the training technique suggest that the length of the indoctrination period is variable and that it is usually defined by the patient's capacity to accept the procedure as well as the length of time it takes him to attain his own depth-level. There is some difference of opinion in the literature regarding the level of trance necessary for proper tratment. Certain clinicians express a preference for light (relaxing) levels; others for greater hypnotic depths (cataleptic, somnambulistic). The writer believes that this is more of an academic than a realistic controversy, since, in his experience, the patient will find his own level, one which will be most functional for him and one that will fluctuate between the various levels of depth consistent with the analytic content being worked on at the time.

The conclusion of the training period may be determined by the patient's ability to meet the three criteria that R. Lindner (6) has proposed: Upon signal from the hypnoanalyst, he must be able immediately to enter the hypnotic trance; he must be able to carry out posthypnotic suggestions, especially for posthypnotic amnesia; he must be able to execute *memorial reversion.* As regards the last criterion, R. Lindner makes a distinction not made previously, or necessarily followed, by other workers, that memorial reversion actually consists of two kinds, both of equal importance: regression and revivification. *Hypnotic regression,* as he uses the term, is the usual recall of previous events which the patient considers in respect to his present outlook on them.

Hypnotic revivification, however, which appears to be more dramatic, is the term he applies to memorial reversion during which the patient psychically returns to the previous biographical situation and reparticipates in the events as though he were reliving them at the moment. R. Lindner further suggests that, since these two types of memorial reversion are crucial to the hypnoanalytic treatment, before concluding the training period the hypnoanalyst must be certain that the patient is capable of achieving both phenomena.

Because this writer has had most of his experience with the first or more structured method, the section on Hypnoanalytic Technique (below) follows that method and the practice of R. Lindner. Although a personal bias for the structured method is noted here, both methods are in general use among clinicians. The present writer has successfully utilized each with certain types of patients.

The other major method is more flexible and allows for greater clinical freedom in the utilization of specialized hypnotic techniques (Erickson, Schneck, LeCron and Bordeaux, Wolberg, Rosen). The special appeal of this method is said by its proponents to rest in the facility with which hypnotic techniques may be applied to meet the patient's varying needs. In addition to the memory searches contained in all hypnoanalytic and psychoanalytic procedures, herein use is made of such hypnotic techniques as are considered to "decrease anxiety at appropriate moments and to encourage the working through of various problems . . . to . . . facilitate the gaining of insight and production of change," in the words of Schneck (12, pp. 310, 311).

In addition to these free introductions of various hypnotic tools at different times during the course of treatment, the adherents of what we term the second major method claim for it a kinship with psychoanalysis. The point, however, is debatable, as illustrated by the following excerpts from A System of Brief Hypnoanalysis, a chapter in the LeCron and Bordeaux textbook:

In the following pages we describe a procedure formulated by taking the most suitable and helpful elements from several systems and combining them to make a reasonable, logical plan. Basically it is psychoanalysis, though not of the orthodox type, with the addition of some points taken from other schools of psychotherapy and the supplemental application of hypnotism. (*4*, *p. 220*)

In the same chapter, while discussing the hypnotic training period at the beginning of hypnoanalysis, these authors say:

At the same time, strong suggestions of eventual cure should be made. Modification and disappearance of symptoms as progress is made should also be suggested. Their relative unimportance because they are only incidental should be stressed. . . . In this period it is desirable to develop confidence on the part of the patient and to instill a capacity for acceptance of whatever comes forth during the analysis. (*4*, *p. 223*)

They also write:

It has been an axiom of standard psychoanalysis that the actual causes of a neurosis must be learned so that the energies generated by the repressed conflict and memories can be discharged by the patient as a part of cure. Undoubtedly a knowledge of causative factors is valuable, for it aids both patient and analyst to understand the situation. When they are known, these factors may be worked through and the patient given insight and taught to readjust. If the cause, such as an environmental matter, is still active, there will either be a relapse or no cure will be effected unless the cause is uncovered. But causes may extend back into child-

> *hood and be completely inactive though still motivating behavior. If dynamic energy is still being generated, this would explain the presence of symptoms arising out of such old causes, and it would be necessary to remove them through knowledge of the causes. However, if they are considered as being still exhibited because they have become habits or conditional reflexes, the case is different and it is not so important to know the causes, though it would still be desirable.* (*4, p. 225*)

In our final quotation from these spokesmen for the second major method of hypnoanalysis, we are told:

> *In our consideration of brief hypnoanalysis, we have mentioned some matters not concerned with either hypnosis or psychoanalysis but which can be incorporated supplementally to advantage in the treatment of many cases. And if medicine can also be employed, as is sometimes possible, then by all means it should be used. The main thing is to bring relief to the patient no matter what the means. Essentially the method of psychotherapy being outlined is hypnoanalysis, but nothing which can be of service should be overlooked or neglected.* (*4, p. 229*)

From these excerpts it should be obvious that while this second method is referred to as a form of hypnoanalysis, and its proponents pay tribute to psychoanalysis and a psychoanalytic orientation, it is not, even by loose definition, substitutive.

As regards those hypnotic techniques which are so liberally employed in the practice of this treatment method for the breaking down of repressions and the recall of forgotten situations and buried memories, use is made of most known hypnotic phenomena. Such hypnotic tools are freely employed without any formalized or rigid considerations other than the individual therapist's own preferences or predilections. The commonly practiced techniques include:

1. *Dream induction.* Herein the therapist requests the patient to have a specific dream (or through the medium of a dream) to resolve a conflict that had defied conscious examination and solution.
2. *Hypnotic regression and revivification.* The therapist requests the patient to recall previous happenings in his life or to return physically to a previous biographical situation and actually relive the event as though it were happening at the moment, so that a repression, a buried or screen memory, can be examined and verified.
3. *Automatic writing and drawing.* The patient is requested to scribble, write, or draw on blackboard or paper without exerting any manual controls over this activity so that a symbolic relationship can be examined or a repression released.
4. *Crystal and mirror gazing.* The patient is requested to look into a crystal ball or mirror in which he will find and report about a symbolic written or pictured solution to a problem that has defied conscious examination.
5. *Direct suggestion.* The therapist gives the patient direct suggestions in order to facilitate change in habitual response patterns and to provide him with experiences in realistically solving life problems.
6. *Scene visualization.* The patient is requested to visualize a specific scene so that conflictual matters may be clarified, with the therapist helping the patient to handle objectively and resolve these matters which have perplexed him.
7. *Motor activity,* such as hypnotic play therapy and psychodrama. The patient is requested to act-out structured psychodrama roles or unstructured play-therapy situations so that

old response patterns can be realistically reviewed and new patterns and solutions experienced.

8. *The use of symbolic stories.* The patient is requested to solve symbolic stories which the therapist constructs so that an investigation of transference relationships and unconscious insight can be attempted.
9. *The use of projective test material.* The patient is requested to take various projective tests so that an evaluation may be made of unconscious attitudes, interpersonal relationships, and therapeutic status.
10. *The elucidation of visual and auditory hallucinations.* The patient is requested to hallucinate in order to help clarify and work through problems which, because of their symbolic or affective qualities, have not been amenable to less drastic techniques of examination.
11. *Incidental phenomena,* such as the control of associations by resort to signaling the arrival of a pertinent thought or insight, the signal being the mention of a previously specified number, letter, name, tap on wood, stamp of shoe, etc. At the appearance of the prearranged signal, the patient is requested to verbalize a pertinent thought or recall a hidden memory, so that understanding of a therapeutic matter can be reached.
12. *Experimental conflicts.* The patient is requested to resolve conflictual situations which are structured by the therapist so that further understanding of the patient's unconscious mechanisms and dilemmas can be achieved.

It should be sufficient to note that, while it is remotely possible for such authoritative manipulations to be consistent with a psychoanalytic orientation, it remains difficult to discover a plausible rationale for the employment of such devices within the accepted conceptual field of psychoanalysis.

Hypnoanalytic technique

Any interpersonal relationship—and therefore any treatment relationship—commences and has meaning from the moment of the parties' first contact. Hypnotic treatment, by its nature, actually commences before the initial interpersonal relationship may even occur. The patient, by virtue of his a priori biases for and against such therapy, and consistent with his cultural preferences, comes to the hypnotherapist with a frame of reference either for or against hypnotic treatment. This is especially apparent if the therapist has a reputation as a hypnotist, in which case one might observe that the patient is often "hypnotized" before he even approaches the hypnotist. Since hypnoanalysis is essentially similar to psychoanalysis in that it deals with transference phenomena, this places a greater burden upon the hypnoanalyst than it might on other therapists. The hypnoanalyst must recognize that certain resistances and defenses are quite active during the primary sessions but that, by the time the training period has been completed, certain of these have already been worked through and a positive transference exists.

From this admission it might seem that the writer accepts the charge, so often challenging to the hypnoanalyst, that he works only with a positive transference, all the while ignoring other transference phenomena which play so important a therapeutic role in standard analytic practice. The refutation of this charge lies in a deeper understanding of the transference in hypnoanalysis. To quote from R. Lindner: "Due to the narrowing of the attentional field [in hypnosis] and the creation of a new social gestalt, the figure of the analyst is introjected and incorporated into the unconscious ego of the patient. From this literal engulfing of the analyst into the patient's unconscious ego, there is created a highly special and unique form of rapport which accounts for the rapidity with which exploration of the unconscious takes place in hypnoanalysis." (8) By this he means that by introjection the hypnoanalyst becomes incorporated with the patient, although he is still an object toward whom the patient must react in accordance with his own developmental influences. Through this hypnotic avenue, however, the hypoanalyst can avoid being the butt of defenses and resistances which the patient usually projects onto his analyst during the work of the waking state. This duality wherein, during the trance, the hypnoanalyst is both an object and a participant in the unconscious ego permits the rapid pace obtainable only in hypnoanalysis because it localizes the therapist's image in the unconscious ego.

Transference in hypnoanalysis may also be exploited, in certain cases, to perpetuate the treatment, where it might, as in characterological problems, otherwise be incompletely terminated. It may also serve a crucial synthesizing function during the terminal stages of therapy in that it is applicable whenever the therapist finds that its use is indicated. Thus it may be employed to reinforce newly acquired habit patterns, to aid the patient in testing his analytically acquired insights in the process of response changes, or to destroy those sensorimotor patterns that serve to maintain the neurotic structure of defense systems. And finally, hypnosis may be utilized to hasten the dissolution of the transference; hence, treatment by posthypnotic suggestions may be used to help the patient achieve a healthy integration without the painful and time-consuming struggle such matters usually occasion in the nonhypnotic analysis. It does this by rapidly and efficiently helping the patient to redistribute his energies along healthy lines as dictated by the analytic experience, rather than in ways which had previously perpetuated the neurosis and proved to be of pathogenic significance.

Parallel with its parent technique, hypoanalysis deals with associations, dreams, screen memories, etc. The hypnoanalyst interprets as does the psychoanalyst. The difference between the two procedures lies in the duration of resistance analysis. When the psychoanalyst encounters resistance, it must be slowly, painfully, and laboriously worked through in a conscious associative state. The hypnoanalyst, upon encountering these marked resistances, can undercut them by immediately signaling the patient into a hypnotic trance and, in the hypnotic state, securing liberation of material which had consciously defied exhumation. In practice, whenever crucial resistances (e.g., those relating to fundamental personality and character structure, amnesias for traumatic happenings, and habitual defense mechanisms which perpetuate the symptom formation of neurosis) are encountered, the patient is hypnotized and asked to continue to free-associate. The hypnoanalyst may direct the associations toward material excluded from the conscious associations or he may, in historical matters, suggest regression or revivification. When the material has been fully explored in hypnosis, the patient is given a posthypnotic amnesia for all that has occurred in hypnosis and then awakened from the trance, and the usual analytic procedure is continued.

The crucial factor here is, of course, the introduction of a posthypnotic amnesia for the events which transpired during the trance. Since psychoanalytic theory has shown how important it is to involve the total organism in the analysis, this amnesia is mandatory. It guarantees that the patient will have a conscious abreaction and thus secures total therapy, which alone will give lasting therapeutic benefits.

The ancillary product of posthypnotic suggestion is the key to total therapy. It guarantees the readiness of the ego for the reception of repressed, rejected, or otherwise interfered-with memories. It also serves to validate the hypnotically released memories by affording them conscious restatement *if they prove to be valid memories.* This by-product is technically known as the *interim phenomenon.* Once the memory has been disclosed under the cloak of hypnotic trance and posthypnotic amnesia is placed upon it, soon thereafter, in the conscious state, the patient invariably reveals the same material to which he had previously shown such marked resistance. However, only that hypnotic material which is valid—memorially valid—is revealed in the waking state, while any content not valid (e.g., screen memories, etc.) does not make an appearance in the nonhypnotic condition. From this it would seem that revelations in hypnosis exert an effect on the ego, and in the interim between the elicitation of the memory in hypnosis and the conscious free association of that material, the ego has become prepared to accept and work through that material which it had previously repressed or rejected. It is precisely because of this interim phenomenon, which permits the patient consciously to discuss only those disclosures which are memorially valid, that there is no need to analyze resistances at length. The therapist can deal directly with this crucial material in orthodox analytic manner. Thus, by this conscious disclosure and its conscious abreaction, there is obtained a total therapy; and those criticisms of hypnoanalysis which hold that it is a superficial and suggestive therapy can be laid to rest. Hypnoanalysis, like psychoanalysis, holds it a cardinal principle to insure waking-state abreaction so that the total organism is engaged in the therapeutic process. Because of the interim phenomenon an enormous condensation of the course of treatment is permitted which eliminates the expenditure of time-consuming energies in the analysis of major resistances.

In effect, then, the practice of hypnoanalysis—with those reservations outlined above—is identical with the practice of psychoanalysis. It deals with all the phenomena of the usual psychoanalytic treatment and is, as is psychoanalysis, essentially the analysis of resistance and transference. Through the expeditious use of hypnosis it precludes the necessity of laborious resistance analysis. Parenthetically, it should be mentioned that not all resistances are hypnotically undercut, but only the major ones, the usual reluctances and minor blockings being handled through standard analytic techniques of discussion, interpretation, and insight. Essentially, the transference in hypnoanalysis is manipulated as it is in psychoanalysis. Except that hypnotic therapy allows for a more rapid and continuing therapeutic relationship by narrowing the patient's attentional field to the analytic social gestalt, there is no difference in analysis or management between hypnoanalysis and psychoanalysis. In hypnoanalysis, during the last stages of the analytic program, other than on relatively rare occasions (dictated only by the analyst's purpose to insure that the new integration conforms to those insights achieved through therapy) there is a lessening of the use of hypnosis and a more conventional psychoanalytic situation exists. Indeed, in this end phase of therapy where the reeducation and application are very evident, the need for hypnosis is so diminished that only those techniques ordinarily used for psychoanalytic termination are employed.

To illustrate the hypnoanalytic procedure and the operations of the interim phenomenon, the writer has chosen from his case histories a representative example, portions of which will be reported here.

A Condition of Diurnal and Nocturnal Enuresis. Henry was a twenty-six-year-old, healthy, serious-minded white male, who had adjusted fairly well to his Army situation but who was being considered for psychological treatment because of incontinence of urine. Medical findings were negative and GU studies revealed no physiological basis for the condition. The hospital staff were unanimous in the diagnosis of hysterical enuresis.

Hypnoanalytic treatment lasted some two and a half months during which time the patient was seen for five hours each week. Almost the entire first two weeks were spent on training in hypnosis to rapidly achieve a desired trance depth. Henry proved to be an easy subject for hypnosis; the depth-level of trance which he was able to attain fluctuated between the somnambulistic and cataleptic depths. At the end of two weeks the patient was able to enter immediately a deep hypnotic trance state whenever the therapist suggested he do so. By that time it was also obvious that a workable positive transference, based on mutual confidence, had been established.

The reporting of the entire treatment course is beyond our limits here. Essentially, free association was the procedure followed during all sessions. However, when major resistances were encountered, Henry was placed in a hypnotic trance, his last few associations were given him, and he was instructed to continue associating. After the consciously resisted material was revealed in hypnosis and the therapist felt that the block had been hypnotically relieved, he was given a complete amnesia for all that had transpired *after* the associative material of the waking state had ceased flowing, and then he was awakened from the trance. Upon awakening, free association was continued and the hour progressed as would the usual psychoanalytic session. Because of the operations of the interim phenomenon, invariably Henry would (either later in that session or within the next couple of sessions) repeat *in consciousness,* and elaborate upon, the substance of the previous hypnotic session. Thus was accomplished the rapid disintegration of resistances which permitted therapeutic progress to be made in so brief a treatment program.

Henry was born in a small town just outside of Hartford, Connecticut. His birth was normal and the early medical history was without significance. Because his parents were inadequate, his childhood and adolescence were emotionally traumatic. He entered school at the age of six and completed the elementary courses with an average deportmental and scholastic record. In high school his conduct and scholarship deteriorated. He accounted for this as due to his having had to work after school hours. He graduated from high school at the age of eighteen and went directly to work as a shipping clerk, which job he held until his Army induction.

Henry's parents were rural immigrants of Polish descent.

His mother was an illiterate and grossly overburdened housewife, who, after her husband's death when Henry was sixteen, depended upon the children for her support. The father, who had been a farmer and general handyman-repairman, had psychopathic tendencies, was a pathological liar, and a chronic alcoholic. In an alcoholic stupor the man frequently attacked the patient's mother, his brothers, and him. Family history failed to reveal any indications of insanity, feeblemindedness, or epilepsy; the father's alcoholism was an isolated condition in a family history that, otherwise, might have been considered free from any significant psychopathology.

Henry was the first of three siblings. The youngest was a poorly developed, introverted male; the middle son was a robust athletic person. Both his brothers were in the armed forces at the time Henry was undergoing treatment, with the younger reported as having been under psychiatric treatment for somnambulism.

Henry's sexual history reportedly began with masturbation at about age ten. As an adolescent he preferred the company of boys to girls. Initial heterosexual experience was at age eighteen, with casual and infrequent indulgence up to the time of marriage.

Perhaps the most expeditious approach to the task of illustrating portions of the hypnoanalytic technique in this condensed report is through the fantasy basis of Henry's escape into hysteria. The sequence and characters were always the same from the first fantasy experience at about age ten until it underwent a startling alteration at the near-conclusion of the therapeutic program. Henry would experience this fantasy before and during sleep and frequently in daydreams as well. The fantasied scene was an open space. A snake with horns shooting out of its head and with a long biting tongue would chase Henry and attempt, so the patient feared, to bite off his penis.

The key to the fantasy and subsequently to the patient's chief symptomatic manifestations was found in the numerous dreams he brought into treatment and in the hypnoidal reconstruction of the enuretic periods. These enabled Henry to work through the fantasy and to relate it to the symptom formation.

By the end of the twentieth hour Henry was able to discuss the following matters: He remembered that his father was frequently intoxicated. He blamed his father for "making a nervous wreck out of all of us . . . he used to threaten my mother and us kids, and we were always afraid of being killed 'cause he often beat us . . ." At the age of sixteen when his father died, Henry admittedly found relief from much emotional tension. He had been, however, since then, periodically bothered by the memory of the event. He recalled having overheard the comments of some neighbors to the effect that he "didn't cry at his father's funeral."

From the age of sixteen to twenty-two Henry supported the family. He would return home after work and spend the evening with his mother while his brothers were usually out. When he was twenty-two he met a local girl at a factory picnic. She manifested similar inferiority and introtensive feelings, and, quite rapidly, the relationship culminated in marriage. From the time of his marriage to the time of his Army induction (approximately two years), Henry claimed to have spent the happiest years of his life. Just prior to his Army induction his wife gave birth to a boy. During those two years of happy married life his enuresis, which had been a constant disturbance since childhood, was minimal.

When Henry entered the Army he concealed his history of enuresis, hoping, he said, "to get well through the tough life." For four months he trained with an infantry division in the United States and was then shipped overseas to the ETO. From the time of overseas assignment until his return to a hospital in the United States his enuretic attacks were quite frequent. In Europe he saw five days of combat. Throughout those five days he constantly urinated and, due to the conditions of combat, was unable to change his clothing or to rest for any period of time. Following combat he developed a severe anxiety reaction, was evacuated, hospitalized, and finally sent to the hospital where this hypnoanalytic treatment program was conducted.

The initial hospital interview records indicated that the patient was tremulous and depressed, had a severe neurogenic dermatitis, cursed profusely, had vasomotor instability, was irritable, had a stuttering of speech, and suggested strong inferiority feelings. The following memory yielded the main link in the treatment process and, because of a major resistance to its revelation, was first obtained in deep hypnosis. Henry was taken back, via hypnotic revivification, to the ninth year of his life:

> *. . . it's cold and snowy outside and I'm sitting at the kitchen table trying to do multiplications . . . but Mama and he* [*father*] *are yelling and fighting by the stove . . . he's drunk like always . . . damn him, if I wasn't so sure he'd hit me . . . I'd . . . fix him. . . .*

Henry was clearly reliving this experience and clinical notes made during the session confirm the extent of the abreaction: "Patient sweating profusely . . . shaking, tremulous . . . face taut and features suggestive of pain and dread . . ."

> *He's going to hit her again and says he'll beat me too . . . Jim and Ralph are sleeping in the next room . . . they better look out for him too . . . Hey! he's looking at me now . . . he has that butcher knife . . .* STAY AWAY FROM ME . . . PLEASE DON'T . . . *Ohhh . . . I can't get up . . .* HELP ME . . .

Henry's abreaction became so intense that he fell off the office couch on which he had been lying and awoke from his trance state. He was immediately ordered into another hypnotic trance and this time via regression the entire sequence was reviewed:

> *We were in the kitchen. My father was threatening to beat my mother and me. My brothers were sleeping in the other room. At that moment I knew I hated my father. I wished I could kill him. I guess he noticed the expression on my face, for he yelled at me and said that if I didn't stop looking at him like that, he'd fix me for good. Then he picked up a table knife and advanced towards me. I was so scared that I couldn't move. I can see him now . . . holding the knife at about the height of his thigh. In my fear, I fell off the chair and ran out into the yard. It was cold and snowy and so I ran into the barn. I had on only my overalls and I was freezing. I hid myself in the haystack loft. The next morning when I awoke my body and overalls were all sticky and wet from urinating all night. My penis was so swollen that my mother took me to our doctor who said that it was frostbitten . . .*

At this point Henry again became so disturbed that he was given a complete amnesia for the events of these hypnoidal experiences and was then brought back to the waking state.

In the next hour Henry consciously reported these hypnotically exhumed facts and now free-associated the material we had discussed during the previous hypnotic hour. This time, however, he did not block. Through the operations of the interim phenomenon he no longer resisted a discussion of the material, but now recited it at length and revealed its importance to him by engaging in conscious abreaction quite similar to the behavior he had previously exhibited while in hypnosis. Because he was able to get no further with his story than he had gotten in hypnosis, he was again placed in deep hypnosis and the final link was obtained. In hypnosis he repeated the story but added the recollection that, in his fear of his father's cutting off his penis with the knife, he, even in his sleepiness that night in the hayloft, continuously forced himself to urinate by pulling on and squeezing his penis. That is, the castration fear was so great he was compelled by fright to force urination to prove to himself that his father had not cut off his penis and that his father had not carried out his drunken threat to "fix him for good."

Following the conscious working through of these data it became clear that the entire story was uncovered and so the therapeutic task became one of reorientation and reeducation. Within approximately fifteen more hours Henry no longer showed depression or exhibited feelings of inferiority. Henry's speech defect had left him almost completely, his neurogenic dermatitis was minimal, and he was able to converse in more socially acceptable language with more ease and confidence than he had ever shown previously. Most importantly, however, after the following dream was reported and analyzed, the clinical records show that there was no recurrence of either diurnal or nocturnal enuresis:

> . . . *I was standing in the hallway of this hospital building when I saw my father running towards me through the doorway. He ran past me, wild-eyed and hectic-looking. He didn't notice me, but ran up the stairs, jumping two and three at a time, until he came to your room [therapist's office]. I ran after him and watched. He broke open your door by smashing it in, he picked you up, smashed you, beat you, and cursed at you. I yelled to him to stop, but he didn't. I pulled him away from you and hit him. I hit him so hard he disappeared. I felt swell; happy that I was able to help you.* . . .

Indications for and against hypnoanalysis

Since, as has been shown, hypnoanalysis is an adjunct of psychoanalysis, one might expect that the psychoanalytically trained practitioner (and by now it should be realized that only a psychoanalytically trained person should practice hypnoanalysis) may use this alternative method in all types of cases where psychoanalysis has been shown to be effective. That this is not true will be indicated in the section which deals with contraindications to the use of this method.

There is ample evidence to support the contention that hynoanalysis is especially valuable in a variety of diagnostic categories. Success has been reported in the literature in cases of hysterical somnambulism, anxiety neurosis, impulse neuroses, simple adult maladjustment, conversion hysteria, frigidity, homosexuality, and character disturbances (psychopathic personality). It is especially effective in conditions of psychopathic personality because, as was suggested in a previous section of this chapter, it permits the therapist to overcome (via posthypnotic suggestions) the ever-present danger of the patient's discontinuing treatment before he acquires sufficient insight into his defenses and psychogenic symptom formations. Thus it may be used to "bind" the patient to the treatment program until he is ready to make mature rather than infantile judgments about the value of the treatment program.

The method has had a wide field of application and, except for those contraindications set forth below, is available for most pathogenic conditions for any patient who is hypnotizable. Its efficacy lies in its singular advantage of rapidly cutting through resistances to depth-therapy, insuring the perpetuation of therapy until the pathology is relieved, dealing directly with the sadomasochistic factors, analyzing dependency, passivity, and hostile needs—all with enormous savings in time and, nevertheless, with the total participation of the organism in total therapy.

Essentially the indications against employment of hypnoanalytic techniques are but two. The primary contraindication is with conditions of frank or incipient psychosis. Those whose conscious egos are no longer intact, whose egos are debilitated or suggest a fragmentation process, can either not be hypnotized or not participate in hypnoanalytic treatment. Beyond their incapacity to handle this form of treatment there is a real hazard in attempting to treat such patients. Even though the break with realistic thinking may be but borderline, or the condition is in an early stage of the psychotic process, hypnotic therapy is not recommended in such conditions. Those practitioners who have attempted hypnoanalysis with the psychotic (or incipiently psychotic), whether for research or therapeutic purposes, report that the treatment may be so traumatic and threatening as to precipitate a frank psychosis or destroy what little remaining ego strength the psychotic may have available for other therapeutic methods.

The second contraindication is with those who are latently homosexual. (As suggested in the previous section, overt homosexuals can be hypnotized and may profit from hypnoanalysis.) The latent homosexual whose defenses are inadequate cannot submit to hypnosis, and so this treatment method is doomed to failure. There have been reports that certain latent homosexuals —those who have some insight into their sexual pathology and those who are passively feminine—can work with hypnosis and therefore with hypnoanalysis. The latent homosexual who cannot be hypnotized is the one who so strongly fears being attacked that he cannot submit to hypnosis because it is to him, at least in fantasy, an assault.

It would seem, therefore, that hypnoanalysis has certain limitations that do not hold for its parent technique. As hypnotic therapy is not indicated in these special conditions, the treatment of choice for them in the writer's opinion is still psychoanalysis.

Summary

In summary, we have explored those hypnoanalytic principles which, in the literature and in practice, suggest that this method for an advantageous blend of hypnosis and psychoanalysis has reached sufficient maturity to deserve a place in the psychotherapeutic armory.

By virtue of research and practical accomplishments, in terms of the professional interest and labor it has aroused in the past decade, and in view of its potentialities for assisting in the enormous mental hygiene task, hypnoanalysis has earned the respect of serious students and practitioners.

As an offspring of two major methods (hypnosis and psychoanalysis) it has been relegated to the role of "stepchild," having no "school," no "training facility," and no particular academic rostrum. It is parasitic—taking from both hypnotic and psychoanalytic theories and being practiced by specialists of both disciplines.

In view of the clinical importance and interest it has been able to generate—even though a "stepchild"—it would seem that provision for its independent study should be made available. Then, those who wish to take advantage of its singular potentialities for the expeditious treatment of important psychogenic disturbances may obtain the training and theoretical advantages that are usually offered to those who wish to qualify for the practice and study of other psychotherapeutic arts.

REFERENCES

1. Brenman, M., and M. M. Gill: *Hypnotherapy*, New York, International Universities Press, 1947.
2. Erickson, M. H.: "Hypnotic Psychotherapy," *Med. Clinics No. Amer.* 32:571 (1948).
3. ——— and L. B. Hill: "Unconscious Mental Activity in Hypnosis—Psychoanalytic Implications," *Psychoanal. Quart.* 13:60 (1944).
4. LeCron, L. M., and J. Bordeaux: *Hypnotism Today*, New York, Grune & Stratton, Inc., 1947.
5. Lindner, R. M.: *Rebel Without a Cause*, New York, Grune & Stratton, Inc., 1944.
6. ———: "Hypnoanalysis as a Psychotherapy," *Diseases of Nervous System* 6:371–374 (1945).
7. ———: "Hypnoanalysis in a Case of Hysterical Somnambulism," *Psychoanal. Rev.* 32:325 (1945).
8. ———: "Hypnoanalysis as a Psychotherapeutic Technique," in *Specialized Techniques in Psy-*

chotherapy. Ed. by G. Bychowski and J. L. Despert. New York, Basic Books, Inc., 1953, p. 36.

9. Rosen, H.: *Hypnotherapy in Clinical Psychiatry*, New York, Julian Press, Inc., 1953.
10. Schneck, J. M.: "Notes on the Homosexual Component of the Hypnotic Transference," *Brit. J. Med. Hypnotism* 1:24 (1950).
11. ———: "Hypnoanalysis, Hypnotherapy and Card 12M of the Thematic Apperception Test," *J. Gen. Psychol.* 44:293 (1951).
12. ———: "Hypnoanalysis," *Personality* 1:307–317 (1951).
13. Watkins, J. G.: "The Hypnoanalytic Treatment of a Case of Impotence," *J. Clin. Psychopath.* 8:453 (1947).
14. Wolberg, L. R.: *Hypnoanalysis*, New York, Grune & Stratton, Inc., 1945.
15. ———: *Medical Hypnosis*, I & II, New York, Grune & Stratton, Inc., 1945.

Frank J. Kirkner, Ph.D.

11

HYPNOSIS IN A GENERAL HOSPITAL SERVICE *

PSYCHOLOGICAL DISTURBANCES are rather frequently found among medical and surgical patients. Some of these reaction patterns are difficult to cope with as demonstrated by their refractoriness to usual methods of treatment. Hypnotherapy has been found to be useful in many of these cases. This discourse will consist of a description of some of its uses and the principles involved.

For the purpose of orientation, we might think etiologically of two major groups: (1) those in which the illness is precipitated primarily by reaction to emotional stress and (2) those whose psychological reactions are precipitated by physiological stress. The former disorders may be referred to as *psychogenic* and the latter as *somatopsychic*. As a general principle, in either group, if the attitude of the patient can be influenced by hypnosis, the patient has a chance of benefiting from hypnotic treatment.

* The cases represented in the population presented were treated by Drs. Frank J. Kirkner, Hamilton M. Moody, and Charlyne Storment-Seymour, staff psychologists, and Drs. Eugene Blumberg, Claude Fiske, David Grossman, and Richard Laux, former clinical psychology trainees, of the Clinical Psychology Section, Veterans' Administration Hospital, Long Beach, California.

In general, the techniques applied are direct symptom relief and indirect symptom relief with direct suggestion, abreaction, and hypnoanalysis. Symptoms such as pain may be controlled by direct suggestion, and those such as hiccoughs by suggestions of relaxation and assurance. Should a symptom, such as that found in conversion hysteria, serve as a strong ego-defense against emotion-laden anxiety, then either intensive hypnoanalysis may be desirable or the ego-defense theoretically may be replaced by a less crippling and more socially approved ego-defense.

It seems reasonable to assume that hypnosis should be applied along with other methods of psychotherapy when it is in the best interest of the patient. Considering its applicability in this light, it would be possible only to speculate on the extent to which it might be optimally helpful. The writer will attempt to suggest its general applicability by presenting a sample of sixty cases. Table 1 lists the complaints, with in a few cases more than one complaint to a patient. All these patients were adult males with the exception of a twenty-eight-year-old divorced female with rheumatoid arthritis who complained of pain. The average age was 40.2 years with a range from 22 to 75 years. The response of patients to hypnotic treatment in age groups for the six-decade range is shown in Table 2. Patients responded throughout the entire age range. The data are inadequate to generalize further from the decade groups.

Table 1. List of Complaints for 60 Sample Patients

Complaint	Frequency	Complaint	Frequency
Pain	20	Fear of death	1
Hiccoughs	18	Discouragement	1
Smoking	7	Paresthesia	1
Skin disorders	3	Anorexia	1
Essential		Headache	1
hypertension	2	Tension	1
Insomnia	2	Gagging	1
Amnesia	1	Somnambulism	1
Nausea	1	Aphasia	1

Table 2. Age and Response to Treatment

Decade	No response	Response
20–29	3	12
30–39	7	9
40–49	0	6
50–59	5	7
60–69	1	7
70–79	1	2

Hypnotic control of pain

In his discussion of hypnosis and severe pain, Rosen (13) describes the nature of pain and its complexity. He points out that pain can be determined organically or functionally. It may be comprised of varying degrees of both organic and emotional determinants. As the emotional determinants become more pronounced, it becomes increasingly difficult to control pain with the usual medical and surgical procedures.

Laux (9) evaluates the effect of preoperative hypnotic relaxation on postoperative pain. This experiment was carried out according to a rigid research design. The subjects were forty urological surgical patients, twenty each in an experimental group and a control group. The only known variable was the hypnotic procedure which was identical for all the patients in the experimental group. There were three hypnotic sessions for each patient in the experimental group prior to surgery. The hypnotist participated actively in the first two sessions and the first part of the third session. During the last part of the third session, just before surgery, the patient listened to a tape recording. The main criterion for determining the effect of preoperative hypnotic relaxation on postoperative pain was the patient's request for anodynes. Fifty-four per cent of the total requests for anodynes for both groups occurred in the first twenty-four-hour postoperative period. In the comparison of the two groups for this period, the request for anodynes by the experimental group was 34 per cent less than for the control group. Statistically, the difference was significant at the 4 per cent level of confidence, that is, the probability of a chance occurrence was 4 in 100. There was a great variation among the experimental patients. It was observed that some responded little, if at all, to trance induction, while others responded with varying depths.

The first twenty cases in the sample, shown in Table 3, suggest the etiology, control, and limits of control of pain by hypnosis.

Table 3. Hypnosis for Control of Pain

Patient	Age	Physical disorder	Complaint	Outcome
1	30	Spinal injury	Pain	Persisted
2	38	Spinal injury	Pain	Relieved
3	44	Spinal injury	Pain	Relieved
4	23	Spinal injury	Pain	Relieved
5	25	Spinal injury	Pain	Relieved
6	22	Spinal injury	Pain	Relieved
7	57	Spinal injury	Pain	Persisted
8	34	Spinal injury	Pain	Persisted
9	33	Spinal injury	Pain	Persisted
10	25	Spinal injury	Pain	Relieved
11	32	Spinal injury	Pain	Persisted
12	56	Spinal injury	Rectal pain	Relieved
13	54	Cervical discogenic disease	Headache, tension and pain in back and shoulders	Terminated
14	29	Fibromyositis of lumbar muscles	Pain	Relieved temporarily
15	65	Carcinoma of the prostate with metastases	Pain	Relieved
16	32	Carcinoma of the rectum	Pain	Relieved
17	45	Episcleritis, sec. to rheumatoid arthritis	Pain	Relieved
18	28	Rheumatoid arthritis	Pain	Relieved
19	29	Rheumatoid arthritis	Pain	Persisted
20	26	Amputation of left leg at calf	Pain Somnambulism	Relieved Stopped

The variables of depth of trance and etiology of pain are important considerations in the hypnotic control of pain. If the patient has severe organogenic pain, a trance depth to meet the criteria of illusions and hallucinations should be reached in order to suppress the pain. Trance depth is usually desirable. However, emotional factors contributing to pain with little organic justification may be worked through in lighter hypnotic trances and psychotherapy if the patient shows responsiveness and ego potential.

In a Veterans' Administration technical bulletin on spinal cord injuries, Bors (3) reviewed pertinent literature and delineates four types of pain: (1) root pain characterized by segmental distribution, (2) sympathetic pain, (3) visceral pain, and (4) psychic pain, which may be a component of the first three pain types. Pain in spinal cord injuries most frequently appears to be of the sympathetic type. It is hypothesized that an H-like substance accrues peripherally in the skin and muscles of the lower extremities which elicits impulses in the autonomic system to the cord above the lesion to the thalamus. The methods of treatment employed for the relief of spinal injury pain include surgical intervention, nerve block, cobra venom, nicotinic acid, gynergen, Depropanex, heat and cold applications, and psychotherapy. It has been observed that pain has decreased with improved nutrition and distractive activities such as occupational therapy, educational endeavors, and recreation.

Dorcus and Kirkner (4) investigated the use of hypnosis to suppress intractable pain in cases of spinal cord injury. Seven patients received hypnotic treatment twice weekly for two months. Pain was induced and terminated in hypnosis. Then two patients were taught self-hypnosis to inhibit the attacks themselves. The efficacy of the hypnotic treatment was checked against the requests for analgesics, which dropped off markedly. Less pain was reported but none was entirely free from pain. The spinal injury group was compared with five dysmenorrhea cases. Pain was induced and eliminated in the trance state. Then the suggestion was made that it would disappear as quickly as it appeared in the waking state. A follow-up over a two-year period indicated that these latter patients remained relatively free from pain.

It is speculated that the fundamental difference between these two groups is the organic persistence at the source of pain. The physiological source of pain is constant for the cases of spinal cord injury and is mostly the result of conditioning in the dysmenorrhea cases. In the former, the inhibitory process is weakened by incoming impulses, and in the latter the pain is enhanced and perpetuated by an expectancy pattern. Thus pain is suppressed in the spinal cord injuries, and the conditioned pattern of expectancy and tension is interrupted in dysmenorrhea.

Livingston (11) discusses pain and the phantom limb. Phantom limb pain is associated with the excitation of the severed sensory nerves and the body scheme. During the learning process that accompanies sensory experience, the individual acquires a perceptual image of his body. This perceptual image is an integrative entity of three *plastic models* which evolve from (1) sensory impulses originating in the receptors of the skin and subcutaneous tissues, (2) sensory impulses from the joints, tendons, and muscles, and (3) visual sensory patterns. In the case of an amputated limb, the body image includes the missing part as a *phantom limb.*

Patient 20, a twenty-six-year-old male, had an amputation of the left leg at calf. He had complained of somnambulism since the age of nine. Following the amputation, he attempted to walk in his sleep and injured the stump. Two goals were set for hypnosis: (1) interruption of the somnambulistic pattern and (2) modification of body image.

Hypnotic suggestions were given to the patient that, when he had the urge to walk in his sleep, he would awake and go back to sleep. The patient reported that he did occasionally awake during the night and went back to sleep, but that he did not sleepwalk. In the hypnotic state, the patient was given suggestions consistent with the realism of the absence of the amputated limb. He began to talk about his stump with no further mention of the phantom limb. However, he complained of a burning pain in the stump. This sensation could be induced and eradicated during hypnosis. The patient learned self-hypnosis during which he was able to control the pain when it became severe and achieve a general overall reduction of pain.

Patient 13, a fifty-four-year-old male, had a diagnosis of a cervical discogenic disease. He complained of pain in the shoulders and neck and a frequent occipital headache. There was a history of a stormy childhood and considerable resentment toward the father. Psychotherapy did not appear promising. The goal was to reduce the tension throughout the body and particularly in the painful areas. The technique of hypnotic relaxation was applied. He slowly relaxed and the pain subsided. Self-hypnosis was taught, to be used when tension was perceived to be mounting. As he began to feel he was getting relief, he showed an inclination to talk either before or following the hypnotic session. His thought processes were directed into his childhood memories. This produced emotional feelings toward his father and authority figures. A six-month checkup indicated that the gains were maintained.

Pain can be controlled by hypnosis. It becomes increasingly difficult to control for longer periods of time when its origin is continuously generated by a physiological process. Even in these cases, which can be rather well controlled sometimes, the threshold tumbles when the patient becomes emotionally disturbed. When pain has little organic basis, an expectancy pattern may prolong it. In such cases, this pattern may be interrupted by hypnotic procedures. Tension pains may be reduced and eliminated by hypnosis. If the tension has served as an ego-defense and the cause remains operative, it probably will have to be worked through to give more than temporary relief from the tension.

Peptic ulcers

Moody (12) evaluated the results of hypnotically induced relaxation in the treatment of chronic peptic ulcers. Ages ranged from twenty-five to forty-five. He matched two groups of ten male patients each, having uncomplicated, "pure" peptic ulcers with at least a six-year ulcer history. Medication was discontinued for the experimental group at the beginning of the investigation and continued for the control group. Each patient in the experimental group had one orientation interview, thirteen one-hour hypnotic sessions, and a follow-up interview. In addition to the hypnotically induced relaxation, it was suggested to the patient in the trance state that he would not be concerned about pain. Beginning in the fourth or fifth session, autohypnosis was taught. A comparison of symptom changes for the control and experimental groups on the bases of pretherapy and posttherapy x-ray plates, clinical notes in the medical chart, and patient reports, was made. The x-ray judgments were made by radiologists, as shown in Table 4. The sample is small, but the trend favoring hypnosis is significant. The

Table 4. Ulcer Improvement Ratings Based on X-ray Judgments

Rating	Control group	Experimental group
Worse	0	0
No improvement	6	2
Slight improvement	4	6
Moderate improvement	0	2
Marked improvement	0	0

clinical notes suggest improvement for five of the control group and nine of the experimental group. All the members of the experimental group thought they had improved. The author considers a follow-up of these patients necessary to evaluate the long-term efficacy of this method of treatment of ulcer patients.

Hiccoughs

In general, the mechanics of hiccoughing consists of rhythmic clonic spasms of the diaphragm followed by sudden inspiration which is abruptly checked by the closure of the glottis. The rate of the spasm varies from one patient to another and even with the same patient during the hypnotic process. Due to the involuntary nature of the spasm, it is usually considered to be a reflex action.

The reflex action may be bilateral but it is more frequently unilateral (14). It is probable that the majority of cases are stimulated via the phrenic and vagus nerves. The overextension of the stomach, inflammation of the diaphragm, and a multitude of other mechanical and physiological conditions are considered suitable to produce the stimulation necessary for the elicitation of hiccoughs. Whether or not this peripherally stimulated reflex action would occur as a link in the chain of events in psychogenic hiccoughs is not known.

Sources from which hiccoughs may arise have been tabulated by Samuels (14), as shown in Table 5.

Table 5. Sources of Hiccoughs Tabulated by Samuels

Psychogenic	Organic			
	Central nervous system damage	Neck region disorders	Thoracic disorders	Abdominal disorders
Malingerers	Hemorrhage	Tumors	Aneurysm	Postoperative aneurysm
Publicity seekers	Thrombosis	Glands	Neuroma	Tumor
Borderline mental cases	Brain injury	Aneurysm	Pericarditis	Gallbladder disorder
Mental shock	Skull fracture	Bronchial cyst	Pneumonia	Pancreatitis
Prolonged anxiety	Neurosyphilis	Diverticulum	Abscess	Abscess
	Anesthesia	Arterio-venous damage	Diaphragm hernia	Ulcer
	Encephalitis		Foreign body	Gastritis
			Coronary thrombosis	Foreign body

The general methods of medical treatment for hiccoughs have been presented by Dorcus and the writer (4). These consist of the inhibition of the reflex action, mental concentration, use of chemical agents, surgical intervention, and hypnosis.

The rhythmic reflex action can be inhibited and broken up sometimes by a strong stimulus, such as a startle, ice packs on the neck, hot bath, pressure on the eyeballs or carotid sinus, pressure or electrical stimulation of the phrenic nerve, pressure in the abdominal and thoracic regions at points of the insertion of the diaphragm, or the inhalation of a strong olfactory stimulant.

The principle of distraction is used in directing mental activity and concentration to influence the reflex action through the alteration of cerebral organization.

Surgical intervention is aimed at the interruption of the neural pathway of the phrenic, sympathetic, or lower thoracic and upper lumbar nerves. One or more of these pathways may be interrupted.

The use of hypnotic treatment for the control of hiccoughs appears promising. The writer and West have reported on a thirty-five-year-old white male who was hospitalized with massive liver metastases of anaplastic adenocarcinoma. During treatment he developed a severe case of hiccoughs which was attributed to a combination of mechanical and inflammatory irritation of the diaphragm. Attempts were made to control the hiccoughing with carbon dioxide inhalation and a phrenic nerve block. The nerve block held for about forty-five minutes. The hiccoughing was brought under control by hypnotic treatment (7). LeCron, Fields, and Levine (10) have reported a case of a sixty-five-year-old male with hiccoughs as a conversion reaction. The hiccoughs began following surgery. Hypnotic treatment was used to uncover the fear and terminate the symptom.

An accumulation of eighteen cases (5) treated with hypnosis over a five-year period is shown in Table 6. The ages are tabulated in decile steps in Table 7, the age range being from twenty-seven to seventy-five years. The distribution of the data indicates that the factor of age probably has no bearing on the onset of the spasm or its termination by hypnosis. A larger sample is needed to determine more accurately the distribution, for it is probable that these differences are due to sampling. These cases show, as did Samuels's article, that hiccoughs occur with a wide variety of

Table 6. Hiccough Cases

Patient	Age	Physical disorder	Onset	Duration of hiccough	Hiccough after therapy
21	54	Arthritis in hip, chronic pleurisy	Following hip surgery	10 days	Terminated
22	35	Acute myeloblastic leukemia	Following perforated ulcer	4 days	Terminated
23	27	Leukemia	Internal hemorrhages	3 days	Persisted
24	57	Hypertensive heart disease, nephrosclerosis	Attempts at vomiting	Irregular for several weeks	Persisted
25	53	Chronic rheumatic with hyperplastic atrophic gastritis	Seemed to follow increased anxiety about his illness	7 days (?)	Terminated
26	50	Chronic myelogenous leukemia	Following repeated vomiting	3 days	Temporary relief only
27	41	Chronic glomerulonephritis	Pain and nausea	10 days	Terminated
28	32	CNS lesion, multiple sclerosis	Nausea and vomiting	2 days	Relieved
29	30	Multiple sclerosis, acute epididymitis	Anger	4 days	Terminated
30	75	Diabetes mellitus	Not determined	8 days	Terminated
31	44	Cerebral arteriosclerosis, epilepsy, right hemiplegia	Hospital transfer	3 days	Terminated
32	57	Chronic, active pulmonary tuberculosis	Seems to arise over anxiety about outcome of x-ray	4 days	Terminated
33	54	Myocardial infarct	Started upon digestion of liquids	4 days	Terminated
34	73	Pulmonary edema associated with cardiovascular disease	Following surgery	6 days	Terminated
35	48	Buerger's disease	Postsurgical	2 days	Terminated
36	66	Perforated peptic ulcer	Postsurgical	8 days	Terminated
37	60	Emphysema	No event established, fears respiratory loss	Intermittent for 2 years	Persisted

Table 6. Hiccough Cases (*Continued*)

Patient	Age	Physical disorder	Onset	Duration of hiccough	Hiccough after therapy
38	35	Massive liver metastases of anaplastic adenocarcinoma	Undetermined	Record not available	Terminated

physical disorders. The onset suggests both physiological and functional determinants. The majority of these patients had had stimulants and depressants, and they were disturbed. The hypnotic approach was to induce complete relaxation and relieve the patient of his concern about his disease and the spasm. The number of hypnotic sessions ranged from one to about ten. There was

Table 7. Age and Hiccoughs

Age	No. patients
20–29	1
30–39	4
40–49	3
50–59	6
60–69	1
70–79	3

no way of knowing beforehand whether or not the patient would be a good hypnotic subject. Fourteen of the eighteen were permanently relieved of the spasm, one was relieved temporarily, and three obtained no relief. As other treatments had been tried in most of these cases before hypnosis, this was proved to be a useful method of treatment. It is presumed that hiccoughs of long duration are more difficult to control. Irrespective of this factor, it is desirable to stop the spasm as soon as possible to relieve the stress on the patient.

Smoking

Smoking's effect on the vascular system is thought detrimental to those with Buerger's disease. When hypnosis was tried to alter the smoking habit, it was found that these cases seemed to be difficult to hypnotize. Baker (2) indicated in her study of this disease entity that smoking is a symbol of masculinity. It was thought from this observation that these patients might be resisting what they interpreted as submission in the hypnotic process. With a modification of the hypnotic induction technique, these patients responded to hypnosis. The understanding between the patient and the therapist was that the patient would hypnotize himself with the aid of the hypnotist. The results of a group of Buerger's disease patients treated for the alteration of the smoking habit are shown in Table 8. In general, the aims of the hyp-

Table 8. Alteration of Smoking Habit in Patients with Buerger's Disease

Patient	Age	Outcome of habit
39	56	Reduced
40	25	Persisted
41	58	Persisted
42	38	Persisted
43	56	Persisted
44	22	Stopped
45	41	Stopped

notic suggestions were to arouse negative feelings toward smoking and positive awarding feelings. On the one hand, suggestions were given to build up obnoxious feelings toward smoking around the gustatory and olfactory senses; and, on the other hand, to reinforce pleasant feelings associated with the recovery of acuity in these senses, etc. Posthypnotic suggestions were given conducive to the reduction of tension. There was no long-term follow-up on these cases.

Miscellaneous cases

The remainder of the sixty-case sample is shown in Table 9, which includes the age, physical disorder, complaint, and outcome. No attempt will be made to discuss all these cases. The approaches to treatment in cases of psoriasis, essential hypertension, and mutism might be of interest.

Table 9. Miscellaneous Cases and Results of Treatment

Patient	Age	Disorder	Complaint	Outcome
46	52	Psoriasis		Persisted
47	26	Neurodermatitis	Itching	Relieved
48	26	Psoriasis		Remission
49	33	Essential hypertension		Reduced
50	35	Essential hypertension		Reduced
51	64	Arteriosclerotic heart disease	Insomnia	Reduced
52	60	Tuberculosis	Nausea	Terminated
			Insomnia	Reduced
53	62	Postoperative hypernephroma of left kidney with pulmonary metastases	Anorexia	Persisted
54	30	Hodgkin's disease	Discouragement	Persisted
55	65	Arteriosclerotic heart disease, toxic psychosis	Fear of death	Sporadically relieved
56	30	Ulcerative colitis		Persisted
57	57	Adhesive, chronic arachnoiditis of cerebral spine	Numbness and weakness of hands	Reduced
58	29	Multiple fracture of ribs	Anterograde amnesia	Limited recall
59	41	Cerebral embolism	Mutism	Vocalization
60	25	Postoperative abdominal adhesions	Gagging	Stopped

Patient 48 was a twenty-six-year-old divorced male, who had psoriasis from the waist down with patches on his elbows, scalp, and face. A rough estimate of body structure suggested the asthenic type. He carried "a chip on his shoulder," had had a few fights and near fights, and minor skirmishes with the law. He was suspected of being psychotic. A psychological evaluation revealed a neurotic personality with intelligence at the bright normal level. There were rather strong feelings of passivity with a low threshold for frustration. The psychotherapeutic potential was estimated as fair.

It was decided to try hypnotic relaxation. After several distributed sessions, his skin cleared up considerably. However, he was not satisfied with these sessions, which was interpreted to mean that he did not consider his psoriasis his main problem. Following a few sessions of psychotherapy, he seemed to become more anxious and developed general psoriasis. It was thought that anxiety might be better controlled by a hypnoanalytic approach.

The patient was regressed year by year back to the age of three, with sensory associations carefully reinstated in these regressive steps. He was then told that he would begin to have feelings of events that happened during his life and they would become so strong he would want to talk about them. Many childhood experiences were elicited. The crucial period which precipitated the pattern of his present behavior apparently occurred when he was falsely accused of stealing money in the fifth grade. Even though it was found later that he did not do it, he felt this experience keenly as one in which he was rejected and distrusted. His passive behavior changed to aggressive behavior which subsequently continued. During therapy, he automatically related earlier experiences to later experiences. The repressive mechanism was permitted to operate without interference from the hypnotherapist. The patient became more friendly in his contacts throughout the hospital and experienced a complete remission of his psoriasis for the first time in six years. There were nineteen deep hypnotherapy sessions. Further psychotherapy was recommended to the patient when he left the hospital, but the patient failed to follow through with the recommendation. The remission held for nine months until about the time the patient remarried. At that time he returned to the hospital, but the psoriasis was not considered severe enough for further hospitalization.

Patient 49 was a thirty-three-year-old white married male, with the diagnosis of essential hypertension with Grade 1 eye-ground change. Psychological testing indicated that the patient was in a state of panic in relation to his marital adjustment. He showed considerable concern about his blood pressure which fluctuated around 180/130, ranging from 156/98 to 200/130.

The plan of therapy was to utilize the patient's concern about his blood pressure to relate its fluctuations with his emotional reactions and follow each session with psychotherapy. There were fifteen sessions. The patient gradually accepted the etiology of his difficulty, lost interest in his blood pressure, and dwelled considerably on his feelings toward an authoritative father. His fears about heredity and a short span of life subsided, marital and occupational adjustments improved, and his blood pressure stabilized at 145/110. At the beginning of hypnosis the blood pressure rose, and then it dropped during hypnosis. The patient was taught self-hypnosis as an adjunctive measure. In this case, it is predicted that the blood pressure will approach normal in time, if somatic changes do not interfere.

Patient 59 was a forty-one-year-old married male. His diagnosis was cerebral embolism, with motor loss on the right side and aphasia. There was no record of phonation for a year and a half after the accident. Six weeks of attempted speech retraining failed to produce a sound. The patient was poorly motivated, but his comprehension was good.

During the first hypnotic session the patient was induced to hum faintly. During the following seven hypnotic sessions the speech therapist conducted speech retraining which progressed at a normal rate. At the time when he did as well without hypnosis as with it (probably when he reached his ability for the time being) hypnosis was discontinued (7). Since then, a similar case has responded in the same manner.

There are some other types of cases, for which complete information is not available. Among these are three torticollis and three impotency cases. The spasm in all the torticollis cases subsided completely during hypnosis. In sustaining the spasm relief, uncovering hypnotherapy failed in one case, was successful in the second, and has made good progress in the third. Two of the impotent patients became potent with hypnotic treatment.

Two other types of cases are reported by psychologists in other treatment centers. Arnold (1) has found a variation in the persistence of emotional factors in asthma. Some of these cases respond quickly to hypnotic treatment while a proportion of other cases can be controlled by longer treatment. Goodwin (6) used hypnotic relaxation in the treatment of a case of pemphigus. The bullae subsided with the reduction of stress.

This has been a presentation of some of the applications of hypnotic treatment in a general hospital. A variety of disorders and complaints were shown in a sample of sixty cases. Fifty-nine of these cases were adult males and one was an adult female. The average age was 40.2 years with an age range of 22 to 75 years. The main emphases of the use of hypnosis have been on sympathetic, root, tension, and conditioned pain; hiccoughs, the smoking habit, peptic ulcers, somnambulism, psoriasis, essential hypertension, and mutism in motor aphasia. The methods of treatment and the results have been discussed.

REFERENCES

1. Arnold, D. C.: Personal communication.
2. Baker, G.: *Personality Factors in Thromboangiitis Obliterans: An Exploratory Study.* (Dissertation, University of Southern California, Los Angeles, California, 1952)
3. Bors, E.: *Spinal Cord Injuries* (Vet. Adm. Tech. Bull. TB10–503) Washington, 1948.
4. Dorcus, R. M., and F. J. Kirkner: "The Use of Hypnosis in the Suppression of Intractable Pain," *J. Abnormal & Soc. Psychology* 43:237–239 (1948).
5. ———: "The Control of Hiccoughs by Hypnotic Treatment." *J. Clin. Exp. Hypnosis* 3:104–108 (1955).
6. Goodwin, P. A.: Personal communication.
7. Kirkner, F. J., and P. M. West: "Hypnotic Treatment of Persistent Hiccup: A Case Report," *Brit. J. Med. Hypnotism* 1:22–24 (1950).
8. Kirkner, F. J., R. M. Dorcus, and G. Seacat: "Hypnotic Motivation of Vocalization in an Organic Motor Aphasic Case," *J. Clin. Exp. Hypnosis* 1:47–49 (1953).

9. Laux, R.: *An Investigation of the Analgesic Effects on Postoperative Pain Resulting from Urological Surgery.* (Dissertation, University of Southern California, Los Angeles, 1953)
10. LeCron, L. M., I. A. Fields, and E. B. Levine: "Postoperative Prolonged Hiccoughs Relieved Through the Uncovering by Hypnosis of the Psychological Cause," *Ann. West. Med. and Surg.* 5:937–938 (1951).
11. Livingston, W. K.: *Pain Mechanisms,* New York, The Macmillan Company, 1944.
12. Moody, Hamilton M.: "An Evaluation of Hypnotically Induced Relaxation for the Reduction of Peptic Ulcer Symptons," *Brit. J. Med. Hypnotism* 4:1–8 (1953).
13. Rosen, H.: "The Hypnotic and Hypnotherapeutic Control of Severe Pain," *Brit. J. Med. Hypnotism* 2:1–12 (1951).
14. Samuels, L.: "Hiccup, a Ten Year Review of Anatomy, Etiology and Treatment," *Can. Med. Assoc. J.* 67:315–322 (1952).

George F. Kuehner, D.D.S.

12

HYPNOSIS IN DENTISTRY

THE SUBJECT OF HYPNOSIS in dentistry is a relatively new one in the field of dental study. It is becoming increasingly important and will in the future, I am sure, be an integral part of every dentist's knowledge. This statement is made in spite of the attitudes expressed by many when treating this subject. The author is well aware that often these attitudes stem, not only from the average practitioner, but also from scientific investigators and men of prestige in other phases of dentistry and medicine. Nevertheless, upon close scrutiny it will be readily seen that such statements resound the ignorance of their authors as to the scope and the role of hypnosis in dental practice.

In the literature you can find numerous references to hypnosis and psychosomatic dentistry. These references imply that *hypnosis* is synonymous with *psychosomatics,* which is erroneous. Actually hypnosis is but one technique in the control of psychosomatic conditions. Physiological medicine, practiced at its best, is not able to cope with ailments showing no anatomical or bacteriological cause for the physiological dysfunction complained about. Psychosomatic medicine has risen to bring medical practice out of this impasse. (5) Dental educators also have come to realize that the day of total divorce of physiological and mechanical dentistry from the psychology of the patient is past, and that some understanding of psychosomatics is not only valuable to the practitioner, but indispensable in recognizing and treating conditions on this basis.

Dentists employing hypnosis to control certain psychosomatic conditions have been accused of using it as a panacea for the cure of all dental ills. These accusations could not be farther from the truth. No one working in the field of psychosomatic medicine or dentistry will claim the ability of curing a truly organic pathological disorder by the use of these methods, and our knowledge of pathology, bacteriology, biochemistry, anatomy, and all the other basic sciences still retain their full import in the diagnosis, cure, prevention, and mitigation of disease.

The role of the dentist as a member of the healing arts is to detect, control, or eliminate diseases in or about the oral cavity. Perhaps the greatest problem associated with this gigantic task is the problem of pain. It is pain that for the most part is responsible for *dentophobia.* This condition keeps millions of potential patients from securing the benefits of dentistry. Every dentist knows how to eliminate organic pain, but most practitioners have been unsuccessful in combating nervous apprehension and the nearly morbid fear which most patients bring to the office with them. Not until dentists generally are able to allay the fear of pain can they be said to be practicing truly modern dentistry with its accompanying benefits to the health services. (2) The control of fear is most readily accomplished through hypnosis and will be referred to later.

Pain in itself is not a bad thing; it has been called the guardian angel of our health, pointing, as it were, with its red-hot sword to the source of disease. But, alas, we do not always understand its silent signs. Often the troubled mind dreams up a pain which has no bodily cause. Physicians and dentists, attempting to heal the cause of pain rather than the pain itself, are thus confronted with numerous problems which sometimes almost defy solution. Let us discuss briefly some of the more salient facts concerning pain.

Pain is nearly always an entirely subjective symptom; that is, only rarely are there visible signs which enable us to tell that a patient is experiencing it. Rarely do we see such objective symptoms as dilatation of the pupils, sweating in a localized area, or other signs which indicate the existence of pain without the patient's verbal declaration of the fact. Usually we must take the word of the patient that he is experiencing pain. Herein lies the first major problem. Is the pain an organic or psychogenic one?

Very often, after examination and reexamination, no pathologic condition is found which would account for the pain, and the dentist is inclined to diagnose hysteric or neurotic pain. This type of diagnosis is not justified, in that we all know how easy it is for the best dentist to overlook an organic source of pain. There are, however, several positive signs which may lead to such a decision. One of these is that the zone of pain circumscribed by the patient may contradict the anatomy of the peripheral and central nervous system innervation. For example, if a patient indicates the area of pain to extend from the ear lobe to the inner corner of the eye, and then down to the corner of the mouth and back again to the ear lobe, the discrepancy between anatomic facts and the assertions of the patient are so evident that a diagnosis of neurotic pain can be made. Another important feature of psychogenic pain is that it is never anything but a symptom of the neurosis. Often the patient betrays to the experienced observer his general neurotic attitude; in other instances it can be detected by several pointed questions. It is, of course, not the duty of the dentist to diagnose a neurosis unless it is openly manifest. However, knowledge concerning the fundamentals of psychogenic and neurotic pain greatly increase his ability to cope with this condition.

Another characteristic sequence of events which many of us have seen is as follows: A patient presents himself, complaining of severe pain localized in one specific tooth. The tooth may contain a large restoration and the patient may evidence soreness upon application of heat and upon percussion. He will insist that this tooth be extracted and the dentist may finally accede to his wishes. When the patient is asked to return on the following day, he will return with nothing but praise for the skill and cleverness of the dentist in accomplishing that piece of surgery. He is bubbling over because now all his troubles are over. Three days or perhaps a week later he is back, and the pain is back, but now he knows exactly which tooth it is! A dentist cannot be criticized for being misled by the signs and symptoms which the patient first presented, but he should never be misled a second time. A complete absence of pain following surgery with its sudden recurrence after a fairly brief interval immediately clinches the diagnosis: A neurosis is causing the patient's complaint. (4)

It is also a known fact that many persons develop great anxiety about physical pain and are ashamed of it, but they can do nothing about it. The idea of being "stuck" with a needle for a local anesthetic fills them with dread and they have great difficulty in returning for additional needed treatment. Aside from the association of pain or discomfort from the loss of teeth, many patients avoid the dentist because the loss of teeth may alter their appearance and the wearing of dentures is a sign of old age, in their minds. This is applicable to both men and women. This is one of the chief reasons, clinical psychologists tell us, why many chronic illnesses of psychosomatic origin can be traced to a dental operation. (7) Usually during this time, the mind of the individual was not educated to the fallacy of such reasoning and a shattering of the ego was the result. Patient education and reeducation is easily accomplished through hypnosis.

There is one other factor to be considered. Occasionally in adults the opposite reaction in regard to pain exists. That is, patients may like to have their teeth and gingivae worked on. They may even derive a certain perverse satisfaction from having teeth extracted. These are the same individuals addicted to polysurgery and they are severe psychoneurotics. When they develop some physical discomfort, having heard of illnesses cured by the removal of *foci of infection,* they become their own diagnosticians and often conclude that a tooth or a group of teeth should be extracted. Like the patient who wants his tonsils or appendix removed, they usually manage to get the operation done. There are many reasons for such behavior and many say that to perform the operation will do no harm, but, contrary to such a view, numerous case reports show that it *will* do harm in cases of confirmed invalidism. (7)

How then can we cope with these and other related problems through hypnotic procedures? In answering this question let us recall that syndromes which are most commonly productive of psychosomatic manifestations are those of anxiety, hostility, and a generalized state of tension. Via hypnosis we are able to remove fear, as was previously mentioned. Removal of pain is often accomplished with hypnosis alone. The first prerequisite for hypnosis is complete relaxation which, when achieved, in itself relieves tension and anxiety, diminishes and sometimes eliminates all hostility. (1) With this in mind it is easy to see the value of hypnosis in dentistry. It will eliminate *fear, anxiety, tension, hostility,* and *pain*—all the states which are the chief reasons for patients' avoiding the dentist and even for the development of many chronic illnesses of psychosomatic origin.

The chief value of hypnosis in dentistry, then, lies in its use as a means of combating mental conflicts and, in its deeper stages, as a means for controlling pain. But its value to the dental practitioner does not end here. It can be used to remove old traumatic memories which persist in the waking state. The elimination of bad habits (such as thumb-sucking, nail-biting, bad sleeping habits) which would be destructive to the individual are amenable to hypnotherapy. The successful cure of bruxism is possible. The prosthodontist will find hypnosis useful in registering the proper centric relation and vertical dimension, as well as in conditioning his patients for the proper attitude in wearing prosthetic appliances. The elimination of gagging is of tremendous value to every dentist. These are some of the more common fields of usefulness in dentistry, but it should be apparent that other possibilities exist and new areas of usefulness will certainly be found in the future.

In employing hypnosis in the dental office many and varied techniques are employed. It is well if the operator is thoroughly familiar with several procedures as it is often advisable to change methods from one sitting to another. There are several reasons for this. First, not every individual will respond to the same technique. For this reason the dentist may start out with one procedure and be compelled to change. Also, during the training period it is well to deviate from time to time so as to maintain the air of expectation which is so desirable in a good patient. In the literature you will find statements indicating that, once a patient has been trained to enter the trance at a given signal, he will always do so for life. The author has found that this is not the case. In many instances it is true, and even after intervals of years a patient may respond to a given signal and enter the trance state instantly. But it has been my experience that, on occasion, a patient who was easily placed in a trance repeatedly by the same method and signal, at another sitting was completely refractory, so that in order to achieve the trance state a new method was needed. Therefore, the larger the repertory of techniques, the higher the degree of success.

Fortunately, these difficulties do not occur frequently in individuals in whom only a light trance is desired. It has been my observation that, whereas a somnambulistic trance would be desirable in all patients, it is achieved only through the realm of increasing complexities. In other words, as you progress down the ladder of trance depth, the more difficulties and problems you encounter. It should also be stated that, as you proceed toward somnambulism, your percentage of successful cases will also decrease. There are many figures to be found in the literature as to the percentage of patients who can be induced into the somnambulistic stage. These figures are, by and large, estimates which vary greatly among operators. I would say that, if it were imperative to achieve somnambulism in the dental patient before hypnosis were of value, it would be a worthless dental tool. Fortunately, this is not the case.

Originally, those in the dental profession who began employing hypnosis in their practice used it almost exclusively for the purpose of obtaining hypnoanesthesia. The anesthesia produced in this manner is just as profound and perhaps more so than chemical anesthesia. From the standpoint of safety there could be nothing safer. It has distinct advantages. However, from experience it has been found that the time and effort involved in training a patient to enter the trance to a sufficient depth to produce this phenomenon preclude its general use to great degree. The aforementioned fact that it was not always certain whether the patient would achieve an equal depth or deeper trance at another sitting has tended to minimize this specific use. The comparatively small number of total patients who will achieve this state is another inhibiting factor.

However, many of the patients who come into the dental office are sufficiently suggestible to permit induction of at least a light trance. In most instances this is sufficient to accomplish routine operative procedures. A technique which I have found to be very effective is as follows:

The dental assistant seats the patient in the operatory, which is void of instruments to the inquisitive eye, all instruments being concealed in drawers readily accessible to me when the work begins. Upon entering the room, the patient will usually evidence some uneasiness either in manner or by verbal declaration. The patient is given a pleasant greeting and we immediately proceed to make positive suggestions such as: "It is fortunate for you that you have come to have this dental work done now, as it will save you much time in the future as well as future discomfort and expense. In order for us to do the good quality of work you desire it will be necessary for you to be as relaxed as possible. Let's take a few minutes and I will help you to become completely relaxed so that the time you spend with us will be very pleasant."

At this point I make the patient as comfortable in the chair as possible. Male patients are asked to loosen their collars and belts. The patient is asked if he is comfortable and if he assures us he is, we proceed: "To help you relax, please gaze upward at the ceiling and fix your eyes on that little black dot." I have placed a penciled dot about a quarter of an inch in diameter upward and backward of the normal point of vision. "As you gaze at the dot, take three very deep breaths, filling your lungs to their complete capacity and then slowly exhale." The operator does this with the patient so as to reinforce the suggestion. "One, inhale—that's fine—a little more—exhale—push it all out. Two, inhale,—" etc., through the count of three. "As you continue to gaze at the dot you will relax quickly and deeply." *Wait five seconds.* During this time I gently stroke the patient's arm. "Because you are relaxing, your legs are growing heavy." *Wait five seconds.* "Your arms are becoming heavy—very heavy. Your arms and legs are becoming heavier and heavier because you are more relaxed." *Wait five seconds.* "Your entire body is feeling very, very heavy—you are so very relaxed." *Wait five seconds.* "You are so relaxed that your eyelids feel heavy and tired—so heavy and tired." *Wait five seconds.* "Your eyelids are becoming so heavy you want to close them —you may close them. Close them whenever you like." Usually the patient will close his eyes. If not, you make more positive suggestions such as: "You are now so relaxed that you want to close your eyes; you can close your eyes; you must close your eyes. Now as you close your eyes, you will enjoy perfect relaxation." After the eyes have closed, I repeat the words "deeply, deeply relaxed" several times.

In most instances this is all that is necessary to relax a patient sufficiently for dental work or to achieve some depth of hypnosis. It is wise, however, to test the patient's state of relaxation at this point. This may be accomplished by several methods. One is to question the patient through a positive suggestion such as: "You do feel deeply and pleasantly relaxed, don't you?" When a patient has achieved a sufficient depth of relaxation, the response will be a slow, sluggish response in the affirmative. The disadvantage of this technique, which I have encountered, is that it calls for active participation on the patient's part, and in such indivduals where only a slight degree of relaxation has been achieved this participation on their part may tend to arouse them or undo what has been thus far accomplished. Various challenges are sometimes made to the patient, with similar results. I have come to avoid all challenges to the patient, except in cases where I am attempting to develop a somnambulistic trance and then only after a considerable period of induction time has been spent or perhaps not until after several induction sessions, depending upon the case.

A better method of testing is a procedure which will tend to deepen the stage of relaxation or hypnosis and at the same time give the operator visual evidence of the effect. The procedure I like to use is as follows: "I will now take your arm, the one nearest to me, and slowly raise it to shoulder level. With every inch your arm rises, you will become more and more relaxed. Here we go. The arm is being raised and you are sinking into a deeper state of relaxation—deeply, deeply relaxed. You are almost completely relaxed—there, you are completely relaxed, more relaxed than you have ever been before in your life. It is a very, very pleasant feeling." At this point, I release the arm and observe the reaction. In a good subject the arm will remain outstretched without support. It may even evidence the rigidity of catalepsy, in which case you could go on to produce hypnoanesthesia if desired. If the patient begins to lower the arm, this is usually indicative of the fact that only the slightest relaxation has been accomplished and little if any actual trance depth. As soon as this is noticed, I take the arm and say: "That is fine, now we will put the arm back in your lap," and continue as if complete success had been achieved. On occasion, it has been noted that the arm when released fell cataleptically to the lap, and in each case this was evidence of a deep trance as tested by other methods.

After these tests have been made, and the condition of my patient is ascertained, I proceed as follows: "You will remain as completely relaxed as you are now while I do my work. For no reason will you arouse yourself from this very pleasant state you are now enjoying until I ask you to. Although you may be faintly aware of what I am doing, it will not bother you. You should have no discomfort whatsoever and any slight discomfort you may perceive will be easily tolerated and will not arouse you." The statements regarding slight discomfort are made because there are patients who expect and want to be hurt regardless of the type of anesthesia employed. This statement gives them a means to satisfy this mental attitude. At this point a local anesthetic is usually administered, the volume being adjusted to the depth of patient relaxation or hypnosis achieved.

However, our responsibilities related to hypnosis have only begun. Throughout the operating time we must make fortifying suggestions to keep the patient at ease and maintain the level of relaxation. We achieve constant rapport with the patient by speaking to him directly. Every new procedure must be properly introduced and between these introductions it is wise to repeat the words, "deeply, deeply relaxed," from time to time.

In introducing procedures we come to another very important

consideration—that of semantics. We must gear our vocabulary so as not to upset the patient but keep his mind at ease. The patient always carries mental pictures of dental procedures, which are usually erroneously magnified. At this point in our work we can either fortify these erroneous ideas or change them. For example, the average patient has a horror of the dental drill and may even imagine it to be a gigantic monster six feet long and a foot thick. Everything that suggests *drill* will make him shudder, to the point of even reducing the trance effects. Therefore, we must substitute words which produce a pleasing reaction or suggest a more pleasant connotation. A partial list of some phrases to be avoided, along with their substitutes, follows.

1. *Not:* I am going to *drill* your tooth.
   But: I am going to *clean out* your tooth.
2. *Not:* I am going to *grind* your tooth.
   But: I am going to *polish* your tooth.
3. *Not:* I am going to *chisel* this away.
   But: I am going to *plane* this surface.
4. *Not:* I am going to *pound* this inlay into place.
   But: I am going to *tap* this inlay into place.
5. *Not:* I am going to *pull* your tooth.
   But: I am going to *remove* your tooth.
6. For the word *pain* or *hurt, discomfort* should always be substituted.

In speaking to the assistant:

1. *Not:* Hand me a *chisel.*
   But: Hand me a *plane.* (Call it by number.)
2. *Not:* Hand me a hatchet.
   But: Hand me a *plane.* (Call it by number.)
3. *Not:* Hand me an *excavator.*
   But: Hand me a *cleaning instrument.* (Call it by number.)

4. *Not:* Hand me a *grinding stone.*
   But: Hand me a *polishing wheel.*
5. *Not:* Hand me a *knife* or *scalpel.*
   But: Hand me a Bard Parker #12, etc.

This will suggest how the vocabulary can be polished to remove the "acid" from an unintentionally caustic-sounding statement.

As you do your work, then, always introduce each step in a pleasant way through a "streamlined vocabulary." Upon completion of the work, you begin the awakening cycle. "I have completed my work for today. You have not experienced any discomfort. In a few moments I will ask you to arouse yourself, and when you do, you will be completely relaxed and refreshed. From now on each time you return for necessary services you will relax quickly and deeply when I ask you to. After you are aroused you will feel no heaviness of the limbs, you will have no headache or other discomfort but will feel, as I said before, completely relaxed and refreshed. Now I want you to count slowly from one to three and at the count of three you will be wide awake and smiling." (3) This procedure is a simple one and, when mastered, will greatly facilitate the management of the nervous and apprehensive patient. It should not require more than five to ten minutes' additional time to induce and arouse the patient.

This procedure, obviously, is indicated when dealing with adults or children of high school age; persons in these age groups will usually evidence a level of intelligence which allows them to comprehend what is being expected of them. Hypnosis or patient-relaxation methods are not relegated to such individuals alone, however; younger children may also benefit from their use where properly employed. When dealing with young children the objective is the same. It must be remembered that in children there is a wide variance between chronological, physiological, and intellectual age. Therefore, before one can attempt hypnotic methods with youngsters, it is necessary to determine their ability to comprehend. Vocabulary varies among children of the same age group and various words will have different meanings or values. It is therefore wise to hold a short visit with the child before beginning your work so as to ascertain what connotation the child gives to certain things. For example, I have found several questions a very good index for achieving hypnotic success with children. I take the child's hand and gently pinch the skin and ask him what it feels like. You may get answers such as "hurt, ouch, owie," etc. Then I press the same area with the ball of my finger and again ask what it feels like. You may get answers such as "no hurt, mush, dull," etc. I then close my eyes as in sleep and appear relaxed and again question the child. He may say I look like "sleepy, night-night, bed," etc. Whatever terms the children use should be carefully noted, and when you begin induction be careful to use the same words they have given you, since these will convey the most potent mental picture. When speaking with a youngster who is to be a patient, try to remember as much of his vocabulary as possible and then use it as much as possible when inducing hypnosis.

Another important feature in managing children, especially at first visit, is to take them into your private office or any room other than the operatory. Here you can visit with the child where he will be at ease and not frightened by the equipment. Often with the very young I have found it advantageous to induce hypnosis in such a room and then, while they are in the trance, carry them to the operatory. In this way they are not frightened before I begin. Upon awakening without having experienced discomfort, they find no dread in the surroundings and so at future visits will readily march directly to the operatory.

One other situation in regard to children should be considered. In the case of the obstreperous child, one should not hesitate to employ the aid of sedatives. Without them it is often impossible to manage such children. When properly sedated these children will be found quite cooperative and in most cases can then be handled like any other child patient.

Another difficulty which every dentist encounters is the management of the gagger. In most instances gagging is a phenomenon mentally induced by the patient, used as an escape mechanism to avoid the dental operation or to delay its progress. It is disconcerting, to say the least, when you have a busy schedule, to find that your patient is a gagger. Often you cannot meet your appointment schedule or complete the amount of work you have outlined for the patient because you are forced to operate spasmodically with continuous interruptions.

The majority of these cases will respond to *waking suggestion,* which eliminates the gag reflex. A simple technique has been devised by Dr. A. A. Moss (3) which is as follows:

> *Stand in front of the patient who is seated and who is looking upward into your face. Request the patient to stare into your eyes while you return the steady gaze back into the patient's eyes. Without any delay (because continued or delayed stare may bring about a hypnotic trance in a highly susceptible subject), request the patient to take a deep breath and hold it while you count to five. Tell him this has killed his gag reflex, but be certain to repeat the same breath-holding procedure and again stress that the gag reflex has been eliminated.*
>
> *When you have ascertained that your patient is a gagger and you want to take an x-ray or an impression, you say (being careful to use the exact verbalization shown below, for best results):*
>
> Step 1: *"I am going to eliminate your gag reflex by a respiratory or breathing exercise. I want you to gaze steadily into my eyes throughout the procedure." Gaze into the patient's eyes, keeping your eyes about twelve inches from his. Do not remove your gaze from his eyes.*

Step 2: *"Take a deep breath and hold it while I count up to five, keeping your eyes constantly on mine!" Take a deep breath yourself to suggest to the patient what you expect of him and then count to five. If the patient relaxes and expires his air before the count of five, or if he removes his gaze from yours, repeat this step. (It may be necessary at times to make two or three tries before a patient can or will hold his breath or keep his gaze steady for the count of five).*

Step 3: *With your gaze continued, say as follows very, very assuredly and with confidence (this is important): "You may now relax and let the air out of your lungs.* NOW YOU WILL NOT GAG. YOU CANNOT GAG EVEN IF YOU TRY TO. YOU NEED HAVE NO FURTHER FEAR OF GAGGING SINCE I HAVE ELIMINATED YOUR GAG REFLEX." *Remove your gaze from the patient and proceed in the usual fashion as with a non-gagger. It is advisable to repeat Step 2 twice before proceeding with Step 3 in severe gaggers.*

A few minutes spent with such a patient going through this simple procedure will often save hours in completing his work or will result in the ability to do work for one who otherwise might be an impossible case. It should be emphasized, however, that when the condition is truly a physiological reflex, topical or local anesthetics may be necessary. Nevertheless, every dentist has encountered patients to whom he has administered chemical anesthetics, only to find the gag still present. In such cases the above technique will work wonders.

Mention was made previously in this chapter of the value of hypnosis to the prosthodontist. Every dentist who constructs any number of prosthetic appliances has come across patients in whom it is difficult to obtain an accurate centric relation. Generally speaking these individuals are quite tense and this tenseness prohibits them from making the full retrusive movement to allow the centric registration. In most of these cases a simple relaxing technique, as previously outlined, will render the musculature sufficiently passive to overcome the protrusive and lateral deflections which tend to produce a false centric relation.

Another problem of the prosthodontist, although not as common, is the one of securing the proper vertical dimension. Methods of obtaining vertical dimension are varied, and much ado is made concerning the subject in the literature. At best, most methods produce results dependent on arbitrary standards. It has been demonstrated in selected cases that a true vertical dimension can be obtained through hypnosis in somnambulistic patients. This was done by taking patients with a natural dentition and recording the measurements on study casts. After complete extraction these patients were asked to close to what they considered to be their correct occlusal position. Obviously the results were inaccurate and varied with each closure. They were then induced into a somnambulistic trance and regressed in age to the years when they had a full complement of teeth. When asked to close their teeth while in the trance, they would without fail return to the same position of vertical dimension and centric relation, which could be substantiated by the study casts and measurements previously recorded. In cases where somnambulism can be achieved in prosthetic patients and age regression is demonstrable, results will be forthcoming which cannot be surpassed by any other known procedure.

Bruxism is another of the many dental problems which may be alleviated by means of hypnotherapy. The author has had occasion to handle several such cases with gratifying results. It is necessary to correct this condition when noted, lest irreparable damage to teeth and peridontium result from prolonged grinding during sleep.

The most effective method calls for development of a deep trance. Appropriately worded posthypnotic suggestions are given and a specific conditioned reflex is set up to operate during the sleep state when and if the peculiar grinding during natural sleep should take place again. This conditioned reflex causes the patient to awaken the moment the muscles of mastication begin to contract to carry on the grinding action.

Following this first session in which you set up the conditioned reflex and give the necessary posthypnotic suggestions, you awaken the patient and then reinduce him in about ten or fifteen minutes. Again the deep trance is achieved and the patient is directed to bring to mind, and repeat out loud, the full set of instructions and posthypnotic suggestions given him during the former trance. The purpose of this is to cause the patient's subconscious mind to play an active role in the therapy as well as to reinforce the suggestions and instructions previously given. Again the patient is awakened and assured in the waking state that he no longer will grind his teeth while asleep (2). In all such cases it is well to have several reinforcement-therapy sessions at later dates to assure best results. The process may be compared to that of a battery which requires recharging after continuous use. The patients who depend on posthypnotic suggestions to give them relief from this malady require, in most cases, a "recharge" of the suggestions.

The control of harmful habits can be accomplished in a similar manner. All that is necessary is to phrase your suggestions to fit the condition at hand.

From time to time the dentist is called upon by his medical colleagues to assist in the diagnosis and treatment of conditions which are vague and do not follow the category of generally known ailments. A statement of caution to the dentist should be interjected at this point. At no time should he attempt to usurp the functions of a physician, for in most instances he will be treating symptoms rather than causes and this can be dangerous. However, upon the physician's request and with his wise cooperation, the dentist's skill may be utilized to the patient's advantage in some situations.

It has been the author's good fortune to assist in several such cases where the cure was facilitated by hypnotherapy. It might be well to go over two of these case histories in the event that similar conditions may arise requiring some knowledge of their management. The first of these came to my attention while on duty with the 1st Marine Division in the Korean campaign. The patient, a white male, was referred to the dental department because of inability to open his mouth. No other diagnosis had been made. Upon examination there was no evidence of any physical injury to any part of the body. The teeth were locked solidly together, but a very slight tremor of the musculature was noted. This one objective symptom suggested that the condition might be due to musculatory spasm. From the meager history available, it was learned that the patient had been very near the point of an artillery shell explosion, and as a result was badly shaken up but otherwise unharmed except for the inability to open his mouth. It was decided to use hypnosis in the hope of bringing about relaxation in this patient. Fortunately, he proved to be a very good subject and was induced to a very deep trance with little difficulty. I then asked him to tell me his name. It could be seen that he was making physical effort to speak, but all that could be heard was an unintelligible sound emerging from behind the locked teeth. This was, however, an indication of co-operation. I proceeded to make increasingly stronger relaxation suggestions directed toward the facial muscles. Soon a gentle smile crossed his face. I again asked him his name and the teeth separated ever so slightly and he answered, although the words could still not be understood. The above procedure was repeated several times and finally an intelligible answer was obtained. He was then encouraged to relate the events that occurred prior to his coming to see us. With increasing clarity of speech he told a story which closely corroborated the history given by his company corpsman. He was then instructed to hallucinate his favorite dish, which happened to be strawberry shortcake. When told he was sitting at a table with strawberry shortcake in front of him, he was instructed to eat. He proceeded to go through all the motions of eating with gusto, and objective salivation was noted.

After completion of his hallucinated meal, the cause of his trouble was explained to him. He was then asked to open and close his mouth normally and to nod his head if he recognized that he was so doing, which he did. He was further instructed that upon awakening from the trance he would recall everything that had transpired, but would forget the harrowing experience which had caused his difficulty, as no useful purpose would be served in remembering it. He was also assured while in the trance that after awakening he would experience no difficulty in opening his mouth.

Upon awakening, the patient was cheerful and spoke freely. He was amazed and wanted to know what had been done. Amnesia was almost complete even for the things he was asked to remember. The only thing he could recall was a faint recollection of having spoken. He was then told not to try to remember any part of the trance, but was again reassured that his difficulty had been overcome. One more reinforcement trance was brought about later on the same day and the patient was discharged to his company with instructions to return if the condition seemed to reappear. After two weeks it was learned that there had been no recurrence of the symptoms, so the case was considered cured. Shortly after this report, the patient was rotated back to the United States and contact with him was lost.

At the time the above case presented itself, the author was unaware of what the condition might be called. However, since then a similar case has appeared in the literature, presented by Kurt H. Thoma (6) and termed trismus hystericus. The treatment was quite different although along the same general lines. Relaxation in this case was obtained with Pentothal Sodium and Flaxedil. The fact that similar cases may be observed from time to time warrants this description of successful treatment methods.

Another case in which cooperation between physician and dentist resulted in a cure is as follows: Several young men were engaged in a "bull session" one evening. One man had some knowledge of hypnosis and was an amateur hypnotist. During the course of the evening he proceeded to hypnotize successfully one of the other young men and left him with the posthypnotic suggestion that each time someone would touch him, he would receive an electric shock. The posthypnotic suggestion was all too effective and offered entertainment for a while. When the novelty wore off the effect remained, and when the subject asked the amateur hypnotist how long the condition would last he was told it would disappear of its own accord in a short while. Nevertheless, the following day found the young man afflicted as the night before and quite distraught. He sought the aid of his physician who, not having knowledge of the hypnotic phenomenon, proceeded to treat him with numerous drugs. Almost a week passed with no improvement and any touch of the patient still resulted in his receiving an electric shock. Finally the physician, knowing the etiology of the affliction and learning of my use of hypnosis in dentistry, called on me for advice. The physician explained to the patient that anything induced by hypnosis can be removed by hypnosis, and I was asked to see the patient. The patient was highly nervous and emotionally upset as a result of his ordeal. In the waking state a similar explanation was given by me as had been given by his physician. He was then asked to cooperate with me and was told that he would be placed in a trance. He was assured that the condition could and would be removed. He responded nicely and was soon in a deep trance. Countersuggestions were made to eliminate the symptoms, and upon awakening he was free of the vexing shocks.

An important posthypnotic suggestion was given this patient to the effect that, from now on, no one could place him in the trance except a competent physician, dentist, or clinical psychologist. This was further explained to him to be a protection, lest he again fall into the hands of an incompetent person who might use hypnosis for some purpose other than a useful one. The point of his protection was stressed in order to make the suggestion more effective. This practice should be employed with all dental patients before awakening them, regardless of trance depth. This tends to elevate the use of hypnosis in the patient's mind and make him cognizant of the fact that its practice is an acceptable one in the healing arts.

The material presented in this chapter comprises a brief outline of some of the uses of hypnosis in dentistry. We have to date but scratched the surface of its import to the dental practitioner, but already its many possibilities can be recognized. It most certainly should not be considered a panacea for curing every affliction, but should be looked upon as another method of therapy which can be employed when warranted. More and more dentists are recognizing the great potentials of the power of suggestion, but, as in all other methods and procedures, it must not be employed on a patient until the therapist is thoroughly familiar with all the principles involved. When properly used, there is no danger in hypnosis, whereas in unskilled hands detrimental conditions may be induced which, if not removed, may lead to serious sequelae. Hypnosis is not an art to be mastered only by a few. Any conscientious physician or dentist interested in its use and having a sincere desire to learn can master the technique, which will afford him new avenues of approach in dealing with his patients.

REFERENCES

1. Ament, P.: "Illuminating Facts in Psychosomatic Dentistry," *Northwest Dentistry* 29:107 (1950).
2. Burgess, T. O.: "Hypnodontia—Hypnosis as Applied to Dentistry," *Cal Magazine* 13:4 (1951).
3. Moss, A. A.: Unpublished case report, Bernardsville, New Jersey, 1949.
4. Sicher, H.: "The Problems of Pain in Dentistry," *The Bur* 44:3 (1944).
5. Stolzenberg, J.: *Psychosomatics and Suggestion Therapy in Dentistry*, New York, Philosophical Library, Inc., 1950, p. 1.
6. Thoma, K. H.: "Trismus Hystericus," *Oral Surg., Oral Med. Oral Pathol.* 6:449–452 (1953).
7. Weiss, E., and O. S. English: *Psychosomatic Medicine*, Philadelphia and London, W. B. Saunders Company, 1943, pp. 501–502.

INDEX